MINDS THAT CAME BACK

MINDS THAT CAME BACK

WALTER C. ALVAREZ, M.D.

Emeritus Professor of Medicine,
University of Minnesota
(Mayo Foundation)

J. B. LIPPINCOTT COMPANY

PHILADELPHIA
NEW YORK

Preface

In the past fifty years I have gathered what I imagine is the world's largest collection of autobiographies of people who have been mentally upset, highly eccentric, alcoholic, or otherwise ill or handicapped. To me, most of these books have been fascinating and invaluable; many are great books because the people wrote with the frankness of a little child. They had no reticences, and so they can teach us much about human nature and the workings of the human mind. I do not know of any books more worthy of study by us physicians, and especially psychiatrists. Readers can find in the abstracts of these books, which I have gathered here into one volume, much hope and encouragement. Why? Because most of the authors show that, when nervously ill, we can often fight our way back to health and a useful life again.

In writing this book I have used the abstracts I made of the stories of seventy-five persons who, after having been neurotic, psychotic, or actually insane, wrote up their experiences. I include the stories of a few persons who cracked up because of alcoholism or a bit too much religion. A few told of being psychoanalyzed.

It is a pleasure to express here my great appreciation for the tremendous help given me by my wife. Working almost every day for the last two years, she has typed and several times retyped every page of this book.

It is a pleasure also to express my indebtedness to my good friends Mr. and Mrs. M. E. Gilfond, tireless and expert book finders of Washington, D.C., who searched through the world's second-hand bookstores for most of the approximately four hundred volumes now in my collection.

WALTER C. ALVAREZ, M.D.

Contents

Introduction

My great pleasure in reading *Minds That Came Back* makes vivid again the memory of my earliest acquaintance with the writings of Dr. Walter C. Alvarez. Approximately thirty years ago, when I was the youngest member of an informal study group of interns, resident physicians, and medical school faculty members, it fell my lot to discuss his classic study, *The Mechanics of the Digestive Tract*. Having already arrived at the conclusion that even the most learned medical writers were wont to conceal their wisdom in tedious and opaque verbiage, I found this book in its sparkling clarity, its fresh and stimulating substance, like an April morning that dawns after a long and trying winter. What I learned from it is much better remembered than most of the material I have read in the last few years.

After encountering Dr. Alvarez's beautiful demonstration of neurologic function in the gastrointestinal tract, I was not surprised to find during my early years of practice that the best physicians I knew, in whatever speciality they worked, often turned to his *Nervousness, Indigestion and Pain* for guidance in dealing with their numerous and puzzling patients whose symptoms throve despite the absence of any demonstrable lesion, toxin, or other clearly acceptable cause. After almost three decades I still see that wise internists, general practitioners, surgeons, gynecologists, otolaryngologists, and others find in this delightful book valuable and practical help in handling some of their most difficult patients. There is also much in it that psychiatrists can read with profit.

Unlike many of the other eminent medical specialists of our time, Dr. Alvarez has always been profoundly concerned with the emotional and personal problems of his patients and has accepted these problems as part of his interest and

9

his task as a physician. Unlike many psychiatrists, who chose these problems as their specific field of endeavor, he has been able to communicate his observations and his thought in clear, accurate, and arresting language, language un-cluttered with pretentious polysyllabic technical jargon, un-clouded by the distorting framework of dogmatic and du-bious psychologic theories. Such theorizing has perhaps obscured as often as it has clarified interpretations of per-sonality disorder.

Dr. Alvarez's present study, *Minds That Came Back*, should be of no less interest to physicians in general than to psychiatrists. It should be of value to social workers, to lawyers, to teachers, to the clergy, to nurses, and to all people whose work involves the behavior and personal problems of others. Since most of us, whatever our work may be, must find the pursuit of life's goals, the fulfillments and the failures of human effort, a subject second to none in its enthralling interest and in its mystery, this book should indeed appeal to every thoughtful adult.

A prodigious amount of study and thought is summarized in this volume. A great number of human beings affected by a wide variety of mental and emotional disorder, and in al-most every degree of variation from an accepted norm, are allowed to speak for themselves. As the author pertinently says, if we seek to understand what is happening to these people, let us not neglect their own accounts of their ex-perience. Though the opinions of the psychotic are usually colored with delusional ideas, and often with false percep-tions of the objective world, an important reality of the illness can be found only in the subjective reactions they undergo and seek to communicate to us.

Many of the items of human experience presented and discussed here are stimulating and worthy of our most seri-ous thought. Sometimes in the highly personal, imperfectly communicable, inward adventures and discoveries of the psychotic and the neurotic one may find clues to almost inexpressible realities. What reader can fail to be impressed with the report of the Reverend Anton Boisen, the discerning clergyman who carefully evaluated his own psychotic experiences and then devoted so much effort to the help and understanding of others similarly disabled? Should we not all pause to consider carefully Boisen's conclusion that both psychosis and religious conversion are attempts to reorganize the personality after it has been shattered or somehow dislocated by major stress?

A successful attempt, Boisen believes, may lead to rare and profound insight, true fulfillment, and a superior adjustment in life. The failures result in disability, sometimes in the unhappy and tragic disability of permanent psychosis as seen in the chronic wards of the state hospital. This book, like William James's *Varieties of Religious Experience,* should challenge the attention of readers not only now but also in subsequent generations. It raises many questions of the utmost importance, many questions for which there are not yet complete or satisfying answers.

Aside from its relation to genuine mystic experience and religious insight, what is the relation of serious personality disorder to creative achievement in other fields?

Perhaps every child has wondered about Shakespeare's implication in referring to the lunatic, the lover, and the poet. Was A. E. Housman correct in his conclusion that the genuine poem, like the oriental pearl, is always, or nearly always, the product of a pathologic lesion? Shall we accept the opinion of Thomas Mann, expressed in his introduction to *The Short Novels of Dostoevsky,* that the insights of genius arise not so much from the genius despite his afflictions as from the disease itself, from the sometimes virulent and distasteful morbidity that may incapacitate him for normal life as this is ordinarily conceived?

The concise and deeply engrossing accounts presented here of August Strindberg, Vaslav Nijinsky, Friedrich Nietzsche, William Cowper, Guy de Maupassant, Fyodor Dostoevsky, Vincent van Gogh, and others are likely to provoke in the serious reader thought along many lines. This book makes it very clear that those who suffer from major psychosis, as well as those handicapped by lesser mental disorder, sometimes achieve in art, literature, philosophy, or other forms of creative endeavor success that commands the admiration of many generations. Dr. Alvarez's cogent discussion of these people and their psychiatric aberrations is likely to prompt the reader to bring up other important questions.

In what way, for instance, and how much, does the basic anomaly that underlies the overt psychosis of a brilliant novelist, poet, or playwright, the florid disorder which necessitates his temporary confinement to a psychiatric institution, influence pathologically the substance of his works, the reflection of life and of the human condition he offers during his apparently lucid and highly productive periods of endeavor? Because of their generally accepted status as geniuses, can the ordinary reader count on the interpretation of life offered by Strindberg or Nietzsche as authentic, as one likely to yield valuable and true insights? Or will the fundamental defect of a Strindberg be projected insidiously into even his most admirable productions and subtly immerse us in a universe of paranoid misogyny which the author has faithfully mistaken for reality? How much does the disease-induced personal failure and frustration of a Nietzsche enter into the gloom and defeatism of his philosophy, however much this philosophy may be praised in other and sometimes very misleading terms?

One of the many interesting and significant contributions of this book lies in the repeated demonstrations by Dr. Alvarez of minor or abortive manifestations in relatively normal people of what in a more complete expression would be full-blown psychosis. We know that cerebral dysrhythmia, which in one subject gives rise to the dramatic and unmistakable major convulsion of epilepsy, may cause in others only periodic irritability, harrowing nightmares, lapses of attention, unpredictable rare hours of inexpressible elation, or unaccountable episodes of irresponsible conduct. Many of the cases discussed in this book strongly suggest that the person who has never shown recognizable signs of psychosis may occasionally, or often, demonstrate in his inexplicable acts reflections of fleeting psychotic motivation that probably arise from paranoid, cyclothymic, or schizoid traits and potentialities that remain relatively dormant and never become sufficiently organized or dominant to be distinctly recognized as illness.

The relation of these subliminal or incomplete twists of normal response, these *formes frustes* of psychotic behavior that never emerge into full clinical recognition, to the obvious and familiar patterns of madness, as this is conceived by the layman, becomes impressively plain in many vivid illustrations. The discerning reader is likely also to wonder if the stress of these challenges to happy social adjustment and to sanity may sometimes act as a stimulus to growth, to positive reorganizations of the self, and to the expression of wisdom gained from insight acquired in these inner struggles against subjective turmoils and threats to the basic integration of personality.

Dr. Alvarez, as a physician of excellent judgment and immense clinical experience, is not so naïve as to offer glib and authoritative explanations for the diverse marvels and mysteries of human life exemplified in the many interesting lives he brings to our attention. He presents enough of Schreber's fantastic journal for us to feel the weird disorder that is depicted in such detail and at such length in that remarkable volume of memoirs. Unlike Freud, he does not insist on resolving these mysteries according to a rigid formula; he does not force this strange material into a simple schematic artifact, or by a rule of thumb (based on gratuitous assumptions) interpret it with the confidence of a Roman augur.

It is both a pleasure and a privilege to introduce the reader to this delightful and significant book. It is a fine distillation of the observations and the thought of one of the greatest physicians of our century. Its subject is scarcely less broad than the whole scope of human life, and it is presented with the simple clarity, the vitality, and the charm of an accomplished writer.

HERVEY M. CLECKLEY, M.D.

CHAPTER 1

The Great Educational Value of Books by the Mentally Disturbed

Of all the books I have written, this one has given me the greatest pleasure, and has excited in me the greatest interest. Why? Because the many autobiographies on which I have based this volume have been so fascinating and instructive. As I studied them, I learned so much that I could not learn elsewhere, and that has been very helpful to me as a physician. I am sure there is much also that will be helpful and of great interest to thousands of laymen.

A word of hope. Many men and women—and especially those with some personal interest in psychosis, which perhaps has shown up either in themselves or a relative—may at first feel a bit afraid of a book like this; but actually, all of them can find here, not only much information that can help them, but also much that can give them comfort and inspiration. What cheers me is that so large a percentage of the persons whose experience with a mental breakdown is here described came out of their spell, either cured or almost well.

Another point that cheers me much is that usually when one of these persons recovered, perhaps after years of mental confusion, he found that his mind was not injured: it was as clear as it had ever been. Also, most of these people say

15

that even when they were badly confused, a part of their mind retained its sanity, and it was this good part that helped them to get well.

This book can give us all hope, also, because it shows that through the years the care of mental patients has been improving; it has become more humane, more kindly, more helpful, and more sensible. Already, many mental hospitals are restful and friendly places to be in—places in which many of the doors are left open, and the patients are kept busy making things in shops and studios.

Everyone is interested in the workings of the human mind. Few topics are more engrossing to us men and women than that of how our minds work. We are interested in how they work in health, and we are interested in how they work in disease; we are even interested in their workings when we are tense, tired, discouraged, depressed, much worried, full of fear and anxiety, or elated, "all lit up," "blowing our top," or somewhat under the influence of alcohol. Those of us who have a tendency to great nervousness or to difficulties in adjustment are always looking for help in learning to live with our handicap; and those of us who are unfortunate enough to have a mentally disturbed relative are always glad to pick up information that will help us in handling the difficult situation with which we have to struggle.

Most of us are interested in the autobiographies of people who have no reticences. Each one of us knows much about how his own mind works, but he can only guess what is going on in his neighbor's mind. He knows what some of his own motives were when he did something unusual, but he cannot tell what induced his neighbor to do what he did. Because of this, most of us are fascinated when we find a book written by such men as Samuel Pepys or Benvenuto Cellini, men who had so few reticences that they did not mind telling us about the despicable things they did, and why they did them.

As one would expect, the people in this world who have the fewest reticences—and hence are the most likely, metaphorically, to disrobe in public—are those who are psychotic, or decidedly eccentric. As Lara Jefferson said (see Chapter 3), the insane have lost all of those inhibitions which control most of us. They will blurt out anything they know, as Nietzsche did; and some will not mind walking out onto the front lawn as naked as a jay bird. Many, even some who are just eccentric, will publish without shame or reserve details about their sexual life which no "average" woman would ever think of talking about, even to her close relatives or intimates.

Very instructive to me was the behavior of a friend of mine who, for all her adult life, had been a charming, gracious, and able woman. For thirty years she had kept the peace with her unpleasant stepmother, in spite of the fact that, when she was a girl, the woman had often been very unkind to her. Recently, when my friend went into a spell of mania, she so lost her ladylike inhibitions that she rang up the stepmother and spent a half hour telling her, in the eloquent language of a fishwife, just what a skunk she was and always had been!

Books by the insane are highly instructive. If only because of the great frankness of the insane, their books must always be of great interest and value, not only to every psychologist and every psychiatrist, but to every thoughtful man and woman. In these books we can all learn what, in many cases, were the earliest symptoms of a nervous breakdown and what were the exciting causes which kept driving the patient mad. Psychiatrists should be interested to see what actually were the thoughts and motives that caused these people to behave as they did—unwisely, and often to their own detriment. It is strange that in the past so few of these invaluable autobiographies have been used by us physicians. Actually, they should for long have been among our best and most trustworthy textbooks.

When a man wants to learn about a little-known land, such as Thibet, he reads all of the books he can find by travelers who have gone to Thibet, or have lived there. Similarly, when I want to know about psychosis, I like to read the books written by the people who have been to that topsy-

turvy land of the mind—psychosis. What could be more
logical than that?

Some characteristics of the insane. In this book one of the
best descriptions of what the insane keep thinking about is
given by that able hospital chaplain Rev. Anton Boisen. He
found that often the patients' three main concerns are with the
coming of the end of the world, with the all-important role
they expect to play in the new "Kingdom," and with their
close, chummy relationship with God. Many expect that
when the world comes to an end, they will be either the
Messiah or a sort of Noah who will repopulate the earth.

The best description of the wild onrush of madness is by
Lara Jefferson, and the best description of paranoia is by
Strindberg. Interesting are the conclusions of a formerly
alcoholic editor who studied insanity as he observed it in
his fellow patients during the months which he spent in
a mental hospital. He was there, not because he was insane,
but because, for a while, he had to be kept away from
alcohol (*Behind the Door of Delusion*). He said that in the
minds of most of the strange persons with whom he had
chatted, the outstanding emotion had been fear—an unreasoning and often vague and formless fear. I have been
much impressed on noting in the stories of many of the
psychotic autobiographers their statements that their minds
were seething often with hates and resentments. Evidently,
to hate and resent one's fellows is often a characteristic of
psychosis.

A remarkable explanation of the horror of insanity. In
The Maniac, the author, a woman journalist, gives us the
best description I have seen of the horror of insanity. She
reminds us, first, of the tremendous feeling of relief we all
have when, on waking from an awful nightmare, we find
that it was just a dream. Then she says, just imagine waking
from a horrifying nightmare to find that it is real. That is
what madness is. That is why madness can cause many a
person to be so frantic with terror that he or she will gladly
commit suicide.

*The insane are honest, and their memory is usually re-
markably good.* I can imagine many persons asking now,
"But can we trust what the ex-insane person says he can

remember of the time when he was 'out of his mind'? Will he get things straight, and will he be honest?" Yes; I am sure we can trust him. After several interviews with Miss Hillyer (*Reluctantly Told*), Dr. Joseph Collins, the eminent psychiatrist, wrote that he thought her recollections were remarkably clear and trustworthy. Several ex-patients, when they came to write their books, reinforced their memory, as did Miss King (*The Recovery of Myself*), by turning to notes, diaries, and family letters which they wrote while they were ill. A few of the insane, like Lara Jefferson (*These Are My Sisters*, Chapter 3), wrote sections of their books during those times in the hospital when they were lucid.

What has impressed me much is that so many of the ex-insane say that—especially when they were manic—their thoughts were so unusually vivid that nearly everything they experienced became deeply etched on their memory. As one woman put it, her memories of her first days in the mental hospital were as vivid and as detailed as were her memories of her wedding day. Arthur Symons, speaking of some of his experiences during his spell of insanity, said they were branded on his memory as if with "the hot iron applied to a convict's arm."

Many a person who once was manic has marveled at the excellence of his memory during that time. As he became elated, he found he could quote long passages from the Bible and Shakespeare—passages which he thought he had forgotten. John Custance found one day that he could remember a long passage from a book which he had read years before. Several persons wrote that when they became manic, they discovered that they could write rapidly in verse, as they had never done before.

As to the honesty of the insane, there can be no question. As Beers and others have said, they tend to be as honest as little children. A few of the writers, such as William Moore and Paul Hackett, said that when they knew they could obtain their release from the hospital by telling the doctors that their delusions and hatreds were all gone, they were too honest to do this!

The ex-insane help us much, by telling us how they slowly lost their reason. One of the very helpful things that the ex-insane do is to tell us what their thoughts and feelings were as they slowly slipped into their breakdown. This information can be of great value to psychiatrists and physicians, and it can serve to warn laymen as they watch a relative drifting into the world of mental confusion. As several of the writers, such as Lenore McCall, say, if only they, their relatives, or their doctor had quickly realized what was happening to them, the period of their illness might have been much shortened.

The books here abstracted can be of tremendous help to all those who have to take care of the insane. Obviously, the reading of books by the insane can be of great value to all the attendants, nurses, and resident physicians in mental hospitals because the ex-patients tell us why they were rebellious and difficult, and what could easily have been done to gain their cooperation and obedience to requests.

Too often in the past, poorly trained attendants have looked on a frightened and confused patient as just "ornery" and hence have treated him roughly. In the autobiographies we learn why, for months, many an insane person does not say a word, or answer a question, or visit with his relatives. He has his reasons for this behavior.

That there is still need for improvement in the training of workers in mental hospitals was shown by the complaint of the superintendent of a mental hospital who said that the recent graduates in psychiatry who were being sent to him as resident physicians knew nothing about the *handling* of the insane. He told how one of these young doctors had just come to him to report that the new patient whose history he had been sent to get had only cursed him and ordered him out of his room. The superintendent said, "You probably frightened him by a too-abrupt approach—let's go and see."

The superintendent went with the young doctor and greeted the patient courteously. He explained to him where he was and why he was there; he explained to him that it would be to his advantage to be protected for a while from the buffets of the outside world. Then the superintendent identified himself. He said that he would like to do everything possible to make the man comfortable; also, he would be happy to let him go home as soon as he was well enough to leave. He said, "If you have any trouble, send word to me and I will come and help you." With this, the man calmed right down and became cooperative. He felt he was safe because he had a friend at court. On reading the books here abstracted, we find that until recently this sort of explaining was rarely met with in mental hospitals.

Fortunately, now, as I write, more and more superintendents are putting some sense and kindliness and humanity into the care of their patients. No longer are these unfortunates being ordered about contemptuously—much like "jailbirds" without any rights. Many of the hospital doors are being left open, and great efforts are being made to find attendants who will be kindly.

Many of the ex-insane who wrote a book did it with the hope of improving the care of the mentally disturbed. It should be noted that several of the persons who, through the years, have written up their experiences in a mental hospital did it with the hope of improving the care of the insane. In 1873, Mrs. Packard (see the Bibliography following the last chapter of this book) campaigned and kept campaigning until she got the governor of Illinois to appoint a committee to investigate her charges against the superintendent of the mental hospital in which for years she had been mistreated. When the committee found every one of her charges valid, the man had to resign.

How I came to collect this library of unusual books. It was my great interest in Clifford Beers' book, *A Mind That Found Itself,* which I read in 1909, which caused me to start collecting all similar books that I could find. Later, I collected all books I could find written by alcoholics, or decidedly eccentric or "screwbally" people. Along the way I collected autobiographies of the sexually mixed-up, the ill with some disease, the blind, the deaf, the crippled, the drug addicts, a few hoboes, a few criminals, and a few prostitutes.

Not all the writers quoted in this book were insane. I should emphasize the fact that in this volume I include abstracts of a few books written by people *who were not insane.* Two of them described their remarkable phobias; a few described their vivid hallucinations; one—a great religious leader—described the depressions that saddened his early years; a few described the mental disturbances that went with their epilepsy, their paranoia, their hypochondriasis, and a few told of the progress of their psychoanalysis.

CHAPTER **2**

A Brief Description of the Several Types
of Mental Aberration

A simple classification of nervous patients. For the benefit of
those many readers who may not have studied psychiatry, I
will note here that the average physician, who is not interested in the long and detailed and official classification
of the psychoses (mental diseases), divides his patients into
two main groups—the nervous and neurotic, who suffer from
neuroses, and the psychotic, who suffer from *psychoses.* The
dividing line between a severe neurosis and a mild psychosis
is so vague that probably no two psychiatrists will ever
agree on where it is.

Actually, many of us physicians straddle the line, and
speak of *psychoneuroses.* These are supposed to be somewhere in the middle—but just where, again, no two authori-
ties can be expected to agree.

Many psychiatrists believe that neuroses never change
into psychoses, while a few believe that this can happen.
Others say what may well be correct, which is that if a
person was supposed in his youth to have only a neurosis
later becomes psychotic, it is because from earliest life he
was more psychotic than neurotic.

People with great nervousness or a neurosis. The wise
doctor diagnoses "just nervousness" when one of his nice,
friendly, well-behaved, well-adjusted, and successful pa-

23

tients, after a period of overwork, strain, sorrow, disaster, or insomnia, becomes very tired, tense, on-edge, irritable, nervous, and anxious; and then perhaps feels some distress in his heart, or stomach, or bowels. Such a person is still well adjusted and sensible; and after a vacation, a few nights of good sleep, and perhaps the taking of a sedative drug, he or she is back at work.

People with a mild, often unrecognized, psychosis. An observant and experienced doctor will usually recognize at a glance, or in a few minutes, the type of nervous patient who, for all of his or her life, has been odd, eccentric, a "screwball," difficult, mixed-up in some of his or her thinking, or perhaps overly shy, reserved, and hard to get along with. Perhaps the person is undisciplined, unsocial, unemployable, or too fond of alcohol.

The old family type of doctor will often be influenced in his discouraged outlook about a mildly psychotic patient by the fact that he knows the man's family, and knows that the fellow resembles some of his "difficult" or ne'er-do-well or "goofy" relatives. Old doctors will say he is a "chip off the old block," or he has his grandfather's love of the bottle, or his uncle's love of loose women or gambling. A wise doctor will try to help such a person with his present flare-up of trouble, and he may send him to a psychiatrist, but he will have no illusions as to anyone's ability to make the fellow over so perfectly that he never again will slip back into a nervous episode or a spell of dissipation.

Several types of psychosis. By definition, a psychotic person who is committed to a mental hospital is "insane." The two commonest forms of mental trouble are *schizophrenia* and *manic-depressive psychosis.* In each division there are some minor and often unrecognized forms of the disease. For instance: as we shall see, schizoids with a slight tendency to schizophrenia are often just abnormally shy, reserved, unaffectionate, and "touch-me-not." Some of them are too shy ever to go out with a woman, and some live alone all their days.

Cyclothymics are people who inherited just enough of the manic-depressive tendency of a melancholic ancestor so that they tend to swing too widely in their moods. At times they will be a bit too jovial, merry, talkative, social, clever, and full of "pep" and drive. At other times they are a bit too silent, moody, discouraged, unsocial, and averse to seeing people. Many have days when they just feel mean and quarrelsome.

Many of the women in the cyclothymic group are very tense and depressed at the time of menstruation, or after the menopause. A few mildly depressed persons will have only great feelings of fatigue in the mornings—a fatigue that is gone by 5 o'clock in the afternoon. Others are "sadsacks," or *anhedonics,* who get no pleasure out of life; they have no enthusiasms, or they are always fearing the worst. Some of them or their relatives will drink heavily in spells in order to get relief from the great distress they feel when in their depressions.

Some depressed persons keep thinking of suicide. Many feel very tired and toxic or full of aches and pains. Some feel very sinful but, as we shall see, are vague as to what the sin was. Many manic-depressives never seem to have a manic spell; they are either fairly normal or else a bit depressed. Rarely, one will find a person who seems always a bit manic—so that usually he is tireless, remarkably energetic, and decidedly talkative. A few persons—usually old women—go into what is called an *agitated depression,* which causes them such suffering that they tend to keep constantly walking about, day and night, saying that their distress is more than they can bear.

Psychoses that come late in life. As most of us know, there are many persons, who *in their later years,* become *mentally confused* and perhaps childish and hard to get along with. Occasionally, a woman will get a bit upset after her menopause. She may be said then to have an *involutional psychosis,* ushered in, perhaps, by the loss of function in her ovaries.

Persons on the fringes of psychosis. On the fringes of psychosis are many *alcoholics,* some *epileptics,* and many *crackpots,* recluses, criminals, delinquents, drug addicts, unemployables, ne'er-do-wells, and people who seem never to be able to learn to live sensibly, or to learn to get along comfortably with their fellow human beings. Often they are spoken of as poorly adjusted persons, or persons with psychopathic personalities. Characteristic of families full of such persons is the fact that they all dislike each other, and often quarrel when they get together.

Besides these people, there are a few million others whose small inheritance of nervous trouble shows up in them as a tendency always to be sickly and ailing and complaining. Some, we doctors call "constitutionally frail," or *"inadequate to stand up to the strains of life,"* and some have the *"habit of illness,"* or *"the habit of being operated on."* A while back, when a company doctor went over the records of hundreds of the employees to see how many days of illness they had had, he found many persons who, in the course of years, had been absent from work for only a few days, while a few sickly ones had been absent for over 100 days, with all sorts of complaints. Some had had half a dozen operations.

Millions of mentally disturbed people have only a mild form of psychosis. People who have been mentally disturbed, or who have a loved one who has once gone through a spell of psychosis, should not be too pessimistic about the future, because some mental diseases, even schizophrenia, can exist for a lifetime in mild forms. An occasional schizophrenic has to be committed, but even he may later recover and go back to work. Only *some* of those schizophrenics who have to be committed degenerate to the point where they become incurable. Thousands of schizophrenics never have a single severe episode. A few will have one depression or bad spell, perhaps when they are around twenty. Some of these will then quickly recover sufficiently to go back to work; a few will never have to go back into a hospital, but will never be capable of holding a job. They may just sit around at home. An occasional schizophrenic will succeed well in business.

In David Martens' book, *The Abrupt Self* (see Chapter 4 in the present volume), we get the picture of a sex-hating and asocial bachelor who was psychotic enough to want to spend his summer holidays all alone on an island, trying to figure out why his mental processes were as confused as they were. Yet, with all this, during the remainder of the year, this character with a somewhat muddled mind was able to be a successful university professor and a writer of some salable books.

Paranoiacs. Paranoiacs and paranoid persons are always thinking people have it in for them, or are planning evil against them. Sometimes they think people are controlling their thoughts or beaming radar at them. Too often they think some harmless action of someone is directed at them. Many of the paranoiacs get by well enough in this world until perhaps they feel that someone's malicious persecutions have become more than they can bear. For instance, a man and his wife rented their spare bedroom to their best friend, an apparently normal man. At the close of World War II they said to him, "We are awfully sorry, but our son is coming home; he will want his old room, so would you mind hunting up a new place?" All that the man, a paranoiac, could see was that his friends were deliberately baiting him; he brooded over the injustice being done him until he took down his rifle and shot his friends dead.

Many mildly psychotic persons "get by" all their days. There is many a businessman who gets along well enough with most of his customers, and who, to all appearance, is sane, but who, when he reaches home at night, turns into a psychotic "devil," perhaps mean, suspicious, parsimonious, cruel, or even dangerous. His temper may be so violent that his wife and children go in daily fear of him.

As will be seen from reading some of the abstracts in this book, there are many people who, even after having been committed, just cannot believe that they were ever mentally disturbed, or disturbed enough to have been locked up. Doubtless, many a one could easily have been kept out of a mental hospital if he had only had some kindly, understanding, and well-to-do relatives, willing and able to take care of him at home.

Persons with a sudden mental crisis. Remarkable are a few cases, in which able men, like Rev. Anton Boisen, perhaps twice in a lifetime will suddenly go into a brief spell of violent delirium. It would be interesting to know how sane these people are in the interims between spells. Are they then perfectly normal, or do they remain always somewhat eccentric and odd?

I do know this, that often when in his early twenties a brilliant young man in college goes into a spell of mania, or commits suicide, his mother will keep saying, over and over again, "I knew it; I knew it; I have seen this coming ever since he was a little boy."

Phobias, compulsions, amnesias, fugues, and hysteria. As we shall see, mildly psychotic or eccentric persons, like William Ellery Leonard (see Chapter 7), suffer much from unreasonable fears, which are called *phobias*. Some of these phobias are so distressing and so restrictive of the person's activities as to make it almost impossible for him to get about and earn his living.

Other persons waste much of their time on *compulsions* which cause them to keep performing certain ritualistic acts —such as washing their hands a dozen times—before they can get down to work. Some will say that this ritualistic compulsion is designed to save the life or health of a loved one. Even a child, when neurotic, may really believe that he had better step on every crack on the sidewalk or "the pursuing demons" will get him.

An *amnesia* is a state in which the person's memory appears to have left him. Often, when found, he says he does not know his name or where he came from, or if he is married, or what he did while away from home. Sometimes, as when the claim of amnesia is all that stands between the person and serious trouble with the law, experts are doubtful as to the genuineness of the loss of memory, but there are some cases in which there is no reason to doubt the honesty of the man's statements. In such cases the person may have had a little stroke, or he may have a rare form of epilepsy.

Fugues are runnings-away, either mental or mental and physical. Every so often an erratic husband may drop out of sight for six months. This habit may easily be explained by the presence in the home of a shrewish wife, but sometimes it seems to be a manifestation of epilepsy or some type of psychosis.

Hysteria is a strange disease in which a person—usually of unstable nervous make-up—develops a paralysis, or goes into a sort of convulsion, or an apparent trance, or gets a spasm of some muscles, or a peculiar walk, a blindness, a deafness, an apparently severe pain, or an inability to talk above a whisper or to take a step. Often a wise physician with much experience will recognize hysteria at a glance. Curiously, a woman in an hysterical trance with supposedly anesthetic or numb legs will allow the physician to run an old-fashioned hatpin into her thigh without objection, when she cannot stand any tickling of the soles of her feet!

People with such troubles can often be helped by the doctor who shows them, first, that their nerves are playing tricks on them and, second, that the reasons for this are an unstable nervous system, plus perhaps some strain that is greater than the person can stand (as in war), or a desire to punish someone, such as a mother who would be much inconvenienced by the person's illness. According to some experts, hysteria is a neurosis, while to other experts it looks more like a mild form of psychosis.

Most of us presumably normal persons are mixtures of sanity and insanity. Actually, most of us are such mixtures of sanity and psychosis that no lawyer has ever been able to make a definition of insanity that will stand up in a court of law. All persons interested in this problem of defining insanity should read a very wise and interesting book called *One Mind Common to All,* written by one of America's great psychiatrists, Dr. Earl D. Bond (Macmillan, 1958). His thesis is that if we were to set up a scale of sanity, running from one to ten units, with a "crazy" man at the bottom and, let us say, Benjamin Franklin at the top, most of us would rate around five.

Bond tells us that most insane men in a mental hospital are perhaps ten per cent sane. For instance, Lara Jefferson (see Chapter 3 in this book) told how, when in a mental hospital, a small element of sanity in her fought off a large element of insanity that was telling her to kill her little nurse.

I thought of this when, the other day, a psychiatrist was telling me about a patient of his. She was a woman who practically always in the past had been gracious and able, and only at times psychotic—but who recently became manic and barricaded herself in her apartment. That night, at

2 A.M., she called her doctor on the phone to talk aimlessly and rapidly and at great length. When he asked her to excuse him, she begged his pardon and promptly rang off. Next day, while still somewhat violent and uncontrollable, she called him to apologize humbly for having disturbed his rest. In spite of all her mental commotion, there was a small part of her in which she still was a lady.

A number of times in my life, when I have found a charming man or woman whose personality and conversation and wide knowledge I could enjoy, I have been shocked later to find him or her psychotic and untrustworthy. As we shall see later, one evening Clifford Beers, still technically insane and living in a mental hospital, went out with his attendant and spent a pleasant evening with a group of able men who did not notice anything wrong with him. Another author tells of a brilliant lawyer who was borrowed for a while from a mental hospital to help with a hard-fought legal battle! Another "insane" inmate of a hospital was borrowed one night by a theatrical group who needed him to take the place of their leading actor who had suddenly fallen ill!

To show how easily one can be deceived as to the sanity of a psychotic man, an able psychiatrist once told me this story on himself. He said that one Monday a well-dressed, wide-awake, and nice-looking executive came in and said he wanted a thorough examination. He said people were following him. He went to the police for protection, but they only laughed at him. So he wanted to go back to them with a certificate to the effect that he was sane. My friend had no illusions about the man but thought it best to humor him; so he turned him over to his assistants for an examination.

On Friday my friend called the patient into his office and said, "I have an abject apology to make to you; when you first came in I assumed, as did the police, that you were an ordinary paranoiac, but every day, when you have come in, my secretary, looking out of the window, has seen two men following you. They wait; and when you go out, they follow you again."

"Oh, hell, no," said the man; "don't pay any attention to

00, he had a severe attack of grippe, which left
depressed condition. On June fifteenth some terri-
ations seized him and rendered him almost help-
e days later he got his first delusion—the idea that
hopeless epileptic. He thought the best thing he
would be to commit suicide. For three or four
slept hardly at all, and sedatives had little effect on
remained in bed, speaking but seldom, and think-
antly of the best way of killing himself. Eventually,
ed out of a window of the fourth floor of his house.
all he did was to injure his ankles, but with this
e "went over the edge" and became mentally con-
He was put in a room with bars on the windows—
ich had a demoralizing effect on him. Soon he was
elirium with high fever. He heard false voices and
rappings on the walls and ceiling of his room.
descent into a psychosis. He became suspicious of all
him, but not until about a month after he had hurt
f did he refuse to recognize his relatives. One of
s greatest difficulties, which lasted for many months,
is conviction that since, in attempting suicide he had
n the law, the police must be after him. During all
first year in a mental hospital, the inability of anyone
lp him was due to his firm belief that all of the people
t him were detectives who were trying to get evidence
could later be used against him when in court he would
ied for his life. Naturally, he refused to talk.
eers showed in his book that often the difficulty attend-
and nurses have in handling an obstreperous insane
is all due to the fact that they do not know why he is
behaving. Worse yet, they often do not ask him with
icient sympathy and skill so that he will tell them what
is afraid of.

A mistake in handling the situation. Early in Beers's ill-
ss a serious mistake was made in taking care of him. His
ler brother, who had taken over the responsibility for his
eatment, had promised Clifford that none of the nurses
ho had attended him during his first brief stay in a hospital
ould be re-employed, but because few nurses were then
vailable, the brother asked one of them to remain. This

those fellows; they are the detectives I hire to keep the other fellows farther back!"

Many mentally disturbed persons have such a mixture of symptoms it is hard to classify them. In the cases of some patients, there is such a mixture of symptoms that no two psychiatrists can ever be expected to agree as to the classification of their psychosis. As one of the ranking psychiatrists in our armed forces once wrote, a mentally disturbed soldier seen at the front may seem to be in a severe fatigue state. At the hospital station, a little farther back, the doctors may diagnose a marked anxiety neurosis; and at the base hospital he may be listed as either a psychoneurotic, a schizophrenic, a manic-depressive, an hysterical person, or a "goldbricker."

The great psychiatrist Dr. Abraham Myerson said he was often puzzled when a decidedly schizophrenic man in his mental hospital would go into a depression typical of a manic-depressive person. Often I will see a mildly psychotic person go into an attack of hysteria; or I will see a primarily epileptic person go into a brief attack of psychosis or into a debauch of hard drinking.

Psychoses and neuroses do not always "breed true." To me, it has been interesting to note in over 1,000 families whose members I have come to know well that when some of these persons were psychotic, one or two others were alcoholic; one might be mildly epileptic, perhaps without seizures; one might be mentally retarded, while others were eccentrics, unemployables, hysterical persons, hoboes, recluses, dope fiends, or criminals. Several were of the type who keep constantly going to doctors with minor mental or physical disturbances, usually labeled neuroses.

I wrote up these many experiences, telling *what actually happened* to the members of some 700 families, and made a book called *Practical Leads to Puzzling Diagnoses: Neuroses That Run through Families* (Lippincott, 1958). The book might just as well have been entitled "The Minor Equivalents of Psychoses and Epilepsy," or "Relatives of the Psychotic." It deals also with the many persons—sometimes odd or eccentric—who are *carriers* of a tendency to mental disease. They are the people who account for the fact that mental disease will seem often to "skip a generation," or for the fact that there is no overt epilepsy in the parents of many an epileptic child. All that one can find in many such families are people with explosive and violent tempers. This temper appears to be their share of the epileptic inheritance. That those who never had a seizure really are epileptics can easily be shown with the help of electroencephalograms (records of the tiny electric currents constantly being formed in the brain).

Some Outstanding Au
by the Ex-Insane

In this chapter I present abstract
have impressed me most. First, I
Beers's well-known book, *A Mind*
because its influence on the thoug
so great. It has been reprinted a
When Beers recovered his sanity, h
helping of psychotic persons and
conditions in mental hospitals every
National Committee for Mental H
came the National Association for M

An Ex-Psychotic Recovers and

The beginning of Beers's breakdown.
June, 1894, when an elder brother wa
looked like epilepsy, he became con
would be going the same way himself.
he kept brooding over this. In Novemb
while seated in a classroom at Yale, hi
snap, and he thought he was going into
the rest of his college years, he never dar
because he felt so sure that this would th
After graduation, he went into business

34

March, 19
him in a
fying sen
less. Thre
he was a
could do
days he
him. He
ing cons
he jump
Luckily,
shock h
fused.
bars wl
in a d
ghostly
The
about
himsel
Beers'
was h
broke
of his
to he
abou
that
be t
B
ants
mai
mis
suf
he
ne
el
tr
w
w
a

was unfortunate because, as Clifford said, this breaking of
a promise "broke the only remaining thread that bound me
to the world." He could not believe that his brother could
have done such a thing, and hence the man who did it could
not be his brother; he had to be an impostor. This is typical
of the logic of the insane.

All relatives of a psychotic person should know that with
the mentally ill every promise—and even every trifling one,
direct or implied—should, if possible, he kept to the letter.
As Beers said, "Suspicion cannot be overcome by being fed
upon untruth, and suspicion is the condition of most unbalanced minds." "To gain the shattered confidence of insane patients, their treatment should be consistently honest
and kind." It was only years later, as Beers regained his
sanity, that he quit blaming his brother and admitted that,
without special training in psychiatry, the brother could
easily have made a mistake. The sane can make allowances
for the mistakes or forgetfulness of loved ones, but the insane cannot.

Like so many persons who have been insane, when Beers
recovered, he was sure that if only the seriousness of his
situation had been recognized more quickly—if only his
family could have seen right away that he was slipping into
a psychosis, and then he had had good treatment—he almost
certainly would have been spared years of suffering.

Why a psychotic person behaves as he does. As I said,
because Beers was convinced that the man who looked and
talked like his brother was a detective trying to get damn-
ing evidence against him, for months he refused to speak
to him. This was bad because it broke all contact with his
family. All those who take care of the insane should keep
constantly remembering that, although these unhappy persons can often reason logically, their senses have become so
disturbed that they supply false information.

As Beers said, soon after he became confused, his senses
began to play tricks on him. "The tricks played upon me by
my perverted senses of taste, touch, smell, hearing and sight
were the source of great mental anguish. I heard false
voices; none of my food had its usual flavor, and this soon
led to that common delusion of the insane that some of it

contained poison." Beers began to see remarkable faces in the dark, and he saw handwriting on the sheets of his bed. He was sure that at night someone was hiding under his bed.

Then he was moved to a private sanatorium. Wisely, his brother told him where he was going, and why; but Clifford didn't believe him. He was sure he was on his way to New York City to be hanged. It was unfortunate that the doctors did not keep trying to convince him that he was in a hospital and not in a jail, as he thought.

Queer ideas Beers had, which should have been inquired into. On being admitted to the hospital, a stupid law demanded that he, an incompetent person, sign a lot of important commitment papers which, for years, might deprive him of his liberty. Naturally, he refused to sign these documents. He felt sure they would later be introduced in court as evidence against him.

A curious reason for Beers's refusing to eat was that he had an idea that the detectives supposedly watching him had worked out a code by which they could catch him incriminating himself. For instance: if he had eaten a burnt crust of bread, that would have been a confession of arson! Still another reason for not touching certain foods was his conviction that they were saturated with the blood of his loved ones!

Beers said, so wisely, that an insane man should be treated as sane in every way that is possible. The psychiatrists of that day thought it unwise to tell a disturbed person that he was insane, but Beers said that it could have saved him a world of anxiety if someone had told him that, since he was temporarily insane when he attempted suicide, he was innocent under the law. Also, he should have been told repeatedly that no legal charge had been laid against him. This, in a moment, could have relieved him of most of his mental suffering. It would have helped him greatly if someone had kept telling him why it was advisable and for his own good that he be kept shut up for a while.

As Beers said, no one should ever say that an insane person is *stubborn,* and no one should ever get angry with him for not doing immediately what he is peremptorily ordered to do. Even many of us who are sane would refuse to go into a room without being told what we were to expect there. Certainly, an insane man should never be punished for failure to obey orders. That would be like punishing a child for having the mumps. We must keep remembering that for a man bereft of his reason to act upon an idea which, to him, seems correct and logical, is sensible; it may even seem to him to be essential to his self-preservation. For a long time Beers would not talk to anyone, but as we have seen, he had good reason for this—fearing, as he did, that detectives would take down anything he said!

The patient who talked again. A while ago I was much impressed by the fact that one day when Governor Stratton of Illinois was inspecting one of the mental hospitals in his state, he stopped to chat for five minutes with a man who, for many years, hadn't spoken a word to anyone. When the governor moved on, reporters and attendants crowded around the man to ask, "How come you talked to the governor?" "He talked to me," was the simple and logical answer! I imagine that what the patient meant was that the governor had talked to him courteously, evidently wanting to learn something that he could tell him. Perhaps for years the attendants had talked to the man only with dislike in their voices.

I have attended many a medical consultation in which within a few minutes the air was crackling with a sort of electricity of hate. Once it was so bad I was glad when I was able to leave the room. What had happened was that the doctor who came in had instantly taken a dislike to the nervous or psychotic patient and, after glancing at his history, had decided he was a cry-baby type of "neuro." Accordingly, when the doctor asked a question, he did it in so accusing or insulting a way that, in a moment, the patient was bristling with anger. This in turn riled the doctor, and in a minute the two men would have liked to go at each other's throats.

The patients in mental hospitals have often been denied books and magazines. Beers tells how, for a while, he refused to read. He would have loved to read; he craved magazines and books, and he should have had plenty of them.

Reading would have speeded his recovery; but he felt that in some way, such reading would have injured his case when he came up before the judge. Later, when he wanted to read, and should have been reading, books were taken away from him by a stupid and vindictive doctor. Many of the ex-insane have told in their books of the great stupidity of old-time superintendents who would not allow them to have any reading matter.

Often, with kindness and frankness, one can get the insane to cooperate. The winning of an insane man's confidence is not always impossible. A number of times in my office I have done it largely by treating the man as if he were sane, and I liked him. This attitude he would greatly appreciate, and soon he would become friendly and trusting. Then I would get him to admit that he had been acting unwisely and to his own detriment, and with this he would say he could see the need for treatment. He would do whatever I advised. I would ask him if, for a while, he would accept treatment in a mental hospital, and he would say, "All right," that he would go and commit himself—and he would.

Ways in which the insane can become confused. Beers tells how difficult it is sometimes to keep from alarming the insane. For instance, even some of the well-meant and harmless statements made to Clifford by his brother frightened him. Several times when his brother said, "We'll soon be straightening you out," this phrase had a dismaying effect because Clifford got the impression that what was meant was that he would be straightened out by the hangman's rope!

No treatment was given. As commonly happens in over-crowded and understaffed hospitals, no attention was paid to Beers except to see that he had three meals a day, a regular bath, and some exercise. So long as he was passive and didn't make trouble, the attendants were kind to him. But when he began to make trouble, war began.

Unfortunately, later, when Beers changed from his silent mood and became manic, his doctor took a dislike to him and started denying him most of his perfectly reasonable requests, such as that for the pencils and reams of paper that had been keeping him quiet and out of mischief. This stupidity on the part of the doctor soon brought much trouble down upon him and the attendants. Beers became so resentful and angry, and so determined to fight for his rights, that he soon was causing everyone much annoyance.

Beers makes trouble. About this time, also, because Beers had decided to write his book about insanity, he wanted to see some of the brutal attendants he had heard about. In order to get to see these, he wanted to be put for a while into the worst ward of all, the one in which the violent patients were kept. In order to get sent there, he had to be violent, and violent he became! By jeering at his doctor and calling him an incompetent ignoramus he soon succeeded in making that pompous man so angry that he lost all control of himself and with his own hands tied his tormentor into a canvas strait jacket. He bound Beers's arms so tightly that the poor fellow suffered tortures all that night and part of the next day.

He got himself transferred to the violent ward, where he ran amok, partly because he was still a bit psychotic, and partly in order to see what the attendants would do to a "difficult" patient. He soon found out. Day after day he got beaten up, knocked down, and choked into unconsciousness. Some of Beers's friends later asked, "But what can attendants do with an insane man when he becomes violent?" Beers's logical answer was, never treat him so nastily that he will get violent. Actually, Beers decided that much of the violence of the patients he studied in the bad ward had been *produced* by the brutal handling they had received when they came into the hospital. As he said, even a sane man, if kicked about for a while, would have begun to fight back.

Instead of explaining to a confused and fearful old man why the doctor wanted him in a certain room, an attendant would simply say, "Get in there." And when the man, perhaps fearing that he might meet torture or death in the room, refused to go in, he was kicked and beaten and thrown in. Occasionally, in those old days, an elderly man would die after such a beating.

As Beers said, the doctors could hardly have approved of such behavior, but if they had fired the offender the other

attendants might have struck, and at that time it was hard
to get attendants who would work in so unpleasant a job
for so small a salary. Hence it was that when a patient was
being beaten up, everyone looked the other way, and no
one dared buck the *system*. Also, in those days, it did not
help to fire a brutal attendant, because all he did was to go
to another hospital nearby, where he was immediately taken
on, with no questions asked. Obviously, this was some sixty
years ago, and conditions today in most hospitals have improved.

Beers doubtless was right in assuming that a really competent psychiatrist could have won the good will of most of
the patients under his care. If occasionally an excited patient did get nasty, a wise doctor would not have paid any
attention to him: he would have known that, since the man
was insane, he was not responsible for what he was saying.

Beers said that he was kept in the violent ward for four
months, although for most of this time he was practically
sane and just studying the behavior of the doctors and attendants, much as if he had been a newspaper reporter
planted in the institution. Beers felt that the physician in
charge, if he had had more sense or kindliness, would have
let him out much earlier than he did.

*Later, Beers was much helped by being transferred to a
better hospital.* When Beers's brother eventually found out
how badly Clifford was being treated by the physician who
hated him, he transferred him to another hospital in which
the assistant superintendent was sensible and kindly. This
man immediately gave Beers all the privileges he dared
give, together with all the books and magazines and writing
paper that he wanted. Although Beers was still a bit manic,
the doctor treated him as if he were sane; he told him he
trusted him, and this so pleased Beers that he tried thereafter
to act so as to be worthy of the trust! He would not "let the
Superintendent down." How different were these two ways of
handling him—one with brutality, and the other with friendliness and mutual trust.

Eventually, Beers became so well that he was allowed to
go out into the city and even go back to work in his office
—so long as an attendant went with him. One day, leaving

his keeper in the lobby of a bank, he went in and talked the bank officers into placing a contract for a building project which would mean the expenditure of $150,000. On another occasion, he was pleased with himself because he went to dinner with a number of old friends who did not know that he was still "insane." They all had a pleasant evening, and then he went back to the hospital for the night. No one had noticed anything wrong with him!

As Beers said, during his last weeks in the hospital, "The doctors and attendants treated me as a gentleman. Therefore, it was not difficult to prove myself one." As he said, if the doctors in the first hospital had treated him with kindliness and intelligence, he probably would have recovered much sooner.

Some of the great lessons that Beers taught were the following: (1) recognize earlier the symptoms of oncoming insanity; (2) in dealing with the insane, be absolutely honest and keep all promises; (3) explain to the insane that they are insane, and why, for a while, they must go into a mental hospital; (4) try to find out why they are refusing to cooperate with the attendants; (5) treat them with kindness and, whenever possible, accede to their requests; (6) keep them supplied with writing materials, books, and magazines; (7) don't try to keep the insane at home; and (8) unless the family is so wealthy that the financial burden is of no concern, send the patient right off to a *state* hospital.

How It Feels to Go Raving Mad

Of all the many books I have found describing personal experiences with insanity, the most brilliant and vivid, and the one that tells most clearly what it feels like to go violently insane, is *These Are My Sisters* (1947). It was written by a woman who used the pen name of Lara Jefferson. Because I think so highly of her contribution to the literature of mental troubles, I am discussing it here, alongside my abstract of Beers's volume. Mrs. Jefferson gives us the most vivid picture of a personality which, while going mad, seemed to separate itself from the body it formerly inhabited, and then to stand off, looking down at this body with contempt. Very remarkable is her description of the great mental relief that can come to a person who, after many long years of struggling to stay sane and to behave herself, finally lets go, and in a sort of wild exultation becomes insane—with no longer any inhibitions or need for worrying about conscience and the results and penalties of wrongdoing.

A woman who had been vowed to God. Lara says, "I was the child of a woman of forty-six and a man of seventy. Five children were born to my mother before I arrived. These five, and the three previous husbands, had all died before I was born. All succumbed to some wasting disease. The oldest child lived fourteen short years—the youngest only a few months." "As my mother approached her menopause, she prayed for a child who would survive, and that prayer was answered. Perhaps it shouldn't have been."

"Before my conception I was pledged to the service of God. The child in her womb was to be made into the world's greatest evangelist. After my birth, mother's menopause came, and lasted sixteen years—sixteen years of ill health, and a determination that I should be a Saint who would pay off her debt to God."

Her education and how it fell short. During all of her unhappy youth the girl was forced daily to memorize texts from the Bible, until she could quote hundreds of them. "My mind was crammed with knowledge no child should have been made to absorb." "I was to spend my life leading people to God, but I was worldly; I could not accept the idea that the salvation of the world depended on me. I wanted to be a girl; not a saint." It did not help matters that because Lara's mother was matron in a state prison (in Oklahoma) the girl was brought up within the stone walls, where the sex-hungry criminals sometimes tried to molest her.

So the mother kept striking back at her by threatening her with insanity. This was to be her punishment if she let her thoughts stray to worldly things. When the mother saw that she could not make a great preacher and saint out of the girl, she tried for the next best thing, which was to make her into an evangelistic musician. But after three years she had to face the fact that the girl was tone deaf! Then the mother became so outraged that she kept saying that Lara "had debased her before God; I had failed in 'My Destiny.' Contempt of me crept upon her; and downward—ever downward—I slid in her regard."

Soon, Lara was taking refuge as best she could "in deliberate forgetfulness, and in fanciful dreams of a world in which there was no music and no efforts toward 'leading the world unto Light.'" In desperation, the mother tried putting her daughter in a convent. The girl left there as soon as she could, but this meant going back home "to face constant contempt and unkind condescension, and a whirlpool of misguided mentality." All the time the mother kept exhorting her to fear the Lord and His vengeance, and kept telling her what would happen to her if she didn't become an evangelist.

When insanity appeared. And then, one day, after 29 years of this constant persecution, the mental breakdown that the girl had for long felt was coming caught up with her and swept her over the edge. As Lara tells us, the germ of insanity had always been present in her mind. From earliest childhood "I had had to contend with it." "It had always been waiting before me . . . or behind . . . pursuing me." "I was only a child when I first felt its hot breath upon me. I started down through the years in headlong flight, trying to escape that which could not be escaped." "The monster was so sure of his prey that he could afford to take his own time in the catching!" In one place in her book, Lara hints that the great religious fanaticism of the mother represented her share of some mental aberration that had come down to her from some eccentric forebears. This is probable.

Somewhere along the way, Lara escaped from her mother long enough to get married, but in the book that is all we are told about this phase of her life. (Mr. Jack Vickers, her publisher, tells me that before her mental crack-up she divorced her husband, and when she came out of the hospital, she remarried him.)

One day, the breaking point came, and Lara—now twentynine, and a big powerful six-footer—picked up a hammer and, coming up behind her mother, was about to brain her with one terrible blow. She says that at the moment, "I was filled with a fierce exultation because I felt as powerful as Samson." But then, "Midway in its swing, my arm was stopped as though another hand had caught it; and I saw it descend gently." "This brought me somewhat to my senses, and I turned and went away. The next hour was a Gethsemane I wish I could forget."

She has herself committed. Lara went straight to the Court House to ask that, for her own protection and that of others, she be locked up. She was declared insane and sent to the Vinita, Oklahoma, mental hospital. Lara says this would have been the end of her story if she could only have stopped thinking. Matters went well enough in the hospital until a letter came from her mother, asking if she could come for a visit. Then, "I felt such a rebellion and bitterness fill me, that it rose and choked me. I could not reason around it; I thought of the thousand ways I had loved her, and would not admit that there was any cause for the hatred I felt."

Her efforts to hang onto her sanity. Then a great fear came over Lara that any minute she would lose self-control and go completely insane—so murderously insane that she would start killing people. So she called the hospital physician and told him she was going mad and must have help. As she said, "The thing is lashing within me, and I feel the walls of my structure crumbling." The doctor sent her to the so-called hydro department of the hospital, where they gave her wet packs.

"A fierce determination came to me—born of new hope and courage; and I made a resolve that no matter how greatly I might be tempted to think with a warped crookedness—I would resist it; I would hold it down and repel it." "So I went about with new courage." But later, "a loneliness seized me—the like of which I had never known. I wanted something but what it was I did not know. I felt the stark madness of the other patients beating in on me, and I could not endure it. Something gave way within me. It was *madness*." I thought of the man I had married. "I remembered the tight stricken look on his face as he said good-bye to me, not daring to kiss me. I thought of the years we had lived together."

And the flood broke. "It all broke in a flood around me." "In that moment my thinking ceased to be thinking and became naked feeling." "I thought of my mother, probably staring out as I was, seeing nothing. I knew she would be sitting somewhere awaiting death, and I would be sitting in the madhouse awaiting madness, and the sooner it came for each of us, the better. And so the monster was out, and the ghost of some old berserk ancestor rose up within me and suggested that I could do something about it; and the fierce hatred exulted because it had possessed itself of a massive and powerful body. And the thing that was in me was not I at all, but *another*—and I knew that no power on earth but a strait-jacket could hold *her*."

The impulse to kill. "So I went to the nurse and said, 'Tie me up quickly; tie me quickly before something terrible happens.' . . . But the nurse did not sense *her* danger and just sent me back to my bed." Lara dared not obey the criminal urge that she felt—the urge to kill. "*I had controlled this urge for years*, but now I knew it was beyond me." "I knew the thoughts that came to me were maniacal; and I knew I could not resist them much longer." So, again, she begged the nurse to put her into restraint, and again the young woman ignored the warning. "I stood over her with my hands gripping my folded arms tightly because I could not trust them to hang free at my side. All my nerves tingled with the madness loose within me—and I thought how pleasant it would be to let my arm swing free and fell her with one mighty blow. I knew I could do it. I knew I *would* if she did not hurry and tie me up."

"If I live for a thousand years I shall never forget the minutes that followed. The nurse stood there before me with no idea that my request was an appeal for help—urgent and necessary. To the nurse's way of thinking, before I could be put in a strait-jacket I would first have to commit some misdemeanor—and I had done nothing. She did not know of that berserk thing in my brain, charging and raging." As Lara said, with her great strength, if she had ever let go, not ten people in that ward would have been able to hold her, or to tie her down. Fortunately, she could still cling to the "decency that was left."

But still the nurse was in great danger. As Lara said, "For one split second I had the feeling I had stepped out of my body and was standing there watching." "I kept praying a desperate prayer—don't kill her; don't kill her." "I looked on the person who I knew was not myself—and knew I had never seen—she was so deadly and menacing that I felt a nausea of fear, and prayed God to make the nurse hurry!"

Again, the nurse simply said, "Go back to your bed. I am not going to tie you"; and again Lara warned the girl that if something awful happened to her, it would be her own fault. As if she hadn't already been stupid enough, the nurse now dared her to come on and fight; she said that that morning she'd enjoy a good fight! Fortunately, soon after this the young woman gave in and put Lara into a strait jacket. Then there came to her a great flood of tears—tears of relief that at least she was safe—she had not killed any-one.

Then she heard in her disturbed mind the voice of her mother, "filled with cruelty, sneering, 'You poor ungodly thing.'" "I wondered if she were feeling delight in knowing that at last I was meriting the contempt she had felt for me when I had failed. I hated her with a fierceness I could not control—had I wanted to. It raged through me."

Exultation in madness. "And once the great Madness in me had found a voice, there was no stopping it. It rolled out in such a tumult I was amazed at it—I wondered where it all came from. It seemed obscene and terrible that I should be answering in adult language, things said to me in my childhood—things I had forgotten, until they again began to pour about me in a flood of bitter memories."

"All my fear of pain and loss of reason and eventual death was drowned in wild exultation. I stood upon the brink of everything I had ever feared, and knew that now it did not matter how far I fell. I knew I was falling, and this wild thing within me stood erect, and laughed great peals of laughter not good to hear. It made even my own flesh creep and crawl to hear it, because that laughter was not mine—but something wild and terrible." "I prayed to God to keep me from filling my mouth with the slimy obscenities that the patients around me were constantly screaming out."

The relief that can come with insanity. Very thought-producing and somewhat startling is Lara's statement that "when a soul sails out on that uncharted sea called Madness it has gained a release which is much greater than its loss." "Those who have experienced what I am speaking of know the wild hysteria of Madness means salvation—release and escape, and salvation from a much greater pain which is the *fear of* Madness. It means escape from that which could not be endured. And this is why Madness came—as deliverance: pure, simple, deliverance!"

"Madness knows nothing of the fears which formerly held us. It knows nothing of wrong-doing—has no such thing as conscience—has no fear of God or Devils. Nothing in this world can stay it when it has claimed its own. The one whom it has chosen has no choice in the matter; he or she must follow and obey." "No phenomenon of nature is so awe inspiring. A typhoon—a Niagara can be caught and held in harness as easily as one can catch and hold a deranged mind!" "I have felt it sweep me, and take me—where —I did not know, all the way through Hell, and far, far, on the other side. It has given me a keener sense of feeling than has the dull edge of reason."

How true is her statement that she learned that "nothing is as terrible when it is actually happening to us as when we were dreading and anticipating it." "When the thing we have feared comes upon us, we are so enveloped and enmeshed in it we do not have time to worry about it. Worry is what fills vacuity." "*Even Madness—the thing from which I had fled for most of my life, was not so terrible when it actually overtook me as it was in all the years during which I tried to escape it.*"

When "the last connected and coherent element in my thinking gave way, the madness filled me and rejoiced." "It shouted and exulted with a noise that tore my throat out, charging through me till it nearly dragged the life out of me." How remarkable is her statement that a part of her mind "stood there and took in the whole situation, yet could do nothing about it." Many a psychotic patient has told me this story. As one mildly psychotic but beautiful woman said to me, she could never have a satisfactory sex life because, when in the arms of a lover, part of her always stood off to one side and jeered at the other half for the "silly things" it was doing! As Lara says, "The thing that was raging did not seem wrong to me then—but the rightest thing in the world —a magnificent accomplishment."

Insanity can be more interesting than sanity. Curiously, Lara says in several places in her book that insanity can be more interesting than is the dull prosaic thing called sanity —which she had fought so hard and so long to keep. She says, "The loss of it was not worth grieving over." Also, curiously, she says "there came to me a feeling of rest and freedom, as I floated on the current of my thoughts without any of the old struggle to keep my thinking in the channels I had been taught were right! So I let my thoughts run wild and free. All the things I had striven for, during a life-time of fierce wanting, fell so far away from me I did not know I had ever suffered disappointment—or unrest—or fear."

So she went ahead and sang at the top of her voice as so many of her fellow-patients were doing. "As one of these women said to me, 'You are enjoying your insanity!' And she was right."

When hallucinations came. Then, for a while, she "saw things"—birds and bats that flitted about in her mind's eye. "Presently over in the corner I saw a creature about two feet tall, jumping up and down. He looked like pictures I had seen of imps, and seemed in high glee. I was not afraid of him—he amused me; I just asked the little squirt what he wanted, and what he was laughing at."

Chemical changes in the insane body. During five days and nights of wild raving, "I had been wringing wet with perspiration, and the stench which assailed me when the strait-jacket was loosened, was asphyxiating." "It seemed as if something in me had died and decomposed." How amazingly modern Lara was when she wrote, "My whole body chemistry was changed. Truly I was a different person."

Lara writes up her thoughts. All through her hospital experience, during intervals when Lara was lucid, she kept writing notes on scraps of paper—notes which later she turned over to Mr. Jack Vickers for publication. This writing helped her to cling to what little sanity she had left. As she said, "Something has broken loose within me and I am insane"; but still "I have sense enough to know it." Also, most of what she wrote was perfectly logical; it apparently had been written by the half of her brain which remained so sane that it could watch with disapproval what the other half did.

The best psychiatrist or philosopher in the land could hardly have written more wisely than she wrote in the next few pages. As she said, "Here I sit—mad as a hatter—with nothing to do but either become madder and madder—or else recover enough of my sanity to be allowed to go back to the life which drove me mad." "Unless I learn to think differently, I shall shortly be incurably insane." "It is up to me—to the power of the life still within me. There is nothing another person can do to help me. The job is mine to do. Nothing has yet been discovered which will enable [the psychiatrists] to reach into the dim caverns of a crooked brain and make the crooked places straight. The doctors have endless ideas and theories—but when it comes down to actual performance of making an insane person sane— they are helpless."

The inability often of physicians to help the insane. "They have a list of long Greek and Latin words to define the several types of insanity, and when they observe such and such symptoms, they paste a label on us—and that is the end of the matter. I cannot see that they have accomplished much, simply because they were able to remember a long-handled name for our madness. We, who have learned what madness is by going through it—are separated from all others by a gulf so wide that it cannot be bridged."

She doubted "if the doctors in the hospital were as sure of what they thought they knew as they would like others to have believed—or would like to have believed themselves." Often she sat and thought of what might be ahead of her—perhaps nothing but "insanity with nakedness and loneliness—unless I can learn to think differently." But, "How, How, How? In the name of God—How does a per-

son learn to think differently? I who am crazy wild this
minute—how can I learn to think straight?"

The two persons at odds in her body. "Something has
happened to me—I do not know what. The self that was
formerly mine has crumbled and fallen in, and a creature
has emerged of whom I know nothing. She is a stranger
to me." "How can I escape the fate stretching out before
me? The easy way out would be to cease from all caring or
striving. But, as long as there is a shred of me left, I dare
not do other than try to find some sort of balance between
the conflicting forces fighting within me."

"I can recall with humor the odd sensation I had [when
first put in the hospital] on finding that a crazy woman had
moved into my body—a crazy woman who had no sense,
and who refused to be governed by reason—who acknowl-
edged no law higher than her own whim—and who had no
fear of anything." "This person is not real—she is not I—
I never saw her before; I must have dreamed her up. I am
dreaming her now."

Sometimes Lara thought that she might wake up some
day and find it all a dream. She hoped someone would come
and waken her so that she could go free. But then she
doubted if this could be. "There is only a shadow remaining
of the person I used to be. My whole former life has fallen
away so completely it might be an existence lived in the
Stone Age—leaving only a few uncertain bones to mark its
passing. If the person whom I used to be could not prevent
the birth of the person I have now become, there is not
much chance that the latter powerful creature will be controlled by the ghost of the old person whom she succeeded."

Curiously, Lara had the feeling that she didn't want to go
back into the body of the old person she formerly was. "I
would not call her back if I could. None can write her obitu-
ary better than I—for she was I—a pitiful creature who could
not cope with life as she found it—nor could she escape it—
nor adjust herself to it. So she became mad, and died in
anguish—of frustration and raving. The worst that could be
said of her is that she was a fool and a coward. The best:—
that she did have the foresight to see Madness coming, and
to make grim preparations for its advent—And God alone,

who knows all about our inner emotions, is the one able to judge whether her end was a defeat—or a triumph!"

Some of Lara's remarkably clear thoughts about insanity. "All my life I have been in the throes of either mania or depression, one or the other, and I have an empty sick feeling when I think of the energy I wasted in trying to hold my moods down to something like reason." How well she describes the problem of the manic-depressive person!

Remarkable is her thought that "If the weak, fearful creature that I used to be, had the ability to generate, out of her weakness and fright, such a powerful creature as I have become—then the world must have had her all wrong. She was not an imbecile—but a genius; even though the creature that has grown out of her failure is a monstrosity." "I do not know what to do with her—nor how to withstand her, nor how to educate her." "But she mocks me—and tells me that it does not matter whether life is lived inside an asylum or out of it." "Life is the important thing—not the classification of it. Life—to live it—and not to fear it. Let it rip—let it roar —let it be destructive if it must; the essential thing is to live it."

Her pictures of fellow patients. Lara gives us vivid pen pictures of half a dozen strange personalities in her ward. As she says, it is remarkable to see someone who was brought up as a puritan suddenly with the coming of insanity start hurling out obscenities that would make a sailor blush.

Many of us have noticed what strange piercing and moving—and even frightening—eyes some eccentric people have. Speaking of one of the women in her ward, Lara says, "To feel her eyes sweep you is to feel a chillness blown from caverns of hatred—black, vast and bottomless. You know then that you have seen naked madness—heavy, and pregnant with horror unborn."

Lara's wonderings about why the incurably insane are allowed to suffer on and on through the years. As Lara lived day after day in this awful pandemonium and watched her terrible fellow patients—many of them so far gone that they urinated and defecated wherever they stood—she got a strong feeling that if our legislators had more sense and

more kindness and *more human sympathy,* they would order the sterilization of those many persons who, if they ever
were to have children, would probably have some resembling the women in that awful ward.

Lara also wondered if it wouldn't be immensely kind to
grant many of the hopelessly incurable creatures a release
to a permanent sleep. She thought that if the people outside
such a ward could live for even two days watching these
patients, they wouldn't be able to stand it. They would demand that many of the hopeless ones be put out of their
misery.

*Lara's puzzlings over why we allow probably doomed
children to be born.* As Lara said, "If there is no chance of
freeing some of us, once the snare of Madness has caught
us—and if the trap is sprung most often along the path of
heredity; won't someone please try to decide who is fit to
bequeath the heritage of [a fine useful] life to a child—and
then dam up the life-stream of the other [persons who cannot be trusted to have children]. Please give the half-damned
children the freedom of never being born into a life of suffering. For it is better that a life not begin than that it have
to *gamble* with the probability of reaching an awful ending." By which she meant geneticists know how bad
the gamble is for the children of, let us say, two schizophrenics. Professor Franz Kallmann of Columbia, who has
spent his life gathering statistics on this problem, can tell
us that under such circumstances at least half the children
born to the couple are likely to be psychotic.

Lara went on to say, "Once defective children are born,
there is that in our modern thinking which recoils from the
heathen custom of strangling them. Because we have no
sacred rivers into which we can throw our poorly born
babies, they grow up and mature, and perhaps beget others.
Some of the largest institutions in the land are now given
over to the care of those who came out of the shambles—
creatures who were faced, even before they were formed,
with the possibility of being a terrible burden to others—
and a source of unspeakable torture to themselves!"

Lara said she knew that many of the hopelessly insane
about her would gladly have accepted a judge's decision

that their sufferings be ended. Obviously, many of the thousands of insane who try each year to commit suicide would be grateful if a judge were to permit someone to help them in their repeated efforts to get out of this world—a world which, for them, is full of nothing but agony.

I hope that no one will now write me savagely to accuse me of wishing to put to death his mother who is a bit disturbed mentally. All I have done is to quote the words of a thoughtful woman who knows immensely more than I can ever know about the horrors of raving madness—of people who sit all day in nakedness and filth and spit at anyone who comes near. Because she lived in a hell and watched scores of people going through that hell, we might at least listen to her and think a bit. Before we rush to attack someone who begs for mercy for these people, all of us ought to go at least once through the worst wards of a state hospital. After seeing the horrors there, we would have a little more right to discuss the subject of what to do about the unrestricted breeding of such mentally and physically unfit persons. Unfortunately, the problem is not as simple as Lara thought, because the apparently normal brothers and sisters of a horribly insane woman can breed insane children just as easily as can the insane woman. Few of these "carriers" of insanity will care to be sterilized.

The insane can appreciate and respond to kindness. Worth remembering is Lara's statement that "Though we [in the ward] are insane, and not quite human beings, this very fact gives us a keener appreciation of any kindness shown us. If a nurse treats one of us as a human being she gains for herself a devotion, dog-like in its loyalty."

Lara recovers. The book ends on a hopeful note. Lara says that a nurse had just come to tell her that she was so much better that that night she was to be transferred to "the best ward in the hospital," where she could live in a civilized atmosphere and with almost sane people. Later, Lara got straightened out and after that for a while was employed in her city as a housekeeper. Her publisher, Mr. Jack Vickers, tells me that she is still living, and well. Only once, after leaving the hospital, did she go into a brief spell of madness.

A Remarkable Manic-Depressive Adventuress

Of all the books written by manic-depressive persons, probably the most interesting and instructive is called *Magpie*. It is the story of Lois Vidal, a young Englishwoman born probably about 1890, the well-educated daughter of an English country parson, who, like his daughter, went insane. This book gives us the best available picture of the type of person who, while in a restless spell of mild mania, rambles about the country, unable to settle down anywhere for more than a few days at a time.

Many of the mentally unbalanced can pass as sane. Lois was one of those innumerable persons who, while mentally ill for most of their days, and often so badly that for a while they have to take refuge in a mental hospital, are never violent or unreasonable or confused and can always chat so well with a stranger that they are never thought to have anything worse than a fatigue state or, perhaps, some eccentricity. This young woman's story alone is sufficient to show us why no lawyer has ever been able to think of a definition of insanity that will hold up in a court of law.

As I was writing this, a patient and his wife told me of their next-door neighbor in a suburb—an able, unmarried business woman of thirty-five—who, after receiving much kindness at their hands, turned on them and showed herself to be a dangerous paranoiac, capable even of attacking them. To their surprise, she started accusing them of all sorts of malicious persecution. She became so threatening that they became frightened and moved away. What interested my patient was that this crazed woman could still, on occasions, be so attractive and ingratiating that, when last heard from, she had a wealthy widower who was planning to marry her! If he *did* take her to the altar, what a terrible awakening he must soon have had!

Apparently a poor nervous inheritance. Miss Vidal's nervous heredity was much against her. She tells us that her father died after 10 years in a mental hospital. The mother was an able and sensible person. Several of the children started out with poor health. Mary and Mark died by the time they were twenty. We are not told what the cause was. Peter had some mental difficulties off and on for much of his life. His health was poor, and more than once he had to be in a "home of rest." For a while he was a "veritable skeleton, with hardly more impulse to live than a crushed beetle." In later years, he had Lois's tendency to travel about. At sixteen, Bridget had St. Vitus's dance and hysteria. She was expelled from two schools for insubordination, and she had to spend time in what was probably a mental hospital. Occasionally she was so manic that she would not stop talking for even a minute. When she was twenty-nine, she said she had had enough and committed suicide. Dorothy, from the age of eleven, was constantly struggling with a "terribly irritable nervous system," and a jealousy that often made her a thorn in the flesh of her family. She often had "a terrible neuralgia." Many manic-depressive persons complain, mainly of pain in the face, chest, abdomen, or lower back. John and Lancelot appear to have been the only stable ones in the group of eight sibs.

Marked ill health soon came to Lois. Early in life Lois was taken out of school for a term because of a pigeon breast and a painful kink in her spine. She says that school games tired her abnormally. She early came to sense that "we were a family with a 'skeleton,' and Lord help me if I got touched with its ghoulish breath, or whatever way a skeleton affects one." When she was seventeen, she had her first spell of depression, with "three months of misery and deadness." So many persons, when they go into a depression, speak of feeling dead; there "is no life in them." A little later she had another "breakdown" and for a while had to retire to the country. After this, she had an attack of mania "when I had perhaps one hour's sleep in 48." Then she entered a mental hospital which was to be her haven off and on for years.

Repeated hospitalizations. As usually happens when a person first starts going insane, her family tried hard to keep her out of a mental hospital. As Lois says, when she was eighteen her mother strove "in an agony of love to keep me from this." But something had to be done. "For some months I had not slept properly; and had not ceased to see visions." In her first maniacal spell, with her brain racing, she found herself able to recite long passages from Shakespeare and the Bible. She soon left the hospital, but from time to time she had to go back in. Once, she had to remain for six months "until the fires of that over-lit spirit were finally burned out, leaving it ashy and lifeless." She tried to curb her "undisciplined emotions and imagination," but this was hard to do. For a time, as sometimes happens when the brain is not working well, she put on much weight, until she, a small woman, weighed 182 pounds. Later, this fat came off, and she became petite again.

A series of brief and unfortunate engagements with worthless men. During one of her convalescent periods, Lois started on her series of precipitate and amazing courtships which after a few days, would end in an engagement—always short-lived. Usually the man was interesting and intelligent, but always he had no job, no money, and no prospects. One of the great difficulties of some mildly psychotic women is that, when it comes to picking friends and beaus, they have no sense.

The first fiancé promptly "borrowed" £100, which represented all of Lois's savings, and then he left for parts unknown. Several other beaus tried hard to borrow a similar sum, but by the time they arrived on the scene Lois's bank account was empty! With each fiancé she would become devoted enough so that, for a few months, she would write a long letter every day, but then the man would drop out of sight.

Her inability to become aroused sexually. Interesting is the fact which any psychiatrist or good physician could have prophesied, namely, that a psychotic girl would have little if any ability to love with her body. When World War I was started, she went to France for YWCA work. There, she had many experiences with men—weird experiences of the sort she was to keep having for the next twenty years or more. For instance, when she went for a drive with a man he quickly wanted to make love. "I was intrigued and startled, but drew in my horns and assumed the ice-armour that had proved so useful in the past." "No part of my emotional system was really engaged." Any man with any sensitivity at all can quickly realize that a woman like Lois is asexual and without interest in having any intimate contact.

Often as she worked in her office in the YWCA she would get so tired that she would "lose herself in a kind of torpor," a mild manifestation of her tendency to depression. She went on playing a bit with the suitors "who passed in the night," but she remained "practically unawakened." One episode nearly carried her off her feet, "but the habit of 'ice-wearing' just prevented the thrill from reaching its zero-point, and I was left wondering. There were all the signs and portents of ardour, and the innate worthlessness of the man hardly struck me, and never bothered me."

Later, when she got back to England, she found that a new Lois had developed—"a queer, timid, conscientious creature who had never let herself go." Then along came an interesting beau who shared her love of books and reading. "With never the least need for ice-packs, we enjoyed each other's company, and from the first we slipped into a genuine and rather uncommon understanding; but emotionally we left each other untouched. All of which was a blessing, and a salutary background to other possibly less frigid encounters."

She began to go so far as to spend an occasional night in the same room or even the same bed with a man, but she never wanted sex, and she says the man always respected her feelings in this matter. Often he, too, had no interest in a sexual adventure. He had a little money, she had none, and all they wanted was companionship and shelter for the night. Doubtless, many readers will doubt Lois's statements about her lack of sex experience, but I think any psychiatrist who knows how frigid most depressed women are will be able to believe what she says.

In England she suffered from the terrible cold of winter in an unheated house. "The cold turned me to stone; I was numb and senseless with it; all life ebbed out of me. I went through my duties mechanically." I "kept going for months on the very last ounce of my nervous strength." How wonderful if persons of her type, with a cyclic personality, who are alternately too elated and too depressed, could learn how unwise it is to live as they do—when mildly manic, using up every scrap of energy they have: staying up to all hours and going to bed late.

The loss of her old ability as a secretary. One of the results of Lois's undisciplined life was that she soon lost her ability to work as a fast and accurate typist or manager of an office. Because of this loss of her old skills, for many years after she had to work usually as a maid or a cook, or a minor employee in a hotel. But she rarely stayed with any job for more than 10 days. Either she was fired, or she became restless and rambled off somewhere. Occasionally, she had to go back into her old mental hospital. There, the doctors did little besides urge her to "pull herself together," to forget herself, and to get back to work. As she says, "For anyone as emotionally sensitive as I was, it was hell to be thus insensitive, dead and numb, with no more rebound in me than that of a punctured rubber ball."

More spells of depression. Lois tells us that one of the first symptoms that always warned her of an approaching nervous breakdown was an inability to concentrate or to read even a page. She would find herself reading a paragraph over and over again without getting anything out of it or remembering anything of it. Forty years ago my patients taught me that this is one of the surest signs that the brain has become very tired and a bit demoralized. It is an important "danger signal." No one should run past it.

Another difficulty was that her "mind was tortured with a habit of long delving and introspection, till no act or thought or moment of joy in my very clear memory had any virtue. It was all smirched. Always I had been monumentally selfish; always my motives were mean, even when my actions were possibly generous."

So she went back again into the mental hospital. There they tried to teach her to be less self-conscious and less inclined to brood over "the unhealthy thoughts that romped in an empty and exhausted mind." And all the while her devoted family kept appealing to her to *pull herself together* and come and share some of the burden she had 'so shamelessly shelved.'" Very wisely, her doctor said, "Don't let them hurry you. You've done a lot in a month, but you haven't *begun* yet. You've been years running down; isn't it logical to expect you to take at least as many months building up?" I have often felt this way about a patient who for years, wastefully, has been blowing in all of her energies. A tired nervous system insists on its owner's spending a long time paying back into the bank of nervous health some of the wealth that, for months or years, was squandered so stupidly.

Staying at home was bad for her. Then her mother and sister kept trying to care for her in their home, but this worked out badly. One can easily see why the relatives of a mentally disturbed person, not knowing anything about psychiatry, often look on the apparently normal invalid as someone physically well who is "enjoying illness," or is just foolish, stubborn, and so perverse as to keep making a mess of his life.

Because of the bad influence of her loved ones on her, Lois came to hate her home, and so, back she went to the mental hospital for another period of two years. There she became so weak that for much of the time she remained in bed. She didn't improve, and she kept "the same fatigue, the pains, and the sleeplessness."

During this time, she was sane enough to be able to go home occasionally, for weddings and other celebrations, but back to the hospital she always had to go. Later, while on a visit to dear friends, she "sank into a torpor, not caring greatly for man, woman or anything, still less for my own future." And yet, when the opportunity came, she was able to get up and go with her mother on a tour through Italy.

As usual, she met a man and promptly became engaged to him. After six weeks of running around with *two* men who wanted to marry her, she said the experience "was enough to show me that a permanent marital relationship could not be otherwise than flat, stale, and unprofitable." Marriage was "not for her."

Then she tried a secretarial job, but as sometimes happens with persons as mentally disturbed as she was, her right hand soon became so cramped that she could not hold a pen. So she had to quit. Then she thought she would marry one of her beaus, but after he had failed in his efforts to "nick her" for £100, he disappeared and never came back.

Her inability to hold a job even as a housemaid. About this time, she was working as a maid or a cook in homes, but "I was so utterly incapable of tempering or modulating my peculiarities as to make it possible to hold down even an almost-perfect job." During the next several years she was constantly hunting for a job, constantly being hired, and constantly being let out. As she said so wisely, "If I could have reduced the pace at which I was living, all might have been well, but I was running away blindly at break-neck speed from a future I couldn't face." I have often wondered if these people could not avoid some of their long depressions if only, when they are manic, they could be kept from running around all the time and staying up all night. Typical was her tendency in the evenings to "write reams of self-expressive, picturesque rubbish."

And then, one day, "the powder-magazine blew up beneath my careless feet." "I found I was utterly and incorrigibly unemployable. . . . Something in me affronts my employers." And hence, soon she was back at the doors of the mental hospital, asking to be let in. This time she became deeply depressed.

In one place Lois asked, "Why does the soul revel in isolation when that spells death? The lonelier I grew, the deeper I dug into a self-imposed solitude, with separation of mind and spirit." She admits that often she seemed to take a perverse delight in forcing a rift in her relations with her mother and sister.

Months of penniless wandering in Canada. Next Lois took a bit of money that had been willed to her and with it went to Canada, where she wandered around ostensibly looking for work but never finding any. For some four months, she lived without any income. She tells of a number of her interesting experiences with men who gave her a much-needed meal, and then paid for a room in which she stayed for a few days. Most of these men were kind and understanding and did not expect any recompense for what they had done for her.

As one man said when he picked her up, he didn't care

to *use* any woman. "If I wanted a woman for her body, I'd seek her in the accredited quarter and pay her a fitting fee. If I want a woman for her companionship of mind and spirit —such as you can give me, and are giving me—only so reluctantly—and in such little tiny driblets [this is very typical of a psychotic, frigid woman]—I take her where the gods let me find her, if she will. Is that good enough?"

I am sure many of the men soon sensed that Lois wasn't "right in the head" and hence felt protective toward her. They were like the Plains Indians some 130 years ago, who never injured a certain solitary geologist who wandered about in the West. He was safe because he was constantly pouching bits of rock—and hence "obviously insane," and under the protection of the "Great Spirit."

Actually, it raises one's respect for men in general to learn that Lois was able to keep alive for months on the hospitality of men who, after picking her up, felt sorry for her and did not ask for sex. Much of her success in living was probably due to the fact that so many men, when away from home, hate to eat alone and will gladly pay for a meal for a woman who will talk to them and for a little while take away their sense of loneliness.

A return to England, and much hitchhiking. Finally, her much-worried family sent enough money so that she could get back to England. There, almost immediately, she began to wander around again. She took to thumbing her way constantly from place to place. The drivers of lorries were almost always very kind to her. As I said, they realized that she was mentally ill, and hence should be helped and not injured. Often at night, for lack of money for a hotel room, she would sleep out under a hedge somewhere.

Occasionally, she would stay a few days with old army friends, but, as she says, she wasn't always exactly welcome. Her social sense had been shattered by her wanderings, and she implies that she did not always fit well into a menage. Part of this time she kept rambling about aimlessly in London's cheapest night spots when she ought to have been in bed. This kind of restlessness produces many hoboes and half-crazy sailors. Wherever one goes in this world, even in the most out-of-the-way places, one finds a number of eccentric travelers, often of the beachcomber variety. When, in 1887, I went to Hawaii with my parents, we found there many of these mildly psychotic hermits, living by themselves in lonely shacks.

An adventure with an alcoholic physician. Once, for several months, Lois went around in London night spots with a curious alcoholic physician named Peter. Although drunk most of the time, he was always amiable and lovable. He was living on some money that had been left him by a wealthy woman to whom, for a while, he had been married. Lois and Peter liked to pretend to an affinity for the denizens of the underworld. The two lived more or less together for some time, but neither, apparently, was sexually inclined. Fortunately, Lois never drank, but after weeks of spending her nights in bars, she began to go into hysterical "tizzies" that looked like the beginnings of an attack of delirium tremens. One day when Peter saw her in one of these spells he became so frightened he got on the water wagon and stayed there! But curiously, when sober, he decided he would be much better off without Lois, and that was the end of that romance.

With this, there came a run of six nights when she had to sleep out in the park. Again, she had "the usual crop of semi-disreputable adventures." Her tendency to wander then became so strong that it was hard for her to stay for more than a day in any one spot, even when it was a much-needed haven. As she says, "Fatigue and nerve exhaustion were straining me nearly to the breaking point." Naturally, she was riding for a fall.

A sudden descent into severe depression. Many a time a manic-depressive patient has said to me that one minute she was perfectly sane and the next she was in the depths of despondency. Many such persons said, "The curtain came down." This sort of thing happened one day to Lois, after she had worked a few months as a maid. One morning when the second maid came to waken her, "her repeated calls elicited nothing but nonsense." "Fog had descended on me; my will power had snapped; the game was up. A doctor was called, who said I needed complete and immediate rest." A family friend who came to rescue her, took her into his home. There she lay for weeks "in the worst access of depression my up-and-down existence had ever known." After this, she went home for ten months, but that didn't do much good. So she ran away. "I tried a domestic job of some responsibility without the slightest hope of holding it down." Then one day she tried suicide by turning on the gas. But she was rescued. When the doctor asked, "Do you *want* to get well?" she said, "Of course I don't. That would mean work, responsibility, adult citizenship; those are the things I'm trying to avoid. I'm work-shy." As the doctor said, "Of course you are. We all are to some extent, but we tend to grow out of it. Why don't you grow up?" Her answer was, "More fun to be a child."

In a Salvation Army mental hospital. Then, for lack of funds, she, in a way, "hit bottom" in a Salvation Army mental hospital, which was filled with women from the lowest classes. As Lois said, "In the middle of the night when I lay and listened to the orchestra of snorers, the queerness of the situation would come to me and overwhelm me. To end like this: an inefficient, unloved, unloving creature, who could not even dispense one jot of what had been hers, to the hungry little lives around her."

At the end of a year she realized that she was still the same "diffident, dispirited, well-intentioned misfit." So she moved back to the mental hospital in which she had been helped before. Life there became pretty comfortable, but she couldn't relax.

Marriage. Eventually, she got better and left the hospital. But in a week she was adrift again and wandering about London's night spots. She closes the book with the bare announcement that someone showed up and married her. Only a wild optimist could believe that such a couple had any chance of "living happily ever afterwards."

Lois's story shows us how sane an insane woman can be. She shows us how these people are either too elated or too depressed. She shows, also, the habit many manic people have of aimlessly wandering about. She shows us that four out of eight children of an insane man can be psychotic. Interesting is the picture she paints of the foolish engagements to marry that a mildly psychotic woman can get into.

She gives a good description of the way in which a psychotic person loses her old business skills and her ability to hold a job. As I said, many readers will not be able to accept Lois's stories of innocence, but as a physician, I can believe them.

The World's Most Remarkable Picture of Paranoia

The most outspoken, articulate, and self-revealing paranoiac I know of was August Strindberg, the great Swedish playwright. Because he was a man of tremendous industry who wrote fast and well, and because, like many psychotic persons, he felt it his duty to report and describe even his most disgraceful acts, and because he wrote several books of frank autobiography, he has left us a marvelous record of how a paranoiac lives and thinks and suffers. The facts here given were taken from four of his autobiographies—*Legends* (1912), *The Inferno* (1912), *The Son of a Servant* (1913), and *The Confession of a Fool* (1925)—plus a revealing book written by his second wife, Freda (*Marriage with Genius,* 1937). These works deserve an honored place in the library of every psychiatrist who would like to be well-educated. Among the many instructive details to be found in Strindberg's books is the fact that a man who was primarily a paranoiac was also at times depressed, or suffering from what looked like a nonconvulsive type of epilepsy.

Strindberg's heredity and abnormal childhood. Strindberg tells us that he was the son of a shipping agent and a servant girl. His father, an Icelander, was reserved and without any capacity for showing affection. He was of a melancholy nature, so strict and serious that his children were afraid of him. August adored his mother, but even his love for her was tinged with jealousy and hate. She died early, and her going was a great shock to him. She probably gave him some of his poor nervous heredity because she was nervous, excitable, often moody, and sometimes hysterical. August had a brother who, early, had spells of hysteria. Later, for a while, he was melancholic, but then he changed and became—of all things—a comedian! Unfortunately, Strindberg in his books does not tell us anything about his other sibs.

In his book *The Son of a Servant*, Strindberg says he was born frightened, moody, and capricious. Perhaps the best thing about him was that he was very bright. Already, in his childhood, he felt that enemies were everywhere, and he had a great fear of the dark. He was depressed and hence wept often. He was so touchy that the least criticism upset him, and he lived in constant anxiety lest he should do something wrong. He was very sensitive to any action of his parents that suggested unfairness to him. He was always watching what his brothers and sisters got and was outraged if they received any more attention than came to him. Often he became bitter and withdrawn into himself. His tendency to shyness and reserve grew upon him. Even when he received a word of praise, he would go and hide. In his boyhood he was manic-depressive, being "melancholy and boisterous by turns."

Insanity showed up early. By the time he was nine, Strindberg was showing many signs of his lifelong psychosis. One day he seized a knife and threatened to cut his throat. Already he had his often-to-recur desire to do himself injury. All his life he was to be his own worst enemy. Even as a child he found pleasure in self-torment. For instance, when his mother planned some pleasant treat for her children, such as an excursion into the country, and he very much wanted to go, he would insist on remaining at home. Another will, stronger than his own, seemed to command him not to go. But, if someone would come along and jovially pick him up and put him into the wagon, he would go cheerfully because he would feel liberated from the mysterious will that mastered him.

After he was grown, he often felt that his friendly advances to people were not accepted gladly as they should have been, and then he would retire into himself with his feelings hurt. He would do silly things because of the "invisible hand which scourges and chastises me without my knowing its object." Many times in his life, he would find himself unable to speak to people. And yet, a while later, when he would be in a manic spell, he would become so talkative that his friends would run when they saw him coming.

At other times, he would withdraw completely from those about him. He might even go into a prolonged sort of trance in which he would not even take food. For instance, he once locked the door to his room, and for three or four days did not open it or respond to the anxious questions of his wife and family. Then he came out, very cheerful, and apparently unable to understand why his relatives should be annoyed with him!

He once wrote that "his new ego revolted against his old one, and he lived in discord like an unhappy married couple, unable to get a separation." At times he was greatly handicapped by his inability to make even a small decision. For example, one day he knew that a friend was expecting him, and he wanted to go to him, but he couldn't make up his mind to start.

One reads in his book *The Inferno* how all his life he had had to struggle with four terrible inner foes—doubt, suspicion, fear, and sensuality. His ceaseless suspicions made it impossible for him to be happy in either friendship or love; his fear of invisible powers and his doubts robbed him of all peace of mind, and his sensuality dragged him repeatedly into the mire. With all these handicaps it is remarkable how much money he earned with his pen, how many books and articles he wrote, and how famous he became. The world looked on him as a genius and one of the greatest of all Scandinavian writers. Like many psychotic persons, Strindberg suffered much from pains which often "drove him wild" and which he thought were due to the "unknown forces" that were persecuting him.

His tendency to turn angrily on his friends. The frequent inability of this psychotic man to direct his affairs with any sense is shown by the way in which, once, without cause, he insulted and drove from his door a wonderfully kind and eminent friend who, for some time, had been supporting him financially. As a result, for a while he was left without any income. In his later life, when he was broke and one of his best friends brought him money, he insulted him and refused to see him. He said that one reason for this type of behavior was his passionate desire to be free and independent.

Another reason for his turning suddenly on an old and good friend was probably his unfounded conviction that the man was trying to persecute him. Once, without any justification, he turned on his most admiring and devoted pupil, and wrote, "He hated me with a deadly hatred, hindered my plays from being accepted, wove intrigues, and deprived me of the barest means of subsistence!"

Manic-depressive symptoms. Although most of Strindberg's symptoms were those of paranoia, as we have seen, he was occasionally depressed, occasionally manic, and probably at times epileptic. When Strindberg was depressed, he might quite typically accuse himself of having committed every crime in the calendar. Then he would go into the manic phase, when he would frighten friends by the vehemence of his speech. Back in a depression, Strindberg would shut himself up, and for a while become a recluse. Often, like many a psychotic person, he would take long solitary walks—rambling about all through his city and the neighboring country.

His paranoia. At times he would get much upset by little things that a normal person would never have even noticed. One day in the street he found a scrap of paper with the world *marten* written on it, and in another street he found a similar scrap with the world *vulture* written (he thought) by the same hand. Instantly, for no clear reason, he concluded that a man had come from Paris to kill him!

Often, when in a hotel, Strindberg would become outraged because he thought the man in the next room was trying to annoy him by aping his actions. If Strindberg moved a chair, the man moved a chair; if Strindberg lay down on his bed, the man lay down on his bed, and so on. Sometimes, when this sort of thing happened, Strindberg would get so frightened that he would check out and flee. As he said, "when wolves are near, I scent danger, and I pack my box ready for flight."

Like many paranoiacs, he would wonder if it would do any good to go to the police for help, but apparently he soon learned this was useless. As he said, he never could get anyone to protect him. At times he would become so frightened he would hide himself behind the furniture, but this did not help "because everywhere the furies could find him." Once, suddenly, he was convinced that he had been condemned to death. He was not sure by whom, or why; all he was sure of was that his enemies would be glad to get rid of him. Another time, when he was convinced that he had been condemned to death, he sealed up in an envelope the names of his supposed murderers so that when he was found dead his friends and the police would know whom to blame.

His colossal conceit. Occasionally, like many a psychotic person, Strindberg would feel proud of the fact that he was being persecuted. He said, "My pious vanity is tickled by the idea. I am proud of the distinction of being persecuted by misfortune, and am never weary of saying 'how I have suffered.'" Illustrative of his great conceit was his statement that "Every lightning flash is a personal attack on me," also his belief that when, in a church, people crossed themselves, they were doing it to protect themselves from him!

Typical distresses of a paranoiac. Typical of paranoiacs was his conviction often that people in the rooms above or below his in a hotel were sending smoke into his room, or were directing electric rays at him. In his book *The Inferno* he wrote, "I hear shuffling footsteps, and the moving of furniture. I change my room, I go into another hotel, and still there is the noise overhead. I go to a restaurant, but as soon as I sit down to a meal, the noise begins there also. I ask those present whether they hear the noise, they say 'yes'; and their description of it tallies with mine." Apparently his neighbors preferred to humor him rather than get into an argument.

Once, when there were noises about him, Strindberg ran out into the hall to find the attendant, but when he couldn't, he was sure that his own enemies had done away with the poor fellow. But then the thought came, perhaps the attendant was one of the conspirators, and so he fled the city. Later, he said that, since after this flight he felt better, he could not have been suffering from the delusions of mental disease, but really must have been persecuted by enemies. Like most paranoiacs, after fleeing a city, he was convinced that, in spite of all of his efforts to throw his enemies off his trail, they had traced him, and were in the next room to torment him again!

Once, on going to his room, he heard a tremendous racket overhead. There seemed to be at least a score of young people up there singing, stamping their feet, and pushing things about. The disturbance lasted till morning. When day came, Strindberg got some friends to go with him to search the attic, but naturally, they found no one there.

At times, after this sort of experience, he wondered if he was going mad, but his doctors assured him he wasn't. Finally, he did accept the idea that he must be mentally ill, and went back to Sweden to see a physician, an old friend of his. The doctor put him in a sanatorium, but Strindberg got no rest there because, on looking at his bedspring, he concluded that it was an electric apparatus designed to kill him. Also, he felt someone was watching him from the darkness, touching him, and "feeling for his heart in order to suck his blood." Naturally, he sprang out of bed, flung open his window, and jumped down into the courtyard. Next day he decided the doctor had been paid by one of his enemies "to do him down." As Strindberg concluded, "Every man has his price." When he got home, he still had no peace because the first thing he noticed was that the lightning rod on the house was fastened right over his bed.

Once he thought he was dead and was sure he could hear men hammering as they made his coffin. Like most paranoiacs, at times he was much annoyed because he felt that people around him were reading his most secret thoughts. They were "picking his brains," and using his brilliant ideas for their own literary purposes. Sometimes when he went into his room, it seemed to him that it was full of hostile creatures through whom he had to force his way, in order to reach his bed. "The room is filled with all kinds of demons, who drag me out of bed and try to stifle me under the blankets. But if I come home at midnight intoxicated, I sleep like an angel, and wake up strong as a young god, ready to work like a galley-slave." No wonder, then, that often at night he went to a beer hall and got a bit tipsy. Fortunately, he never became an alcoholic. He explained that at times, "One's lower nature breaks through, and then the brutal instincts find expression; it is so pleasant to be an animal for a while."

Strindberg's first marriage. As was to be expected, Strindberg, with his paranoia, just could not be happy in any marriage, even with an angelic and very devoted woman. He had constantly to be suspecting her of infidelity, and in his case to *suspect* such a thing was the same as being *sure* of it. The next compulsion was to *accuse* his wife of being untrue to him. His first wife, Siri, Countess von Wrangel, managed to stick it out for fourteen years, but his second wife had to quit in less than two years, and his third threw in the towel in a few months.

Strindberg metaphorically stripped himself and his first wife naked before the world in his book entitled *The Confession of a Fool.* (In German, the title was *Pleas of One Insane.*) He told in detail how he took Siri over from Baron Wrangel when the Baron, his devoted friend, became involved with a mistress. Then he told everything about his stormy marriage. Although infatuated with Siri, he kept constantly accusing her of being unfaithful. To show how suspicious he was, one evening when there was a young girls' party in the house, and Siri was being affectionate with the guests, Strindberg flew into a rage and accused her of being a Lesbian.

True to his paranoiac tendencies, he suffered terribly because of his constant fear that his children were not really his. He wrote up this suspicion in his play, *The Father.* As he said, "My old suspicions tormented me. I shrank from the renewal of old relations with former friends, some of whom might quite conceivably have been my wife's lovers. To put an end to my doubts I determined to cross-examine her." He was constantly setting traps for her. Typical of a paranoiac was his reaction when she would come to sit on his knees to be affectionate. He would say, "What wrong have you committed today that you caress me like this?" He admitted that he had no evidence against her that would satisfy a jury; but what he had was sufficient for him.

Curiously, once, after leaving his wife and fleeing to Vienna, he "wrote her love-letters twice a day." Then he returned, and for the next six months they were ecstatic in their renewed love. Evidently at times he could be a charming lover. But soon again he would be so terribly jealous and so full of accusations that he and Siri would get to hating each other thoroughly. Naturally, Strindberg's friends took his wife's part and turned against him with disgust.

He had sense enough left to admit that he "was a madman whose lunacy consisted in believing himself saddled with an unfaithful wife." How strange that although occasionally he could see this truth, he still went ahead, and in his book kept throwing mud on the lovely mother of his children. He did this in spite of the fact that she had forgiven him a hundred times.

He tells again and again of his great desire to be sure that his adored children were his. "Make inquiries? It was like beating my head against a stone wall. People listened to what I had to say with a furtive smile, and stared at me as if I were a rare animal. No information was vouchsafed me; I was deserted by everyone, especially by those who secretly yearned for my ruin, so that they might rise over my fallen body."

Again, he fled from his home, and again he returned, but this time he fell so severely ill—probably from violent emotion—that for a while they thought he was dying. He planned suicide, but decided, egoistically, that first, as "one of the world's great artists," he must write up the whole story—as he saw it with his crazed mind. "I could see plainly now that I had been in the power of a vampire. I only wanted to live long enough to cleanse my name from the filth with which she had sullied it. I wanted to live long enough to revenge myself, but first of all I must have proofs of her infidelity. I hated her now with a hatred more fatal than indifference because it is the antithesis of love; *I hated her because I loved her.*" Then, one day, to his shame, he struck Siri a number of times. But even after this, she forgave him, and became very loving—trying to win him back. But, again, he left her.

He decided that in order to deceive the world, she had invented the myth that he was insane. As he said, "To hide your crime more completely you meant to torture me to

death; you are a criminal; I have no longer any doubt of it;
I shall divorce you." Again, for a while, his wife forgave.
She forgave so completely that they had another child, and
later, another.

One day he rushed downstairs to accuse his wife of all
sorts of crimes, and found her on the bed with the children,
looking so beautiful that his heart softened, and he just had
to kiss her. But doubt remained in his mind. He had doubts
of everything—"Of my wife's constancy, my children's legiti-
mate birth, my sanity—doubts which persecuted me relent-
lessly and unremittingly." "If only I could have absolute
certainty. Either a crime had been committed in secret, or
else I was mad. I must know the truth." "To be a deceived
husband: what did I care, as long as I knew it. I should be
the first to laugh at it! Was there a single man in the world
who could be absolutely certain that he was his wife's only
lover?" "I determined to make the most searching investiga-
tions. Was that monomania, the paroxysm of rage of a
lunatic? It is not for me to say." Eventually, he got a divorce
and practically abandoned his wife and his children. He
did not continue to support them.

The book he wrote describing all this so outraged public
opinion—especially in Germany—that he was threatened
with prosecution and imprisonment and had to flee the
country.

Strindberg's second marriage. Much light on Strindberg's
character is thrown by the book written by his second wife,
an able young woman of twenty or so—the daughter of a
newspaper editor—who had inherited her father's gift for
writing. After a brief and stormy courtship which should
have shown the girl that she was headed for serious trouble, she married the man. Immediately their difficulties
began, and in seven weeks she was glad for a while to live
away from him.

Again and again she had to forgive him for his cruel and
insane treatment of her. Again and again, he accused her
of being unfaithful, when there was absolutely no reason
for his fearing this. During much of their marriage, Strindberg had no money and hence had to live off his wife's

people. This enraged him and made him all the harder to live with. Time and again he insulted and turned from his door good friends who would gladly have come to his rescue with much-needed money or the offer of a job.

In her book, Freda Strindberg shows very clearly that Strindberg was his own worst enemy. Like so many psychotic persons, at times he was brilliant and lovable, but he had in him a devil who, at any minute, would take over control. Strindberg used to ask, "Why is it possible to hate one whom one loves?" He even wondered, "Can one love and not hate?" With his nature, this was impossible.

Probable epilepsy. He wrote Freda that sometimes he was close to epilepsy, and at times he probably was. On a number of occasions, Freda saw him go into what looked like an epileptic "blackout." For instance, one day, while out walking in a crowded street, he suddenly stopped "with his face as if turned to stone, and his eyes riveted in front of him." His wife took his arm, asked what was the trouble, begged him to move on with her, but he made no response. Passers-by began to notice him, and some stopped to ask what was wrong. Then his face began to twitch, and slowly he regained consciousness. Freda got him into a cab where "he lay back, his brow beaded with sweat. The attack was over." "He slept exhausted," as a man would after an attack of epilepsy. A while later, Strindberg wrote to a friend that he was working "with such wild energy that I feel the approach of epilepsy," and later he said, "I am ill, and oscillate between epileptic attacks of furious urge to work, and general paralysis."

His mother-in-law described sudden spells something like *petit mal* in which, wherever he was, when in company, he would seem to forget that anyone was present. Then he might remain as if absorbed in his thoughts for a quarter of an hour, saying not a word and not hearing what was said to him. Mrs. Weyr never lost her fear that any minute he might go insane. She felt he was close to it. But with all this, she was much impressed with his genius. She wrote, "He is a kind of hermit whose company is more painful than pleasant." "The man is melancholic by nature—a pessimist. He has suffered so cruelly that any big emotion or grief will throw him off his balance." "He is embittered, eccentric, and full of fixed ideas."

Curiously, while out walking with Strindberg, Freda might look to one side for a few seconds, and when she looked back, he would be gone. What had happened was that he had seen someone who he thought was an enemy come from a distance to kill him; hence he had fled. Even if, for a moment, he felt displeased at something, he would turn and hurry away, without a word to his wife, or without finishing a purchase he was making in a shop.

Suicide. He spoke often of his desire for suicide. He told of once having flung himself "head first into the sea to drown my black devils." Once he wrote, "The old suicidal mania has come back; life is so repellent to me that I can take no food." Another time he wrote, "I long to leave earth, and find peace." This desire for peace is the greatest wish of many a psychotic person. He knew he was close to insanity, and was always afraid that some day he would be locked up. He would ask Freda if she thought he was mad.

His eccentricities. To show how erratic Strindberg was: the day his fiancée arrived in the city to marry him, he didn't go to the station to meet her because he was tired out, having spent a night or two in a debauch with a woman. Stupidly, but with the strict honesty of the psychotic person, he described the whole affair in detail to his fiancée. She should have left him on the spot, but she forgave him and went ahead to marry him.

Curiously, Strindberg, without any training, became a painter—of pictures good enough to sell. Having a number of crackpot ideas about science, he wasted much of his time playing with alchemy. He was sure he was about to make gold out of some base metal.

Part insane and part sane. What has often impressed me while reading Strindberg's books is to see that while one part of him was acting insanely, another part of him was standing off to one side—like Lara Jefferson's alter ego—criticizing him and pointing out what a disgraceful thing he was doing. For instance, after writing the terrible and shameless book about his first marriage, he admitted it was

disgraceful, and said to Freda—after she had been shocked
by reading it—"Think of the horrors of the [writing] profession! To skin one's nearest and dearest, and then offer
the skin for sale!" "To spy out people's scerets, to find the
moles on a woman's body, to vivisect humans like rabbits;
to kill, to violate, to burn down—ugh!" But, in justification
of his action, he went on to say, "No pain can be too high
a price for any experience which is so vital that it becomes
through you the property of the world. Is it not your supreme law to express yourself and to create?" Poor Freda
then realized that she would be the next person to be exposed and vilified by him.

Strindberg was jealous of his little wife and her publisher,
when he saw her writing late into the night, even when she
was striving desperately to earn money so that they would
have some food to eat. Instead of being grateful to Freda
and trying to collaborate with her, he accused her of stealing his thoughts and using them for her private advantage.
As he said, "She is a devil."

After ruining himself by his crazy behavior, he wrote to
his wife, in his usual fashion, saying, "I have only one desire,
to defend my honour, revenge myself, and shake off everything which has disgraced me." "You hate me out of a feeling of inferiority; I am a superior who has done you nothing
but good; and I hate you as an enemy, for you act like one."
He forgot that he had been living off her and her relatives
for months at a time. As a reward for this, he wrote, "My
god-like insouciance has bewitched me into a marriage in
which I have been treated like a beggar, worse than a serv-
ing-man." When old friends rallied and planned a benefit
banquet for him, he called it off, saying, "I have a horror
of people."

Freda really loved him. Curiously, after all the terrible
suffering she had endured at the hands of her "crazy husband," she said, "I hate the idea of parting from him," and
"I feel a constant burning urge to return to him." Evidently,
she remained for long in love with him, even after their
divorce, because she followed him around all over Europe
—at a safe distance—watching what he did. When asked if
she would marry him a second time, she said, "Oh, yes, and

without a moment's thought or doubt. At any price!" Evidently, at times, he had a way with women!

His third marriage, and his death. About 1901, Strindberg fell in love with Harriet Bosse, a young actress. He married her, but soon her troubles began—with his jealousies and his paranoia. For instance, to make amends for some of his doings, he promised her a vacation trip; but then he suddenly discovered that "the powers were hostile," and so he called it off. From the start, Harriet found no happiness; and hence, like Freda before her, she soon started leaving him for weeks at a time. She had a child by him, but soon after that she got a divorce.

Shortly before Strindberg died, another charming young woman became interested in him, but this time he had the wisdom and kindness to tell the girl to keep away—he was old; and besides there was no chance of her finding any happiness with him. In 1912, he died of a cancer of the stomach.

Summary. As we have seen, Strindberg's books can teach us most of what we need to know about paranoia, and the sufferings day and night of the paranoiac—the constant suspicion of everyone, and even of loved ones; the great self-centeredness, which of course is typical of many psychotic persons; the mixture of suspiciousness with occasional mania, or depression, or trance states, and even mild epilepsy; the tendency of the person to be his own worst enemy; his constant fear of injury or even death at the hands of his persecutors; the occasional and very natural desire to commit suicide; and the occasional mixture of sanity and lack of sanity.

Strindberg shows us so clearly the great amount of suffering that must be endured almost constantly by the paranoiac. His books show the terrible fears he must endure, as when he feels sure his room is full of demons. He can never have any comfort because any little happening can convince him that his enemies are closing in on him.

Perhaps, worst of all, he cannot trust anyone, even those nearest and dearest to him. He cannot trust his wife to be faithful to him; and when his children show him a kindness or some affection, his only thought must be, "I wonder what they want to get out of me now." He cannot trust his friends, and he cannot trust a doctor to whom he has appealed for help—he is so sure they have all gone over to the enemy.

What often adds to the sadness of the story is that in some ways the paranoiac may be brilliant and able, and successful. At times, he can be very ingratiating; and because of a certain singleness of purpose and a great pertinacity, he will sometimes become a leader of men. If only he did not have the one mixed-up idea, he could be a great man.

As we can see from the story of Strindberg, a tendency to paranoia can endure for the man's lifetime. Unfortunately, it is difficult for a psychiatrist or anyone to help the person. Even when, as in Strindberg's case, the man will admit the possibility that he is not sane, he will usually tell the doctor who argues with him, "You are too simple and ignorant; you don't know what's going on; and you haven't sense enough to realize that I am perfectly right about these people who are following me everywhere." One can rarely talk the paranoiac out of any of his ideas of persecution— he is too sure he is right.

There are many men and women who are paranoid, which means that they think somewhat like paranoiacs. Often their tendency to suspect others, or to think that what others did was directed at them, or to think that people "have it in for them" is so little obvious that only relatives and close friends know about it.

CHAPTER 4

Some Schizophrenics

Schizophrenia is the commonest form of psychosis. Actually, there are several schizophrenias, some severe, some of moderate severity, and some so mild that the person is called (by psychiatrists) schizoid, or looked on by laymen as normal. I know many unhappy, lonely, shy, retiring, and "touch-me-not" schizophrenics who never had to go into a hospital. Some have been so successful in business that today they are millionaires. Most of the people whose stories I abstract here suffered from the schizophrenic's greatest difficulty, which is not being able to come close to his fellow human beings.

John Matheu is a good example of an able schizophrenic who loves the life of a recluse on a lonely island. Nijinsky is an example of those schizophrenics who go insane and never quite recover. Judge Schreber and Marguerite Sechehaye show us how the mind of a schizophrenic works when it is all mixed up. Nietzsche shows us how a schizophrenic in a mental hospital can seem half insane and half sane at the same time.

The Random Thoughts of an Able Schizoid Man

One of the best diaries of a schizoid type of antisocial bachelor—of the type who likes to shut himself away from the world—was left us by a certain John Matheu, and later published by his friend, David Martens (*The Abrupt Self*, 1946). This journal tells us much about what went on in the mind of a middle-aged man who, during part of each year, fled from society and lived by himself in a lonely shack on an island.

Matheu described the constant conflict that can go on between two personalities in a man: one craving success and power and spiritual greatness, and the other jeering at success and holding it to be of no account. Matheu's story is different from that of most of the other people quoted in this volume in that apparently he never "cracked up."

Matheu's father died young, and so John and his mother had a hard struggle with poverty. Somehow, he got through college; he got a Ph.D. degree, and eventually a professorship in English. Early in his life he published a book of poems and essays which sold well. For a while, during his early days, John sometimes drank to excess. At such times, he would become talkative, and then he would keep telling of his unhappy childhood, his failures, his emotional solitude, and his dream of an eventual triumphant achievement. He would have liked to become a great religious and moral teacher.

Fears. As is the case with many psychotic persons, Matheu kept saying that his biggest problem was fear, but he did not say what he feared. Once or twice he admitted that the fear was groundless. Often he feared some vague disaster, or perhaps a crumbling of his mind. He spoke of an "engulfing nebulous terror, an impersonal malevolence of the universe planted in the unreachable depths of the individual where most times it cannot be overcome and cannot be combatted."

So often, as I read the books by psychotic persons, I find much about their fears, terrors, and "horrors." As we shall see later, an able alcoholic who spent much time in a mental hospital wrote that the most characteristic feature of most of the men around him was a nameless but terrible fear.

The love of isolation and solitude. On his island, John loved to go about naked in the sun. At night he would get up several times to stroll about. As one man said who, like

Matheu, loved to live alone on a ranch, "It is delightful to be all alone, because then there is no one around to bother you." Other men and women of this type have told me they would never marry because no spouse would ever want to put up with their erratic habits of living and sleeping. Sometimes when an American like Matheu is thirty-five or forty, he will marry a foreign woman of little education, and perhaps ten years older than himself—a woman who will satisfy his sexual needs and will keep house for him but will never feel she has the right to complain about his queer ways.

The passion these schizoid people have for solitude was shown by the first settler in what is now Estes Park in Colorado. I have read that a hundred years ago, when someone homesteaded thirty miles away from him, he felt compelled to move on and to go farther west. As he said, "the place was getting too crowded"!

Many inner conflicts. Matheu seemed to have two personalities, neither of which could ever get very far before it was thwarted and blocked by the other. As a result, he could not make up his mind what he wanted most to do and what path he should follow. On one page of his diary he wrote that he was suffering terribly from loneliness, and on the next he wrote that he had chosen loneliness and was "stuck with it." "You wanted to be by yourself, and by God, you are by yourself." "You have not been willing to give your friendship to such as came your way, and now you go home at night like a kicked dog, dragging its tail behind it, and no one gives a damn, which is as it should be." "Maybe you prefer your solitude to the ways available for breaking it."

In other places in the diary, we find a conflict between the man's desire for austerity, selflessness, and avoidance of gathering possessions, and ideas of great vanity and great personal importance. There is a struggle also between ideas of honest humility and ideas of pride, a desire for power, and the ability to lord it over others. There is a conflict between his desire to live as a hermit and his desire to communicate with others. Once, Matheu said, "There are too many veils of pride, egotism, and sensuality for me to come

easily to sincerity and truth." Too often "pride dictates."
Highly significant is his statement "And all this desperate
enterprise will come to nothing, be worse than barren, be
rotten, if it stems from posture, vanity, falsehood."

He goes on to speak of a "self-strangling: the strange
harshness of a self to a self, tightening with his own hand
the rope which will hang him. Using the shovel himself
for the grave to bury his life. Pulling down the curtain in
front of his eyes, barricading his heart."

Once Matheu confessed that, if years before, he had had
private means, he would have withdrawn permanently from
life. Like many of the saints of olden time, he had the idea
that in solitude he "would reach some lofty spiritual su-
periority, and there would be some product which would
mark me high with men."

One half of him kept saying to the other, "All right, go
this way and be lost, for sensuality can take over a life, and
then it is not long before that life is even without the possibilities of sensual satisfaction. The appetite loses itself,
becomes mechanical; finally incapable of pleasure." At
times, he had the hermit's thought that one can find life
only by withdrawing from it. He tried to show contempt
for a successful life by representing it as sour grapes—"It is
a life of catastrophic horror to too many, and of trivial contention for others."

*But his retreat from life did not bring the hoped-for hap-
piness or spiritual riches.* Unfortunately, Matheu found that
his withdrawal from life did not bring him happiness—it
brought only suffering. He wrote, "If I tried, I might be put
in touch with new wisdom, be illumined in some fresh and
invigorating way; and find a spring of life." Actually, he
probably would have done better to remain in his lecture
room, finding happiness in his teaching.

Once Matheu saw that his retreat from life had gotten
him nowhere. Curiously, he says he suspected this failure
was due to the fact that in his secret heart *he did not want
to succeed!* "Each has a place in life which is natural to
him, and I have not found this for myself." How many men
have had this difficulty, although they have kept searching
for years! Honestly he says, "The pretensions and protec-

tions laboriously put up in my life are neither defense nor protection, but obstruction." He speaks of the minds which, although they harass and drive themselves, "achieve nothing but self-torture." He said, "I wanted quiet, and strained for it, perhaps too harshly. It does not come on demand, but unbidden and gently." Also, he learned that it is useless to try to run away from life; one must learn to manage it!

Matheu might have gotten somewhere if he had only stuck to the thought he once had—the thought that "the significance of one's life is only in its bearing on other lives. You can stay a while by yourself, be enriched and fortified thereby, but you must move back with man." "A life has value when it serves others." On one occasion, he wished that he could let his heart "truly be opened" to other people.

The inability to chart a course and then stick to it. At times, he wondered why, when he saw things fairly clearly, he did not take more energetic and certain steps to attain the end that he desired. But what did he desire? The trouble was that he desired one thing one day and another thing the next day. Like so many mildly psychotic persons, and even persons with decided ability and good intelligence such as Matheu had, when it came to directing his life, he often faltered, hesitated, vacillated, and lost his way. He could not map out a course and then stick to it.

Like so many of the psychotic persons whose writings are abstracted in this volume, he felt often that he was two persons one of whom pulled one way and the other the other way. He was like those persons with a dual personality who, when in a mental hospital, are one day frantic to get well, and the next day are refusing to improve because getting well would mean they would soon have to go out into the world again and work, and face the problems of living.

In one place, Matheu said, "I aim to hear the voice of God." Later, he spoke of regretting his inability to "take his life between his hands and shape it to such ends" as he wished. But, again—he didn't quite know what those ends should be. How true this is of many persons: they are anxious to shape their lives magnificently, but they don't know how to do it. Or, they start out with a good idea and get nowhere with it, perhaps because of the lack of good sense and self-discipline. They start out like a hound after a panther, and then get to chasing rabbits and quail.

Often, in spells of great loneliness, Matheu realized painfully, "How separate each life is from another." It would appear that "we try harder to wall ourselves in than to break the walls down." Typical, of course, of many schizophrenic persons is their desire to build a wall about themselves.

The occasional fear of time's passing. Another great contradiction seen in the lives of many persons like Matheu is their great distress *one day* over their failure to be getting anywhere, and their contentment the *next day* to sit idly and do nothing. Many of them—like a beachcomber—love to do nothing for months at a time. As Matheu puts it: "Even that desperate sense of the passage of time, and that frenzy at the thought of years going, and seeming to take all that is precious in life, passing by, passing by, leaving nothing, each day and hour and minute with less and less chance of—what? Love, accomplishment?" If he so wanted to accomplish things, why did he loaf all summer? Why, also, did he write to his friend saying that anyone who would read his manuscript would see from the agony of his thinking that his very life was at stake—which in a way it was. But why then did he do nothing about it except to lie in the sun?

Signs of mental disorganization. The diary, as it was published, is decidedly disorganized, but this disorganization helps to give the reader an idea of the confusion of the man's mind. Suggestive of schizophrenia is the fact that much of his writing is incoherent and not clear. I had to rewrite this abstract of his book several times before I could get some sequence into it and gather into one paragraph his thoughts on any one subject. Following is a paragraph as Matheu wrote it. I realize that such disjointedness can be found in the pages of many modern writers, but I still think it suggests a mild schizophrenia.

"Falseness, emptiness, a front assumed because it must be assumed, a façade to cover fear, conventions. Desperation represents the reality." "What difference if we are under the ground or over it?" "Perhaps this struggle is not so titanic as the actor would like to picture it."

Apparently at times Matheu realized he shouldn't be making such heavy weather of his life. He wrote, "A play goes on: one dominated by ego and fear, contention for no purpose, to no real end, burdening and oppressive." "All inconsequential, yet with power to wreck the individual life. It is a struggle in trivialities." "It is essentially aimless—for by and large all it points to for anyone is more power, more money, more success, more sensual pleasure, more comfort. It looks to no end in wisdom or truth."

That the man could write well is indicated by the fact that, later, he succeeded in having published a life of Thoreau and a book on the types of men who drift into the Bowery.

At times he wrote as if he wanted success and money, but at other times he said he didn't. When his first book sold well, he might perhaps have ridden forward on the tide of fortune, but for some time all he did was to brood unhappily. Once, with considerable discernment, he said, "Your mind has dimensions beyond which it is fruitless to hope to go." "I am coming to know my dimensions, knowledge I once feared and rebelled against." This reminds me of the statement of a certain very wise man to the effect that most of us can find happiness only as we become willing to accept our average mediocrity!

Occasional signs of discernment. At times, there were signs of discernment in the man, as when he spoke of "the *wholesome* awareness of making a fool of yourself." One day he wrote, "The fierce envy I once had seems largely gone, thank God." Another time he remarked that it was mainly chance that he was not a drunk lying senseless on the street.

At one time, he felt that he should give up. He said to himself, "Don't be for, or toward, or against anything." He had seen that *he did not "have enough wisdom to direct the struggling."* This sums up much of the thought of psychotic persons. Sometimes they give up. Occasionally, there came to Matheu the feeling described by many mentally disturbed persons—that life "just cannot go on." "There was nothing to carry it on but emptiness." Lois Vidal speaks of such emptiness in her. At times Matheu did not feel *strong* enough to go on. Naturally, such feelings can lead to suicide.

Often, when I have in my office a man like Matheu who, instead of striding ahead to do something useful, spends unhappy months trying to figure out what his life is all about, I quote to him this jingle:

> The centipede was happy quite
>   Until a toad in fun
> Said, "Pray, which leg goes after which?"
> That worked her mind to such a pitch
> She lay distracted in a ditch
>   Considering how to run.

I think this little rhyme sums up perfectly what happens to many a person who thinks that figuring things out is going to enrich his life. Often, all he does is to get himself so uncertain how to run that he does nothing, and even has to be supported by his family.

The meaning of schizophrenia. Years ago, the commonest of psychoses was called dementia praecox. Then it was decided to call the disease schizophrenia, which, in the Greek, suggests a split personality such as John Matheu kept complaining about. Nowadays psychiatrists talk less about the split personality and more about the unapproachability and shyness of many a schizophrenic—about his inability to come close to people either physically or mentally or psychically. Often I call these people "touch-me-nots." Many avoid looking anyone in the eye, or they hate to shake hands, and if anyone touches them on the arm they pull away as if they had been seared by a hot iron.

Today, some psychiatrists speak of "the schizophrenias" because there are so many different types of the disease, with varying degrees of severity. For instance, there is the schizophrenic who, in spite of much physical and mental suffering, never in his life has to go into a mental hospital, and never cracks up. I know some of these people who are too odd ever to have married, but who have succeeded eminently in business. Others I see in the office complaining of many queer sensations, such as worms crawling under their skin or blood dripping in their chest. Some of these get operated on time and again. Some, who in their lifetime are never able to hold a job, remain so sane that they never even think of consulting a psychiatrist. Others may have to get psychiatric help once or twice during their life.

Commonly met with are the schizoid persons who have a small touch of schizophrenia. Thousands of them go through life successfully enough, and many marry. But usually they are very shy; some have trouble looking people in the eye, and usually they have a curious, shy handshake that can easily be recognized. Many of these persons crave affection, but they cannot accept it when it is shown them. A schizoid mother may never kiss or fondle or cuddle a child, and a schizoid child may resent any attempt of his mother to kiss him or show him affection.

When I think of schizoids I think of a young woman—an able secretary—who at coffee-break time would always behave as if she didn't know a single one of the girls or young doctors sitting around her—all of whom she had worked with for many months. She did not look at or smile at or greet any one of them unless she was spoken to. Her behavior was loneliness and isolation personified. One day, when I found her alone and crying silently, I was able to break through her protective wall long enough to learn from her that she greatly wanted to be sociable and friendly; she craved affection; but she just could not accept it when it was offered her. She said she knew that she would never be able to marry.

Signs of depression. At times, as is the case with many schizophrenic or schizoid persons, Matheu was either a bit manic or decidedly depressed. He spoke of "The inevitable natural wearisome repetitious swing of the pendulum, the consequence for life, the old familiar feeling of revulsion, apathy. Fear. Hostility. Indifference. Boredom. Self-disgust. Anger. All of these huddled together under the more prepossessing word of melancholy. A pointless, self-pitying business."

Typical of a manic-depressive person was his tendency at times to feel overwhelmed with guilt. He said he had engaged in mean, cruel, calculated actions; or he had been greedy; or he had indulged in thoughtless sensuality. He said, "I have hurt what might have been strengthened. I have grabbed for my own use something which thereby damaged others; I have added my anger and hate to a pool of anger and hate."

Here he is, confessing great sins, and apparently grieving over them, and yet in the next paragraph, he refers to his "towering pride—beyond all sins the greatest." This is the sort of duality of thought that Anton Boisen (see Chapter 6 in this book) found in so many of his patients; one minute they were patting their good pal, God, on the back, and the next they were calling themselves miserable sinners and worms.

Sex could sometimes bring unhappiness. Often Matheu spoke contemptuously of women and sex. Like a psychotic person who cannot love, he said he had no interest in women except when occasionally they satisfied his physical need. He was distressed because his body kept demanding occasionally that he give in to its hunger. Once, after he gave in, he said, "A good sexual experience is invigorating, creating and stabilizing." But another time, his reaction was not so satisfying. He said, "A storm possessed me. Sensuality grabbed my body, held it up, shook it, in indifferent mastery." Then, shame came over him because he had yielded. But as he added so wisely, "Why shame?" Another time, he admitted that he wasn't so self-sufficient as he liked to make out, and he did want some love. But he might have added that if some woman had shown her willingness to give him love, he probably would have pushed her away rudely.

That he could occasionally see some beauty in sex was shown by his statement that "I would not give up the sexual part of my nature, the excitement of a beautiful body, the beauty of sexual love. They are too precious a part of life." "Perhaps the fact of actual sexual exercise is not so important." "To get rid of the vanities of the mind or the tyranny of the sensual body is no easy job; and yet, to find freedom from them, and to use their initiating energies is my purpose." Here we find the mental conflict of an ancient anchorite in his desert cave.

His difficulties with sex are reflected in his statement,

"The centers of life are the mind and the genitals." Apparently while brooding over his lack of normal sexuality, he wrote, "for there are some eunuchs which were so born from their mother's womb; and there are some eunuchs which were made eunuchs of men; and there be eunuchs which have made themselves eunuchs for the kingdom-of-heaven's sake. He that is able to receive it, let him receive it."

Sometimes, he saw that he was troubled by vanity. As he said, "Urgency and vanity. You can be worn down by them; finally bored by them. Let them go for a while. Shake them off."

Why a descent into the slums? I have often wondered why, when a person from a family of education, refinement, and perhaps wealth becomes mildly psychotic, he is likely to go down into the slums and cheap bars to associate with degenerates and alcoholics. Matheu, who did spend much time in the slums, explains why. He says, "the outcast, the crack-pot, the 'offside', the 'queer,' those who mutter as they walk, the half-mad, the drunk: these I go naturally with: one among others; *they make no requirements.*" In other words, they make no demands on another psychotic person. Perhaps Matheu was pleased to think that some of them looked up to him as a man who could write and could be a professor. Perhaps he was like Conrad's Lord Jim, who was happy when he found men who would call him "Lord." And yet, he shows his contempt for success by saying, "What difference does success or failure make?"

Is self-searching of much value, or is work better? Apparently, it never occurs to these mixed-up people that a good honest eight hours of work done day after day and year after year is very worthwhile, and surely one of the most satisfying things in this world. There is nothing so good: nothing so health-giving as work, and nothing so likely to maintain sanity. It is so much more satisfying than days and nights spent in trying to analyze one's life—to see why one is living and where one expects to go. John Matheu does not seem to have gotten anywhere with all his searchings into himself.

Matheu's later years. After writing his diary, Matheu lived on for ten years. His friend David Martens says John eventually achieved a basic serenity and gained some strength to carry him through his difficulties. He still had "attacks of self-consciousness." "On the whole, John had become a human whom it was good to have at hand; not gregarious, or seeking company, but giving himself more easily and completely." "His professional life went forward satisfactorily." This was evidenced by his two published books—one on Thoreau and one on the derelicts who gather in the Bowery. Then he died suddenly of a heart attack.

The Insanity of Nijinsky

As most people know, one of the greatest of all male ballet dancers was the Russian Vaslav Nijinsky (see his *Diary,* 1936). For background information the reader can turn to the book *Nijinsky* (1936) by his wife, Romola, and her *The Last Years of Nijinsky* (1952). Vaslav's brother, Stanislav, from childhood on was mentally undeveloped and insane. Young Nijinsky ran into difficulties when he met the famous Diaghilev, the producer of ballets. He, a decided homosexual, became attached to Vaslav and induced him to live with him for several years. As was to be expected, when Vaslav married Romola, Diaghilev became bitter and vindictive and tried hard to ruin the man he had loved.

The beginnings of Nijinsky's insanity. Mme. Nijinsky tells us how her husband went insane. One of the first strange things he did was to drive his carriage in a crazy way, bumping into the carriages of other people—something which was most unusual for him, because he had always been an excellent driver. Then he had "absent spells," like the epileptic's *petit mal* attacks—spells in which he would stop and for a minute not say a word, and not answer his wife's anxious questions. As she said, "He seemed so far away." Then he began to be irritable and unreasonable and unpleasant in strange ways. One day, he even pushed his wife down a flight of stairs when she had their child in her arms. As she said, "I stood up more astounded than terrified. What was the matter with him?" Then, for a while, Nijinsky again was his normal self.

One of the servants in the house soon made the diagnosis of insanity because he had worked for Nietzsche; he had watched that philosopher lose his mind, and hence he knew the early symptoms. At the start of Nijinsky's trouble, occasionally he would go out and spend several thousand francs for things for which he had no need. Sometimes he would go through the village where they lived, doing silly things. Then, one day, he thundered at his wife, "Silence; this is my marriage with God." About this time he promised to dance for the townspeople, but when they gathered in a hall, he acted very queerly. He made them wait for a half hour or more, while he just sat on the stage and looked at them. Then he danced—and danced well.

Many years of insanity with lucid intervals. Realizing then what was wrong, Mme. Nijinsky took her husband to the world-famous psychiatrist Dr. Paul Eugen Bleuler, who said that Nijinsky was hopelessly insane. Later, Mme. Nijinsky wrote, "Fourteen years have elapsed since the day that Nijinsky's mind became shrouded in darkness, when he withdrew from the world—fourteen years since he has been living in a world where his imaginary creations are real personalities to him, and we—the reality—are only dreamlike apparitions." "He is day-dreaming, unceasingly, but without the loss of his memory. He knows he is Nijinsky." "He is silent for days or weeks or months. He is docile, obedient, patient, and indifferent, but neat and as orderly as ever. His physicians and nurses adore him. His charm is still present. A lightning flash of his old mischievous self will brighten up the monotony of his apparent indifference." To a stranger he would appear as only a silent, quiet, and indifferent man.

At times, Nijinsky would get hallucinations and grow violent, and refuse nourishment. Then he would have to go into a mental hospital. At other times he could stay home with his wife and daughter. In the end, Vaslav went into a coma and died.

Nijinsky's extremely instructive Diary. Shortly after he began to go insane, Nijinsky started writing the *Diary,* which was published in 1936. There were seventeen years in all during which he was mentally upset. As one would expect, the writing in the *Diary* is often unorganized, as most of the writings of schizophrenics are. He jumped from one subject to another. He thought that he was wonderfully wise and all-powerful. Repeatedly, he said he was God or closely related to Him. A sample of his diary runs as follows: "I am God in flesh and feeling. I am man and not God. I am simple. I need not think. I must make myself felt and understood through feeling. Scientists think about me and break their heads, but their thinking will not give any result. They are stupid. I speak simply without any tricks. It is impossible for man to understand God, but God understands God. Man is part of God, and therefore sometimes understands God. I am both God and man. I do not like God when he is bad! I am good and not a beast. I am an animal with a mind. I am flesh, but I do come from flesh. God made flesh. I am God. I am God. I am God. I am happy because I am loved. I love God, and therefore smile to myself."

"People think that I will go mad and lose my reason. Nietzsche lost his reason because he thought too much. I do not think, and therefore cannot go mad." "I want to have millions in order to make the stock exchange tremble. I want to ruin the stock exchange." "God wants me to break the stock exchange." "I took a glass of port and lost consciousness because God so willed." "My task is the task of God, and I therefore want to do everything to fulfill it. I write because God orders me to." "I am the Buddhist God and every kind of God. I know each of them. I have met them all. I pretend to be mad on purpose, for my own aims."

Sometimes he wrote of his bitterness against Diaghilev. "I worked with him for five years without rest. I know all his sly tricks and habits." "I am the bull; a wounded bull. I am God in the bull. I am Apis. I am an Egyptian. I am an Indian. I am a Red Indian. I am a Negro. I am a Chinaman. I am a Japanese." "I am terrified of being locked up and of losing my work." "I am Christ's policy. I am Christ."

Nijinsky tells of a time when his wife's parents arrived. Exactly like one of the old saints he says, "I waited to see what God would tell me to do." "I want to save the entire earth from suffocation. All the scientists must leave their books and come to me, and I will help everyone because

I know so much. I am a man in God." "Everybody will say that Nijinsky has become insane. I do not care. I have already behaved like a madman at home. Everybody will think so, but I will not be put in an asylum, because I dance very well and give money to all those who ask me." "I like insane people; I know how to talk to them. My brother was in the lunatic asylum."

Was he homosexual? According to what Nijinsky and his wife said, he was not homosexual, but it is hard to believe that a man, completely heterosexual, could have lived for years with an aggressive homosexual man. At times, he maintained that his relations with Diaghilev were not physical. He says he hated him, but lived with him because he needed the money that Diaghilev gave him. In another place, however, he admits, "I allowed him to make love to me. I trembled like a leaf. I hated him, but pretended, because I knew that my mother and I would die of hunger otherwise." Nijinsky tells in one place of running after cocottes in Paris. Like many schizophrenics, in his writing, he could get confused about his own sex. He says, "I am husband and wife in one. I love my wife. I love my husband."

Obviously, everyone who would like to understand the workings of an insane mind would do well to read Nijinsky's *Diary*. In many ways his book is better than Judge Schreber's, which we are about to consider.

A Famous Autobiography of a Schizophrenic

One of the best-known of the autobiographies of insane persons is that of Judge Daniel P. Schreber (1955), who came of a distinguished German family. His father was an eccentric and mildly psychotic physician. The judge was a well-educated and cultured man who for years had been president of the Supreme Court of Saxony.

Prior to the commitment in June, 1894, which ended Judge Schreber's career, it appears that he had had a couple of mental upsets. One, in 1884, had lasted about a year. The mental illness described in his *Memoirs* had been going on for ten years. Whenever Schreber was somewhat lucid, he would write. Judging from the rambling nature of his text, practically all of it was written while he was mixed up. Some of the original text was full of obscenities, which were deleted by the editors.

A book full of queer ideas. Schreber wrote down his thoughts as they came to him—usually mixed up, confused, and incoherent. His writing shows how disorganized the mental processes of a schizophrenic can be.

Following is a sample page from his book, chosen at random. "In the circumstances contrary to the Order of the World which have now arisen, this relation has changed—and I wish to mention this at the onset—the weather is now to a certain extent dependent on *my* actions and thoughts; as soon as I indulge in thinking nothing, or in other words stop an activity which proves the existence of the human mind such as playing chess in the garden, the wind arises at once. To anybody who is inclined to doubt such a fantastic statement, I could almost daily give the opportunity of convincing him of its correctness, as in fact I have recently convinced various people about the so-called attacks of bellowing (the doctor, my wife, my sister, etc.). The reason for this is simply that as soon as I indulge in thinking nothing, God, presuming that I am demented, thinks He can withdraw from me."

"Through the light emanating from the sun and the other stars, God is able to perceive (man would say: to see) everything that happens on earth and possibly on other inhabited planets; in this sense one can speak figuratively of the sun and light of the stars as the eye of God. All He sees He enjoys as the fruits of His creative power, much as a human being is pleased with what he has created with his hands or with his mind. Yet things were so ordered—up to the crisis to be described later—that by and large God left the world which He had created and the organic life upon it (plants, animals, human beings) to their own devices and only provided continuous warmth of the sun to enable them to maintain themselves and reproduce, etc."

This one page is enough to give an idea of how a schizophrenic thinks. A few sentences will make sense and then the next few will show nothing but insanity. All teachers of psychiatry should get their students to read this book.

The beginnings of the illness. Schreber started out thinking he was suffering from a softening of the brain which would soon kill him. Then came ideas of persecution and later a great sensitivity to light and noises. Finally, there came many hallucinations.

To show how vivid hallucinations can be, Schreber said that "One day—*in bright daylight*—I saw from my window . . . a magnificent portico arise, just as if the whole building were going to be transformed into a fairy place. Later, the image vanished, but the picture still stands out clearly in my memory."

Often he complained of voices that shouted at him "again and again, hundreds of times every day." As he said, this sort of thing became most fatiguing. He sometimes played the piano to drown out these voices. Occasionally, he got into fights with his attendants because inner voices had told him he should attack people. Sometimes he decided to end his life by starving himself to death.

The curious things schizophrenics feel. Schreber described at length some of the many weird sensations that are so typically those of schizophrenics, such as that "a lung worm was frequently produced in me." "Also, my diaphragm was raised high in my chest." Or his stomach was taken out and an inferior and smaller organ was substituted in its place. Also, there was rottenness and putrefaction in his abdomen. As some of my patients have put it, "their guts were rotting out." At times he claimed that most of his inner organs had been completely removed.

Paranoid ideas. Much of the time he talked about rays which were being directed at him, and this, of course, is typical of paranoia. Like a paranoiac, for a long time he kept inveighing bitterly against Professor Flechsig, who had examined him in the early days, and probably had offended him by declaring him insane.

Like many schizophrenics, he was sure the world had come to an end, and hence everything he saw was just a shell and a sham. Everyone had perished off the face of the earth, and only he was left.

Devils were operating and changing him into a woman.
Day after day he thought devils were performing all sorts
of horrible manipulations on his body. Some of the transformations made by them were for some holy purpose, while
others were designed to change him into a woman so that
his body could be used by men and devils for sexual purposes. He said that God was going to turn him over to the
hospital attendants to be used as a female harlot. He believed he had been changed largely into a woman. He
thought that women's "nerves" had been slipped into his
body to take the place of his own. He had an idea that his
breasts had become feminine in size, and so he took great
pleasure in standing, naked, before a mirror admiring his
feminine body. He thought that already men could have
sexual intercourse with him. Another reason, he felt sure,
for his transformation into a woman was so that he could
redeem the world.

In view of the fact that he had been changed into a
woman, he thought it incumbent on him to offer his wife a
divorce! This would be only fair. In spite of his satisfaction
in having been changed into a woman, he kept worrying
about the supposed shrinkage of his penis. He claimed that
he had a small womb and at times he felt quickening in it.
Once he was sure that, like the Virgin Mary, he had been
impregnated by God. Often he felt guilty because of the
voluptuous feelings he felt because of his feminization. He
thought these feelings must be sinful; and yet, as he said
with some logic, after all the sufferings he had gone through,
he was entitled to some pleasure—by way of compensation.

Strange and remarkable is his idea of "always playing the
woman's part in sexual embraces with himself." These peculiar ideas of the insane resemble the ideas of early man in
Asia Minor in regard to his gods, which might one day be
male, another day have female attributes, and another day
have attributes of animals. The worshipers did not seem to
be at all confused by these ideas. Actually, today, some
worshipers think of God as a man; also, as a woman; also,
perhaps, as a bird with "healing in his wings."

Schreber kept constantly talking about the "divine miracles" that were taking place in him; he said he could have

filled the book with descriptions of them. He said that most
men would have been frightened out of their wits with
these miracles, but he had learned to stand them.

His intimate relations with God. As with so many of the
insane, Schreber felt he was constantly in close communication with God and on intimate terms with Him. So far as
God was concerned, Schreber was the most important man
on earth. He said once that he was the only person who
could mock God and get away with it; at other times he
feared he would have to be annihilated because he constituted too great a threat to God. Sometimes he wouldn't
speak to anyone or do anything because he wanted to remain in a condition of "divine peace."

One of the common forms of behavior of schizophrenics
is to stand immobile in one position all day. Schreber said
that occasionally this was "demanded from me, a duty incumbent on me both in the interests of self-preservation and
of God, so as to liberate Him from the embarrassment in
which He found Himself owing to the 'tested soul.'"

Schizophrenics often feel closely related to the sun, and
Schreber tells us that he often stood gazing at it. He talked
to it!

One can easily see how difficult it was for William James
in his *Varieties of Religious Experience* and for Anton
Boisen in his book, *Exploration of the Inner World,* to guess
how sane was a "saint" who lived each day with every one
of the thoughts that are commonly described by a schizophrenic. As we know, many of the saints thought of nothing
all day but their special and close and affectionate relationship with God. Many also had the schizophrenic's conviction that the world was coming to an end, and that, when
this happened, they would be the Messiah, or perhaps a
Noah—one man left to repopulate the earth.

A curious idea Schreber got was "that God cannot learn
by experience." He felt that God could be surpassed "both
morally and mentally by one . . . human being." As Anton
Boisen said, many insane men often get this idea that they
are superior to God, and then they speak patronizingly
about Him. At one time, Schreber had an idea that there
were two Gods, a higher one and a lower one. He felt that

some of his behavior had been forced on him "through God's having placed Himself into a relationship with me which is contrary to the Order of the World." "There is no possibility of God's freeing Himself from my nerves for the rest of my life."

Like Anton Boisen, Schreber felt that in spite of all his sufferings, his period of mental aberration had been beneficial. As he said, it was "the *holy* time of my life, when my soul was immensely inspired by supernatural things which came over me in ever-increasing number . . . when I was filled with the most sublime ideas about God, and the order of the world." "I have come infinitely closer to the truth than have human beings who have not received divine revelation."

Occasional moments of sanity. Occasionally, he was sane enough to see how fantastic his thinking must seem to other people, and he could admit that he might be mistaken in what he was experiencing.

When Schreber almost recovered. At times Schreber recovered sufficiently so that he could be allowed to go to his home for supper. But even then his behavior was embarrassing to others because suddenly he would make a roaring noise (violent belching?)—a noise that he said he was unable to control.

Another episode of insanity and then death. Apparently, for some years, Judge Schreber was fairly normal, and then, in 1907, he slipped back; he returned to a mental hospital where, later, he died.

Several types of schizophrenia. As I said before, there are many types of schizophrenia, and this fact becomes evident as we study the stories of the three men whose final illnesses are here described.

Matheu was typically the shy, odd, and solitary schizophrenic who, although too upset about sex ever to marry, and much of the time in great conflict with himself, was able to get along with people out in the world well enough to succeed in his work. He found one family whose company he could tolerate, and whose friendship he sometimes would seek. He was the sort of schizophrenic who never cracks up, never needs hospitalization, and never goes near a psychiatrist. Even a physician, when consulted by such a man about one of his physical discomforts due to his schizophrenia, is likely not to notice or recognize his psychosis.

Nijinsky's schizophrenia was worse than Matheu's. With it he apparently became bisexual. For years the disease did not interfere with his becoming a great ballet dancer, but eventually it threw him into a psychosis. Even then, for much of the time, he was pleasant and lovable and docile. At times he was so well-behaved that he could live at home, but for much of the time his thinking was mixed up.

Judge Schreber presented a severe type of the disease with much psychotic thinking, especially along the lines of sexual transformations. He was so badly disturbed that for years he had to be cared for in a mental hospital.

Schizophrenia in a Child

More and more today are psychiatrists coming to see that schizophrenia can often be recognized in childhood—if only one knows the typical symptoms. In *Autobiography of a Schizophrenic Girl* (1951), written about a girl named Renée by Marguerite Sechehaye we are given a vivid picture of the very painful mental processes which a young schizophrenic may have to experience. Part of the time this girl was able to work as a secretary, but part of the time she was so acutely ill she had to be in a mental hospital.

The beginnings of the insanity. The girl wrote, "I remember well the day it happened." Apparently she was then a small child. "At that instant a strange feeling came over me—a disturbing sense of unreality. It seemed to me that I no longer recognized the school; it had become as large as a barracks, and the singing children became prisoners, compelled to sing. It was as though the school, and the children's song, were set apart from the rest of the world. At the same time my eye encountered a field of wheat whose limits I could not see. The yellow vastness, dazzling in the sun, bound up with the song of the children, imprisoned in the school-barracks, filled me with such anxiety that I broke into sobs. I ran home to our garden and began to play 'to make things seem as they usually were,' that is, to return to reality." Later, for some time, she was to see the world in this way with "illimitable vastness and brilliant light."

Renée thought that the thing that had tipped her over was the discovery that her father had a mistress, and that, because of this, her mother was threatening suicide. She says that, in the years that followed, until she was about thirteen, she had several spells in which she experienced these unreal feelings. Later, the sensation became more and more intense and came to her more and more often.

Weird visions and impressions. It is almost impossible to make a good abstract of her book because it is filled with so many descriptions of the awful and frightening and abnormal perceptions that she had of the world about her. Many of them are much like Schreber's. As Renée said, little things would fill her with "excruciating terror"—things that wouldn't bother a normal person.

Especially when the girl was feverish, she had a type of nightmare which would cause her to wake in terror. She would see a haystack, which "fills up the emptiness and engulfs the needle." "The haystack, small at first, swells and swells; and in the center, the needle, endowed with tremendous electrical force, communicates its charge to the hay. The electrical current, the invasion by the hay, and the blinding light combine to augment the fear to a paroxysm of terror, and I wake up screaming, 'The needle, the needle!'"

She says, ". . . the school building became immense, smooth, and unreal; and an inexpressible anguish pressed in on me." "One day, while I was in the principal's office, suddenly the room became enormous, illuminated by a dreadful electric light that cast false shadows. Everything was exact, smooth, artificial, extremely tense; the chairs and tables seemed models placed here and there. Pupils and teachers were puppets revolving without cause, without objective. I recognized nothing, nobody. It was as though reality, attenuated, had slipped away from all these things and these people. Profound dread overwhelmed me, and as though lost, I looked around desperately for help. I heard people talking, but I could not grasp the meaning of the words." "Ghastly fear gripped me." She speaks of these experiences as "crises of unreality." Naturally, she much wanted to get back to reality.

The people around her, who couldn't realize what she was seeing and feeling and hearing, thought she was just hysterical or neurotic. Often she became agitated, cutting capers, laughing at the top of her voice, and "playing the fool." She did this to try to escape from the fear, or to set up a defense against it.

Like so many of the people Anton Boisen described in his book, Renée felt that the world was about to be destroyed and that planes were coming to bomb and annihilate it. During the next year, the girl went in and out of these spells of unreality. She speaks of seeing pasteboard houses, and people around her who were robots. At times the girl suffered from such terrible fear that, like Lara Jefferson, she preferred to escape into madness. When she was pretty much herself, she managed a household of six persons and helped educate her brothers and sisters; she says she was a good student.

Often she heard sneering and mocking voices. She felt she was in an unreal country filled with a blinding light. There was an immense flat and limitless space—a lunar country, cold as the wastes at the North Pole. Everything was immobile, congealed, and crystallized. Objects were like stage trappings—geometric cubes without meaning. Perhaps some modern artists are schizophrenics!

People she saw acted like marionettes. They were phantoms whirling about in the pitiless electric light. She felt lost in it—isolated, cold, stripped, purposeless; a great wall separating her from everybody and everything. In the midst of the desolation, in indescribable distress, terrifyingly alone, she felt that madness had surely come to her.

She hears and obeys voices. Then, one day, voices began to tell Renée to do things. For instance, a voice commanded her to burn her right hand. So she did it. One day she placed the back of her right hand on the incandescent coals and held it there as long as she could stand the pain. She does not say if she was much injured. For some time after this she had to be kept from going into the kitchen because she was in danger of burning herself again. And yet—how strange—in the midst of all her horror and turbulence, she says she carried on with her work as a secretary. One has to doubt this.

Voices screamed at her, saying, "You wretch, you have no right to live; you criminal; you have committed a crime." Voices howled and jeered at her, and she screamed back. She cried out, "See what you have done, you wretches, you ghouls feeding on breasts."

Then followed a period of tremendous weariness when she could hardly do anything. For a while she would just sit in the cellar, unmoving, with her eyes fixed on a spot. At times everything was unreal; also, she saw objects without sensing what their function was—a jug was not something to hold water, and a chair was not something to sit on.

At times she became so manic and restless that she had to go into a mental hospital and be kept constantly in a warm bath. Later, she developed an awful rage against herself; she detested and loathed herself, and felt she deserved death. She sobbed in hate and guilt, and struck herself with violence. In another visit to the mental hospital, she was in a stupor. Everything was dreary, and she was completely passive. And yet, she remembered what went on about her.

Somewhere along the way, Renée went into psychoanalysis and soon became very dependent on her analyst, a woman, whom she called Mama. Apparently, the analyst soon convinced her that her fear was a cover for guilt— guilt infinite and awful. How strange that a child could be thought to be so guilty! The analyst blamed the girl's troubles on masturbation and on the hostility she harbored toward everyone. Renée says she hated people, without knowing why.

Eventually, according to her analyst, she "seemingly recovered to normal adulthood." I regret to say, I do not know what later happened to the girl. As we have already seen, many a schizophrenic remains for all her days sane enough to work.

Nietzsche Tells of His Sins

As many know, the great German philosopher Nietzsche spent many years in a mental hospital. There he wrote a

small book *(My Sister and I,* 1951) which he smuggled out
with the help of a fellow patient. Nietzsche had sense
enough to know that if his sister or his mother had ever
gotten their hands on the manuscript, it would certainly
have been destroyed. Twenty years later, it turned up in
the possession of a clergyman in Canada!

What is remarkable is that, insane as he was, Nietzsche
managed to fill much of this book with brilliant and thought-
provoking statements. Although he was so bitter against
his mother and sister that one wonders how correct his
accusations against them are, the impression I get is that,
like most insane persons, he was ruggedly honest. Certainly
no one but a ruggedly honest man would have confessed so
frankly to years of incestuous physical love with his sister.
No one is likely to confess to such a sin unless, with his insanity, all inhibitions and feeling of shame and reticence
have been wiped away. Interestingly, he said that even in
his worst moments he had never felt like a sinner; and "he
had never sunk so low" that he felt the need to make the
confession just to obtain absolution.

The insanity may have been syphilitic. Nietzsche wrote
that his madness was due to a syphilitic infection which he
had acquired from a beautiful Eurasian girl whom he met
in a brothel. If he did have paresis (syphilis of the brain),
he still could have had a basic and perhaps familial tendency to insanity. Many paretics have this. Nietzsche said
that after an accident his father had some illness of the
brain. Actually, Nietzsche tells how in his early years he had
insane ideas of God's death.

His hatred of his mother. Nietzsche said he hated his
mother. He claimed he was disgusted with her prudishness
and hatred of sex, and her inability ever to show any affection for him. She may have been schizoid, in which case
he might have received some of his tendency to insanity
from her. In some places in his book he said he loathed her.
"Her hypocritical virtue held me in bonds of iron all her
life, and I could only break away by attempting the impossible, the continuation of the desperate love-relationship
with my sister, who was equally in the grip of my mother's
false modesty."

His hunger for love. "I have hungered for the passionate love of a woman who could redeem me from the terror of a world that has witnessed the death of God." He spoke often of loneliness, which he divided into the loneliness of places, the loneliness of a lofty aim, the loneliness which is without any hope of compensation, and the loneliness that is due to the individual's failure to reach some common understanding with the world. "That is the bitterest loneliness of all." Such thoughts do not sound like those of a madman. He said so truly, "Everything can be acquired in solitude—except sanity."

Nietzsche spoke in several places in his book about the greatly oversexed countess who, he says, early seduced him and did much to educate him in sensuality. She had a properly curtained bed "to hide the prying eyes of her conscience from herself!" He thought he had infected this countess with his syphilitic taint, because her second child was an idiot—"no doubt the evil fruit of our liaison." It is more probable that, if the child was his, it was his tendency to insanity which had caused the child's brain to fail to develop properly.

The woman whom he liked best was a certain Lou Salomé, who, he said, was lascivious to a marked degree. His affair with her was ecstatic; and yet, at times, he seemed to be resentful about her. He claimed to have had sexual relations with Cosima, the wife of his friend Richard Wagner.

Incest with his sister. In more than one place in his book, Nietzsche says that from childhood on his sister had loved to crawl into bed with him and to play with his genitalia as a lover would. He maintained that for years their relations had been of this character. He tells how an aunt of his once found out about this affair and reproached him for it. Nietzsche says, "I both loved and resented that wealth of warmth which Elizabeth [his sister] brought to me in those unexpected hours of the night." Of his sister, Nietzsche once said, she grew "into the fierce, perverse little animal she is." In another place, feeling kinder toward Elizabeth, he said she had been both a mother and a father to him. "Without her strict discipline, my genius might have been blighted in early youth when I first realized that God was dead and that we were trapped in a whirling Void, a mean-ingless chaos of being."

Nietzsche's supposed kinship with God. Like so many of the insane, Nietzsche felt he was the son of Odin, and the equal of God. As he once said, he would refuse to play second fiddle to God. In another place, he said that, in crying out against the madness of God, he had gone mad himself.

All in all, I think this is one of the most unusual books ever written. It gives a remarkable picture of a mind which occasionally seems normal enough and even brilliant, but the next minute is mixed up. It shows us that very common tendency of many insane persons to claim a close and unique and chummy relationship with God.

More facts about Nietzsche's last days. Many people who admire the great philosopher may feel inclined to question the authenticity of this diary, but in her book *The Lonely Nietzsche* (1915) the sister, Frau Förster Nietzsche, ad-mitted that there was a manuscript which disappeared.

What happened was that all his days Nietzsche was odd and inclined to suffer from spells of either depresssion or mania. She tells how, in his youth, he had a host of friends "who idolized him even if they did not understand him." Then she tells of several depressions that he had, also spells of mania. She describes (page 152) how "Fine bright days came to his aid, helping him to master his agonies of spirit and to write the first part of Zarathustra in ten days, amid a perfect riot of joy." Evidently he was manic. Nietzsche left letters and memoranda in which he told how at this time "he was literally overwhelmed by the exuberance of his idea."

In a letter written in 1883, he wrote, "You cannot imagine . . . what a deluge of suffering life has brought me, at all times from my earliest childhood." As his sister writes (page 233), "if we now look back at the thirty years of poetic development, we cannot but feel a deep melancholy." One suspects that much of Nietzsche's failure to gain the recogni-tion he craved was due to the mild psychosis which caused him to offend friends and to break with them—as he broke with Wagner.

His sister tells (page 391) how one day late in 1888 her brother fell down with a stroke which left his right side largely paralyzed. After two days of saying nothing, he began to sing and talk loudly to himself. He developed "the wildest fantasies." As his sister said, "His nearest and dearest have become enemies who have torn him to pieces." She went on to say that she and her mother got hold of three sheets of paper which contained attacks on Wagner, Cosima Wagner, "my mother and myself." She said, "Even these notes contain passages of arresting beauty, but on the whole they are clearly the work of a fevered brain." "These papers were all destroyed by my mother." Frau Förster admits (page 392) that some of this abusive material in letter form reached Nietzsche's old friends. Also, she said (page 393), "We suspect . . . that roving manuscript of my brother's fell into strange hands." Frau Förster writes several pages on her brother's affair with Lou Salomé and tells how it came to an end.

She says (page 140) that his illness lasted nearly twelve years. Much of this time he was mentally disturbed and sometimes he was aphasic or unable to talk normally. According to his sister, she and her mother later became reconciled to the invalid; and after that, their relations with him were affectionate to the end. This came in 1900, after several more strokes.

CHAPTER 5

Some Persons Who Were Depressed

This chapter is based on the writings of a number of manic-depressive persons. Their stories tell us much about some of the several types of this disease, and also about the lamentable difficulties we physicians often have in making the diagnosis. In many a case we remain confused for months, partly because the patient complains only of feeling tired or toxic, or full of pain here and there. I remember the mildly depressed daughter of a badly depressed mother who for half a lifetime complained only of a most distressing feeling of fatigue when she tried to get up in the morning. Others of my depressed patients complained only of a stomach-ache, or a headache, and a few complained mainly of paroxysms of fear, or distress over their supposed great sinfulness.

The biographies from which I now quote are remarkable for their magnificent descriptions of some phases of the disease. For instance, Mrs. Lenore McCall's description of the process of drifting into a depression is a classic. Mrs. Judith Kruger's book is noteworthy for its excellent portrayal of the type of depression that sometimes attacks a woman shortly after she has given birth to a child. She shows how serious a problem a psychosis can continue to be for long months after the patient has been discharged from a mental hospital.

Mrs. S. W. Pierce's story is excellent to show, first, how

silly some treatments for a depression are, and second, how slow the recovery is likely to be when electroshocks are not given.

John Custance gives the best description I have ever found of the great activity of a manic brain. He gives the best verbal picture I have seen of the mixture of sense and nonsense that is to be found often in the thinking of a mildly psychotic man.

Robert Dahl's book shows how distressing to a man's relatives and close friends can be their having to tell him that he has lost his sanity—when his only response is to turn on them in anger and bitterness. Dahl brings out an interesting point about entering a mental hospital. He says one of the most unpleasant features of this is that the patient has no idea when he will be freed—granting that some day he will be let out again. As he says, a man entering prison commonly knows how long his sentence is.

Alonzo Graves's book is of interest for two reasons: one, that he supplies such good records of his several depressions, and the other, that he gives the best description I have seen of mental illness as it ran through a family.

Jim Piersall's story is very unusual, first, because for some time his first symptom of mental trouble was clowning, and second, because he had a long period of amnesia (loss of memory) during which time he nevertheless kept playing excellent baseball.

Mrs. Anna Agnew's story is valuable in showing that a person who suddenly goes insane in middle life can have been mildly psychotic and expecting and dreading insanity from early childhood onward.

A Vivid Description of a Depression

An able woman, a trained writer—Lenore McCall—has given us a vivid description of her long and very distressing bout with depression (*Between Us and the Dark*, 1947). Mrs. McCall's book should be read by all students of psychoses, if only so that they may get an idea of how slowly a person can go insane, what the symptoms are during this early stage of the illness, and how the victim often does her best to hide her distress even from those who love her most.

At first, great fatigue. Mrs. McCall tells us how she—a well-educated and well-to-do woman, and the mother of three children—gradually began to feel tired. Soon, she became so tired that she could hardly make the effort to carry on from day to day. All enthusiasm went out of her. For a while, she did not guess what was wrong. As she says, how wonderful it would have been if someone could only have recognized the fact that her symptoms were those of a beginning psychosis. "The signposts were there, but their markings were unintelligible to me. I did not know what horrors lay ahead on that road, and so I did not stop to ask a qualified guide how I might retrace my steps to safety —while there was still time."

She was too fearful to ask for help. Her greatest difficulty was that she was so fearful that someone might see that her mind was slipping. Hoping to avoid being put into a mental hospital, she would not let even her husband know what was going on in her mind. Later, when her husband asked her fine old obstetrician to see her, she turned on the doctor angrily and would take no advice from him. Like so many psychotic people, she had the idea that if she could only keep concealing her mental troubles, she could avoid insanity.

It was not until one September when she had to close her summer place and return to her city home that she realized how seriously ill she was. She just could not force herself to attend to all of the details of closing the house. But still she managed to behave well enough so that nobody knew that she was ill. She did this even after she had "progressed over the border into that strange land of shadows."

She became manic. Then, for a while, she became slightly manic and did too much. She could not relax, and in her there was a restlessness which drove her on to ceaseless activity. "I seemed to be untiring; and parodoxically, the one effort which I could not face was that of resting. I was so thankful, however, that my mental and physical inertia had vanished." She did not realize that what had replaced the depression was equally bad. "So," as she says, "I hurtled on, consuming the last shreds of my resistance, strength and judgment, all of which undoubtedly could have been salvaged and rehabilitated." I often think that if these people could only be restrained during their periods of mania, they might not later go so deeply into the depression that follows.

Her mind began to disintegrate. Eventually, she began to realize that her mental activity and her thinking were becoming disconnected, like the wires of an electrical apparatus. "For example, I sat one day doing a bit of mending for the children. I fumbled in my sewing basket for a pair of scissors, and not finding them, I walked across the room to a table where I might have laid them. By the time I had crossed the short space I had forgotten completely what had brought me there—what it was I was looking for." As she said, all of us have had such experiences, but this was an extreme case, so extreme that with it she became frightened. she saw that this sort of thing was happening to her too often, "as though there were an ever-increasing breach between my will and my brain."

As I shall keep noting in this book, one of the surest signs I have found to show that a person's brain is beginning to function badly is the person's inability to grasp what is read. As Mrs. McCall says, "One night, reading in bed, I realized that I was going over and over the same paragraph, and that its content was an absolute blank to me. Nor could I connect what I was trying to read with any subject-matter which had preceded it, for my mind was wiped clear of what had gone before."

Great loneliness. Then Mrs. McCall began to feel the tremendous loneliness that comes to a person who is losing contact with her fellows. As she said, "I could see people through the invisible wall, I could speak to them and they to me, but the mental and spiritual I, the essence of me, could not reach them, and this was a part of the horror which was enfolding me as I slipped into that dark and unknown world."

Then, she found that she "was numb to all the beauty around; it had no power to assuage the bleakness of my mind. I sat down and, without any warning, I burst into tears. Huddled in a corner of the garden I cried bitterly for some time. Depression far deeper and more pronounced than that of the early summer now took possession of me," "and the hopelessness, and the unreasonable quality of it appalled me."

Horrible fears. "There is no emotion in life more paralyzing than *fear,* no element more devastating." From then on, fear was Mrs. McCall's constant companion, and this fear grew into *horror.* "My fear was based fundamentally upon a terror of myself, of what was happening to me, of the helplessness which was overpowering my faculties." "I began to be afraid of people, of my family and my friends." This was "because of my inability to cope with ordinary human contacts. The world which others inhabited, and to which I rightly belonged, was unreal to me; and I felt myself an alien as I trudged farther and farther into weird and unknown terrain."

About this time, sleep became largely impossible, and specters haunted her as she lay in the dark. Then she began to worry about "little sins of commission or omission." They became "heinous crimes as I lay shivering with fear, dripping with perspiration, my hands and feet ice-cold, my body aching with the tension that was becoming so familiar. Why had I done this, and what would have been the result if I had not done that? I had been wicked, though in what manner I was not quite certain, and this suffering was my punishment." This is so typical of the manic-depressive person. He or she feels a tremendous burden of sin, but with very vague ideas as to what the sin was. This is so typical also of many deeply religious people.

Fear of doctors. In spite of her great suffering, she was "determined she would not seek medical aid." She was too afraid to see a doctor. "I was afraid to find out what was the matter with me." She was afraid of being committed. Curiously, if only some other part of her body below the neck had been misbehaving, she would have gone immediately to a good specialist in that field. "But because my brain was the offender, I could not bring myself to enlist aid from any source."

An inability to make decisions. "I was no longer able to

make the most trivial decision." "I could not decide what to put on when I got up in the morning," and I "couldn't tell the cook what to prepare for luncheon." For a while her love for her children served as an anchor for her, but then that bond failed her. An afternoon came when "I felt that I had sunk beyond their reach, and that I was no longer worthy to share their lives."

Then she turned on her beloved husband and looked on him as her enemy because he kept wanting to find out what was wrong with her. To her sick mind, he was a menace to her safety. "I was determined to be on my guard." She went on avoiding contacts with her children, her husband, and her servants, "while my sick spirit ached for the human relationships now denied me." Then she no longer cared what happened to her. She went out and walked in the snow until she became exhausted. She thought to herself, "I am done for. Someone will find me, but I hope it will be too late." "But the children, what about them? I don't want to live. Not this way."

That night her husband found her, and then a contest began, with him trying to get the doctor to see her, with her objecting strenuously. When the doctor came, she was nasty to him. And when he wanted to call a psychiatrist, she became angrier than ever. Through the years she had thought the doctor was her friend, and now he wanted to betray her! So she hated him.

When a psychiatrist came, she insulted him. But, finally, she felt that there was no longer any use struggling. She no longer had the strength to fight. She said, "Even my children have slipped away from me. I can't hold on to them in my mind. I can't reach out even to my husband. I'm shut away by myself where everything is dim and queer. The only thing that's real now is the horror I'm in."

Problems of hospitalization. She was taken to a *general* hospital for a few days. There she did not want to talk even to her children. She didn't want to see them. She had to force herself to greet them. Then came discussions between her family doctor, her psychiatrist, and her husband in regard to putting her into a mental hospital. She so rebelled against the idea of hospitalization that her poor husband suffered when he had to tell her she just had to go. What was hardest to bear was that she felt that he had failed her and turned against her. She said, "I won't do it." "Henry, you wouldn't do this to me; you couldn't; you wouldn't put me away in a strange place away from everything and everyone I know and care for." She felt trapped, like an animal. She was so angry with her husband she wouldn't let him even touch her. She didn't want him to come back to see her. When her dear old family doctor went to see her, she only cursed him and ordered him out.

Mrs. McCall says she had the idea that "by refusing to accept the idea that I was going to enter a mental hospital I nullified its existence." In many ways this is not a particularly insane reaction; it is the reaction of many supposedly sane people to many a medical emergency.

Loss of contact with the world. Christmas Day came, and she had to steel herself to talk to her children over the telephone. She didn't want to, and she didn't want any presents. She did not want to see her husband. She felt hopeless. She was sure she would never recover. Seeing that eventually she was going to leave the children, she thought it would be better for them if they were to be told that she was dead. One can easily see that when a depressed person feels this way, it is a short step to suicide. Suicide looks like a welcome end to it all. The patient has the idea that her suicide will help her loved ones out of a miserable situation. "It will be better for all concerned." Actually, about this time, Mrs. McCall broke a drinking glass and chewed up and swallowed the pieces. They cut her mouth and her throat but they didn't injure her much. When she woke the next morning and found herself alive, she was much disappointed. "The realization that I was still alive was so bitter that I cursed God."

Life in a mental hospital. For the next year she improved but little. After a while, "I no longer sat for hours weeping bitterly; I gained a modicum of control, and settled into a quiet hopelessness. There was less rebellion in my attitude, because I felt there was nothing to be gained by rebelling. I was done for," and "now I abandoned any hope of escape. This was to be my life for as long as life endured —so I thought."

On the occasions when her husband came, she found no pleasure in his visit; in fact, it was a torture to her. Also, with her sick mind, she got the idea that he must be having a love affair with her best friend. Grief over his wife's illness nearly broke her husband down. It was agonizing, also, to her to realize that Henry, "who had meant everything in life to me had now no more substance in my mind than a shadow." "And yet I could remember how I once had felt toward him." "I loathed the spiritual paralysis which had deadened me, and I was torn to pieces by a sense of bafflement and failure." "I wanted Henry to stay with me, and yet I was glad he was going. The reminders he brought with him of what I had lost were too agonizing; the conflict was too severe, and I was worn out."

It is remarkable that even her mother love left her—that emotion which is perhaps the strongest a woman can have. Later, a horrible obsession laid hold of her: "I became convinced that an unpleasant odor emanated from me, and it caused me unspeakable torture." No one around her could smell anything, but, as always happens, their statements did not cheer her. She was distressed by this hallucination of smell until the day when she got well. When months passed and she did not get any better, she began trying again to figure out another way in which she could commit suicide.

Then it was decided to move her to another hospital where the discipline would be more strict, and where she would be compelled to live by a schedule. It was thought that the program of activities would help her, but it didn't. She still remained rebellious and defiant. She, who had always been a lady, would curse people who were trying to be kind to her. As she said, "I'm all mixed up. I only know that I want to hurt Henry, and that I hate him because he's well, and he's keeping me here in this place."

After nearly four years she was much worse! She was silent and withdrawn. All she did was to try to keep up with the mechanics of everyday living in the hospital. She became very thin, she limped, and her face became etched by lines of suffering.

A cure is found. And then, very fortunately for her, one of the then-new treatments, in which the patient's brain is electrically shocked into health, began to be used. For three months she had a series of these treatments. At first, the shocks did no good, but then, one day she woke up in the morning—well. "I sat up suddenly, my heart pounding. I looked around the room and a sweep of wonder surged over me. God in heaven, I'm well. I'm myself. This is I. . . . My mind is working. I'm glad to see the day; the sunlight is beautiful. I'm well. I've come back from the dead." "I went to bed last night, sicker than I thought I'd ever been, and this morning I'm well. It's a miracle. Tears ran down my cheeks; warm, relieving, happy tears." "I'm going back to everything I thought I'd never see again. Henry, I'm coming back to you and the children. I'll make up to you the rest of my life for all the worry and unhappiness you've gone through the past four years."

"Also, the smell has gone, the dreadful smell I thought I had. I don't think it was ever really there. I think I imagined it." She doubtless did, because I have seen many psychotic persons who were sure they smelled terribly bad when they didn't.

One of the most wonderful things about a depression is that it can clear away in a minute. Many a time a patient has said to me, "One day the curtain went up, and then I was well again."

Mrs. McCall was kept in the hospital another four months, during which time she had to be educated "in the art of living." Just before she went home, she said to her psychiatrist, "One of the essential things you've taught me is to take criticism without my stomach turning over, and without my getting angry. That is something to have learned."

And then her husband came and took her home. "Two tall boys and a slender, leggy girl, her golden pigtails streaming out behind her in the wind," came running to greet her. "It was John and David and Emily, and I was home."

Today, if a woman who has slipped into a persisting depression and perhaps is feeling terribly tired and uninterested in everything, and complaining of abdominal pain and feelings of toxicity, will only go to a good psychiatrist for electroshock treatments, she many find herself much improved within a week.

A Mother's Depression After Her Child Is Born

Many a woman with an inborn tendency to depression goes into a slump after she has given birth to a child, and the best description of this illness that I know of was written by Mrs. Judith Kruger (*My Fight for Sanity*, 1959). When she went insane, her husband was a medical student, starting on his internship.

The slow beginnings of unrecognized insanity. As she says, long before her mind became badly disturbed, there were occasional flurries of anxiety that caused her concern. She was too serious about her housekeeping; there was no fun in her work; she went at every task with tension. What made life hard, also, was her great fear of any change, such as moving to a new apartment.

After her child was born, Mrs. Kruger could not sleep, and in order to get some rest she had to keep taking larger and larger doses of sedatives. She says, "I was consumed in mounting tension. It was like a cloud around me—a choking fog. I had no inkling of what was wrong. I only knew that I was more nervous than I had ever been in my life." "Nothing looked right to me." "When my father and brother made their first visit to us, the sight of their faces upset me." "I moved thickly through the days. Panic was rising and spreading like a slow paralysis." In the evening when her husband came home from the hospital she wanted to be responsive, but "I was different; I was a strange somebody who couldn't see or feel or move beyond a growing wall of fear." "Everything is closing in: steel hands on my chest. I can hardly breathe." Then her hands began to shake, and they kept shaking; "and inside was a great fear."

Finally, she began to wonder if she was "going crazy." She felt dead—"cold and dried up inside." "I can't feel sex or love or anything. Just dead." "I want to sit in a corner and not talk; not say anything." "I want to kill myself." "I want out. Escape. I have to get away from pain and fear."

Then she tried to commit suicide with sleeping pills, but, as so often happens, it was a halfhearted attempt; she called her husband to tell him what she had done.

Hospitalization. After this, they put her in a mental hospital, where soon she was again trying suicide: not once, but twice. She was given some shock treatments, and with these she improved. But she still had feelings of guilt, and when her husband tried to kiss her, she would turn away. From the start she had no use for her baby and could feel neither interest in him nor love for him. Her mother had to take all the care of him. Typical of the concentration on self of psychotic persons is her statement that when her father and husband would make a trip to the hospital to see her, "I would waste precious moments talking to myself instead of to them." Then the doctors let her go home, but she was not much happier there. Like many psychotic persons, she got a diarrhea which lasted for weeks.

Her "emotional control was still very ragged." There was a difficult and unhappy time during which she tried to adjust to living but failed. She could not get along with her husband, and she could not get along with her old family doctor. She had some obsessions, and she couldn't sleep. Any work in the home was almost impossible. She tried to play the role of a mother, but she couldn't do it. She said she was not made for it; that was all. She thought she wanted to be free—out in the world again—to mix with adults. She wanted "kicks and thrills." She did not want her baby, but she could not "give him back." One evening she tried to cook supper, but it took her three hours. *"Three hours!"*

Later, she was so nervous she couldn't listen to the doctor when he talked to her. She was too upset to think straight. It was six months after her baby was born, and still she was in bad shape. She was hating herself because of her inability to love her husband. She begged him to forgive her.

More psychotherapy. She then forced herself to go to a doctor for psychotherapy, but it didn't do her any good. Her harassed husband retreated into a shell and quit talking to her. She began to wonder if she was really a woman. She decided she wanted to be a breadwinner, but only for herself. She said everyone had tried to make her into something she was not fitted for. She felt she was a misfit in marriage. She wanted to leave her husband and the baby; to go back home and just exist—in a room in her parents' apartment. She wanted a simple job. Curiously, she even thought of becoming a prostitute! Then she thought perhaps her doctor wasn't doing a good enough job of psychotherapy, so she asked to see a consultant. He spent ten minutes with her, and she felt she had gotten the "bum's rush." Actually, he probably had sense enough to know that one cannot talk a depressed woman out of her illness; one might as well try to talk an epileptic out of his "fits."

Psychoanalysis. Next, she found a psychoanalyst and liked him. Wisely, he convinced her that there was no sense in her trying to run away from herself; she wouldn't be any happier in a lonely room. With wisdom he told her that even if she didn't learn the origins of all her fears and phobias, she could get well. But, following out the theories of his group, he went ahead to do what he could to prove to Mrs. Kruger that she had been too fond of her father in a sexual way. After the doctor had talked to her awhile, she said, "When my father kisses me now, I want to scream. I feel so dirty; as though I've discovered an ugly secret about us."

She told her analyst she hated him when, near the close of each interview, he started looking at the clock. "It's like a door slamming in my face. I feel so shut out and shut up. Bang! Finished! You're through! Bye, bye!" Soon, the analyst insisted on her believing that her trouble was that she wanted a penis! Then he tried to get her to admit that she was sexually in love with her brother, but that was a bit more than she could stand.

One day, she got the shakes and shook and shook. As she said, "The worst thing about fear is not knowing why you're scared." Then her husband had to go to another city to get the hospital residency he needed, but she wouldn't go with him. Like so many persons who have become dependent on psychoanalysis, she said she just could not leave her analyst, not even so that her man could go where he could earn his living!

She scolded her husband. Eventually, she had a wordy

fight with her husband, accusing him of never having been loving enough. At the same time she said, "I know I am not sufficiently feminine and clinging and passive. But you have never helped me; you have never made me feel like a woman, protected and petted." The poor husband—she felt "it was all his fault!" Then her analyst tried to convince her that her mental trouble was due to the "fact" that when she looked at her husband she saw her mother's image in him.

Mrs. Kruger said, "I've flung myself headlong through life, dragging the demons of hate and guilt and fear: like a cat running down the street with cans tied to its tail." "I have never done a spontaneous thing in my life." As she finished her book, Mrs. Kruger decided she was feeling a little better. One feels sure that she had a long way still to go before she could become "normal" again.

I marvel that in so many of these autobiographies, the person speaks often of the hatred he or she feels for many people. Apparently, a strong tendency to hate one's fellows is a sign of a trend toward psychosis. I know many psychically normal persons who cannot bother to feel hatred even for those persons who tried once to do them great harm.

This account of Mrs. Kruger's illness is so extremely important because it calls attention to a common disease which we physicians usually fail to recognize for what it is. Often psychiatrists—as well as other physicians—fail to recognize that these people only rarely can be helped with psychotherapy or drugs. The treatment most likely to produce real improvement in a short time is electroshock therapy.

Mrs. Kruger shows us so clearly how a person may not be sane for months after return home from a mental hospital, and she shows how the depressed woman loses all ability to love—even her baby and her husband and her parents. She shows how the unhappy woman often drives all love for her out of the heart of her husband.

A Woman Whose Depression Was Treated in Many Ways, Perhaps All of Them Futile

Some forty-odd years ago a woman concert pianist and her husband wrote an excellent story to show how badly, at that time, a severe depression could be diagnosed and treated. Today, a woman like Mrs. Pierce, if fortunate enough to fall into good hands, would probably soon be brought out of her melancholia with the help of a few electroshock treatments. In her day, these were not available.

I might explain that in their book (*A Layman Looks at Doctors*, 1929), Mrs. S. W. and Mr. J. T. Pierce (pseudonyms) described their unfortunate experiences with a series of psychiatrists of a type such as one might well have found before 1919. The specialty of psychiatry was then in its infancy, and many of the exponents of this new science were but poorly trained. In those days, most "psychiatrists" were really superintendents of mental hospitals, whose only job was to run the place and keep the patients locked up. They also did much work in courts as medicolegal experts.

The acute onset of the woman's illness. The Pierces' book is the story of Sally (Mrs. Pierce), a young woman who apparently was well enough until around February, 1919, when she began to have what almost certainly was an hysterical pain and weakness in one arm. She also developed a strange hatred for the mental hospital in which her father worked as a psychiatrist. This hate probably arose when she began to sense that she was headed for the place, or one like it. At this time she married, and apparently was happy and, at first, well adjusted. Seven months later, when she and her husband left on a boat for San Francisco, she promptly went into a terrible panic, and demanded that the ship put back into New York to let her off. The couple got off the boat as soon as they could, at Savannah, but Sally was not better; she continued to pace the floor day and night, wringing her hands in the agony of what psychiatrists today would call an agitated depression. Although this serious disease can easily be recognized from a glance at the patient, we doctors commonly fail to realize what is wrong—because at college no one ever told us about the malady.

A doctor tries to laugh off her psychosis. At the first hospital to which she was taken, the doctor tried to laugh off her troubles. He gave her the impression that they were of no consequence. But this attitude only distressed Sally the more. Actually, she was suffering so much she wanted to die. She felt that her arm *had* died, and yet it was causing her such pain that the agony of it could hardly be endured. She felt trapped in illness. She felt as if her head was encircled in an iron band. She maintained that she was happy in her marriage, and she denied having any personal problems. Her career in music had gone well.

She felt she was never going to get out of bed again, which, of course, is typical of the discouragement of a depressed person. Typically, also, she said her life was over; it had stopped, and she was insane. She was full of fears; she felt she couldn't stand another day of her suffering. She sensed that some terrible danger was all around her, and she was filled with panic. She was afraid to live and afraid to die. Then, as is the case with some psychotic people when they get slightly manic, she found that she could write poetry.

Treatment with contempt and brutality. The second doctor who saw her treated her with contempt and brutality—apparently with the idea that if he could make her angry enough, she could "snap out" of her depression. When he sneered at Sally's talk of suicide, she decided she would "show him," but fortunately she fell to the floor before she could thrust a red-hot poker into her brain. Some months later, she found some codein pills and took them all, but the dose wasn't enough to kill her. As a result, next morning, she woke much disappointed to find herself still alive.

Treatment by making love. Then, a new doctor was found who had the idea that what nervous women need is an extra lover. He said, "The trouble with you, Mrs. Pierce, is that you need another sexual outlet; to put it frankly, surely there must be some good-looking man up at the hotel?" This so disgusted Sally that she would have no more to do with the doctor.

Treatment with classification and long words. The next doctor who saw her loved long words with which to classify his patients. He finally was happy when he figured out that she was "an outstanding example of overspecialization and of community neglect." When she did not get well under the impact of his beloved long words, he was satisfied that her trouble was not with the inefficiency of his brand of psychiatry; it must be with her.

Treatment by glandular products. The next man felt sure that her trouble must all be in her glands of internal secretion. He spent much time and great sums of money on every test he could think of to prove his theory correct, and then he started trying on her, one after the other, the different types of glandular products. As anyone might have prophesied, none of them helped.

Treatment by a "complete examination." Then, as often happens still today, it was decided to call in an internist, to find the *cause* for her depression in some organic disease below her neck. Accordingly, she was put through the whole diagnostic mill. Many physicians and many laymen still have the idea that if someone will only give the patient enough tests, this will in some miraculous way bring a cure. Actually, as could have been foretold, the tests didn't show anything, and the patient got worse.

Treatment by psychoanalysis. Then the husband heard of psychoanalysis and felt sure this was exactly what his wife needed. So she started on her hour-long sessions. At first, the analyst had great difficulty because sometimes Sally was so depressed she could not be induced to talk at all. Also, she had no faith in the procedure, and she had no desire to keep talking about herself—going again and again over what few unpleasant memories she could rake up, together with the apparently meaningless dreams which were of such interest to her analyst.

For months, there was not the slightest improvement. Sally was even more despondent and bewildered and hostile than before, and she rarely spoke to anyone. When she did, she begged her husband to spare her the tedium of the analysis. As she said, she had no idea as to what the analyst was talking about or trying to prove, and she could not believe that he was on the right track. What with all the talking about herself, she became more and more introspective; and often, after her visit with the analyst, she would cry for hours. Then, for two months, she slumped and spent most of her time in bed.

But then, gradually, she began more often to get out of

bed, and even to go for a walk with her nurse. She still had not the least idea of what her doctor was talking about. She became more and more disgusted with the demands that she write down her dreams and then talk at length about them. She didn't absolutely refuse to go on with the analysis, because she didn't know of anything else to try, and because her husband kept clinging to his faith in the method —a faith that had become strong when he had heard of a man who had been helped by it.

After many months, Mrs. Pierce began to talk a bit more, she began to go out more often, and she began to look into shop windows. Then she found she could take her arm out of its sling in which she had kept it all this time. A few months later, she began to buy some clothes, and then she went back to playing her piano. In another six months, she went to tea with someone; and finally, in July, 1923—three years and ten months from the time she had become depressed—she came home well.

A great argument followed as to whether the analysis had worked the cure. The question then was, had the analysis had anything to do with her recovery? Her husband was so sure of it that he had the utmost contempt for the doubts of Sally's psychiatrist father, who said he had seen hundreds of patients, after some years, come out of a depression in just this way—*with no treatment at all.* As he said, psychiatrists haven't the slightest idea why many people go into a depression, or why they find their way out. The father thought the analyst had just been lucky in that Sally had happened to get well toward the end of the long time in which she had been under his care.

The husband, with the infinite wisdom of many untutored persons, said that the father's scepticism "would have been amusing if it had not been so pathetic." Pierce could not know that thirty years later few analysts could be found who would think of going into a mental hospital to try to cure a depressed patient. Even Freud was not inclined to attempt that.

About all that the analyst could draw out of Mrs. Pierce during the course of her long analysis were such facts as that she had often failed to get along well with her neurotic mother and hence had felt more love for her sweet and gentle father. There was a time when, as a girl, Sally had had a little wound on her arm, and, for a few days, her father had fussed over it with considerable concern. This was thought to be the explanation of the fact that the depression had started with the hysterical weakness of one arm.

An old-time psychiatrist like Sally's father could conceive of the possibility that these slight psychic traumas might have upset a person who had been born to be upset, but he could not accept the analyst's idea that Sally's tremendous attack of claustrophobia, which had hit her at the beginning of her mental upset, was due to her "fetal memory of her prolonged birth." The analyst was evidently following the ideas of Otto Rank, who, out of his inner consciousness, when about twenty-two, wrote a book to show that much mental trouble in adults is due to the terror which once overwhelmed the infant as he or she was going through the mother's birth canal.

Sally's analyst was satisfied, also, that her old fear of going on a boat was a relic of the fear she had had as a fetus, when she was unwilling to be torn away from her mother's womb. Today, most brain physiologists would probably find it hard to accept this idea. Why? Because they say a fetus or an infant being born has a brain which is so far from complete it can hardly do any thinking. This brain does not show much of an electroencephalogram until the fourth year of life. Actually the record is not that of an adult until the child is eleven. Few adults can remember anything that happened before they were three or four years old.

All in all, this book raises many interesting questions, and every psychiatrist should have a copy to show to his students. It should serve to keep them thinking.

A Remarkable Description of Mania and Depression

In many ways the best description of mania and depression I have seen is the one written by John Custance (*Wisdom, Madness and Folly: The Philosophy of a Lunatic*, 1952). It ought to be read and studied by every psychologist and psychiatrist. The book is especially good because the man is unusually well-educated, widely read, and articulate.

A mixture of philosophy and mysticism. Custance well sums up his book when he says, "I have perhaps shown that there is a wisdom in 'madness' which has not yet been fully explored." He has filled a number of chapters with a mixture of philosophy, mysticism, ancient religion, anthropology, Freudianism, and present-day psychiatry, the value of which is hard to appraise. It may be pure psychosis, and then again it may some day throw light on the workings of the human mind. Custance himself wondered how psychotic he might still be after he had been dismissed from a mental hospital and had gone into one of his "sane" intervals between a manic spell and a depressed spell. He was obsessed by the idea of opposites, as were the Chinese with their yang and yin.

Part of this book was written while Custance was in a mental hospital. As one reads such parts, one suspects that the man's mind was jumping rapidly from thought to thought, much as it does in cases of schizophrenia; but in other parts of the book, he writes beautifully and clearly and logically.

Curious religious phases of insanity. Interestingly, Custance tells us that, as was the case with Anton Boisen, insanity brought to him "an intense emotional religious experience, very foreign to the temper of staid Anglicanism in which I was brought up." Again and again during the manic or elated periods of his illness, he "felt this sense of a revelation of ultimate harmonies." As with many schizophrenics, the sun came to have "an extraordinary effect" on him. "It seemed to be charged with all power; not merely to symbolize God but actually to be God. Phrases such as 'Light of the World,' 'the Sun of Righteousness that setteth nevermore' ran through my head without ceasing." "I felt impelled to address the sun as a personal God."

One day Custance wrote, "I feel so close to God, so inspired by His Spirit that in a sense I am God. I see the future, plan the Universe, save mankind; I am utterly and completely immortal; I am even male and female." (See Schreber and Nijinsky.) This reminds us of some of the

ancient Syrian gods who had both male and female attributes. Sometimes Custance, like other insane persons,
had a feeling that truths of sciences, even those he hadn't
studied, were made manifest to him by some process of
infusion. (See also Nijinsky.)

Like so many insane persons, Custance felt that he had
become a close friend of God and Jesus; he felt that often
he was in their immediate presence. He said, "I feel that I
talk to Him and He talks to me without the slightest difficulty." Custance said at times he even argued stubbornly
with God, and disagreed with Him on some matters. At
times he had other delusions of grandeur. In many ways
Custance thought like a schizophrenic, and yet he alternated
between mania and depression. His is a beautiful example
of those many psychoses that are hard to classify. As the
famous psychiatrist Dr. Abraham Myerson, of Boston, used
to point out, even after his years of experience with the
insane, he often could not differentiate manic-depressive
psychosis and schizophrenia, because a patient could behave for much of the time like a typical schizophrenic and
then go into a typical depression. In many cases no two
psychiatrists will agree as to the diagnosis, and this is not
so much their fault as it is the fault of our inability to work
out a logical classification.

The great conviction of sin. Like some depressed persons,
Custance was often convinced that, Faust-like, he had sold
his soul to the devil. He made three attempts at suicide. At
times he was sure God had turned His back on him and
left him to Satan. (See, also, William Cowper's Life, *The
Stricken Deer.*)

A hundred times I have been impressed on reading the
writings of religious people to see how horrified they were
over their sinfulness, and yet none of them could ever say
exactly what their sins had been. When Custance kept
telling his wife that his sins were so awful as to be un-
forgivable, she would ask again and again, "But what were
those sins?" And never was Custance sure what they had
been. He brooded over sexual sins which, if really committed, probably wouldn't have bothered him at all if he
had been sane.

I remember an insane patient of mine who was over-whelmed with a sense of sinfulness. When I insisted on his telling me exactly what his sin was, he said he feared he had once been unfaithful to his wife, but he could not re-member when, where, or with whom! And yet he said he would just have to expiate in some way; his only salvation lay in being severely punished.

Custance, like Anton Boisen, thinks there is a place for religion in the treatment of some of the insane. He tells us how insanity causes a man to associate sex with religion, and to get the two mixed up together as they have been in many churches, both ancient and modern. Doubtless, much of the contempt deeply religious people have always had for sex arose in the minds of definitely schizophrenic men and women who came to be looked on as saints. Like many other psychotic persons, Custance felt that he was part of a great pattern of divine purpose.

A good description of a depression. Custance tells us that he was attacked by a manic-depressive psychosis in his middle thirties. He quotes William James who, in describing his own painful experience with depression, speaks of "Des-peration absolute and complete, the whole universe coagu-lating about the sufferer into a material of overwhelming horror, surrounding him without opening or end. Not the conception or intellectual perception of evil, but the grisly, blood-freezing, heart-palsying sensation of it close upon one; and no other conception or sensation is able to live for a moment in its presence." Custance speaks of the depressive state as often "one of misery, dejection, and at times of appalling horror. These states are generally interspersed with periods of more or less complete normality."

Mania. As many writers who have been manic have said, when they are elated, their brains work beautifully, their ideas flow with great ease, and their pens can scarcely keep up with the rapid flow of their ideas. There is a sense of great well-being. Everything in the world then "makes a much more vivid and intense impression than usual." Most of the senses are heightened so that, for instance, lights seem "deeper, more intense, perhaps a trifle more ruddy than usual." People's faces seem to glow so that they almost take on a halo. The sense of touch is heightened, and the hearing becomes acute. The handwriting may become neater, and the person can draw or paint well, or carry out manual operations much better than he can do when he is sane.

Custance gives examples of how rapidly the mind of a manic person jumps from one subject to another in the process of free association. Also, a man will find himself able to remember pages from books read. For instance, one day Custance remembered a long passage from Amiel's *Journal Intime*, which he had read long before. After his recovery he checked back and found that his memory of it had been correct.

He tells us of curious differences in the reaction of a manic and a depressed man to dirt and filth and human excreta. These differences may throw light on that admiration for a lack of cleanliness which was characteristic of many old saints and anchorites in the fourth and fifth centuries A.D.

In one place Custance says, "At one moment a schizophrenic friend of mine feels that he is a devil doomed to eternal torture, and the next that he is a god presiding over eternal bliss." With a manic-depressive, the two states remain farther apart; they may each last for months or years.

Improved health during spells of mania. Remarkable is the fact that during a manic spell Custance could do without his glasses. Apparently, the muscle of accommodation in his eyes became stronger than usual. During mania, his metabolism seemed to have been so speeded up that in cold weather he could walk about out of doors naked without discomfort. Also, during mania, all his old great fears disappeared. As he said, in many ways, it would be wonderful if a man could be manic all the time. The only difficulty is that a manic person is likely to become a nuisance to other people about him, as when he calls them on the telephone at three in the morning! He tends to travel about, using up all of his family's money, perhaps getting drunk, perhaps attacking people, and perhaps getting arrested by the police. Often he has to be committed.

Sufferings during depressions. For a while, after a period of mania, Custance would be pretty normal, and then he would go into a period of depression in which he would feel "miserable and ill." "I am haunted by a sense of guilt; my conscience gives me no rest." "I worry perpetually about my past sins and failures; not for a moment can I forget the mess I seem to have made of my life. However much I may pray for, and think of, forgiveness, no forgiveness comes. Eventually the terrors of hell approach." As Custance says, these sensations are exactly those described by the mystics, most of the saints, and many deeply religious people. Such people are always talking about their overwhelming sense of sin: of sin that is weighing them down. And then, all of a sudden, when they become elated, they feel just wonderful and ecstatic; they have been converted and saved, and Christ is with them.

Later, when depression comes back again, these persons go down to the depths of despair. "God has left them, and they cannot find Him." When depressed, St. Theresa wrote, "All the favours ever granted me were swept out of my memory. My mind was so greatly obscured that I stumbled from doubt to doubt, from fear to fear. I believed myself so wicked that I regarded my sins as the cause of all the evils and all the wickedness that afflicted the world." This, of course, is literally what many a depressed patient says today.

As Custance said, when a man is depressed, "It is appallingly difficult to concentrate; and writing is pain and grief." There are all grades of mania and depression: some with and some without illusions and hallucinations, ecstasies, or horrors. As happens to many people in a depression, Custance never really lost his grip on reality. But at times he "feared poverty, failure in life, inability to educate my children, making my wife miserable, losing her, ending up in the gutter as the most revolting type of beggar, and so on." Sometimes "I was dominated above all by an overpowering sense of fear." He was convinced that he was finished for good and all. "There was no possible chance of my coming out of the hospital alive."

When a man leaves a mental hospital, he may not be perfectly straightened out. In his Epilogue, Custance leaves us with the idea that, even when he was discharged from a mental hospital, he was "really just as mad as ever. The difference was apparent rather than real." "I just do not *appear* to be 'mad,' that is all." He said that when he was manic he had trouble maintaining contact with his fellow creatures. They could not understand him, and he could not understand them. For a while after leaving the hospital, every morning he could see two little devils watching him from the bracket above his bath. "If they should unaccountably disappear, I should be seriously disturbed."

Custance thought it is unsound for doctors to try to teach mental patients to be "normal"; what is necessary is to teach them "to *play* satisfactorily at being normal!"

As I said at the beginning, this is a remarkable book because Custance is so well educated; he is literate, and he is a good observer. I wish thoughtful psychologists and brain physiologists would study this book to see if, perhaps, by his analysis of what goes on in a disturbed brain, he has thrown light on how a normal brain works.

In his book *Adventure into the Unconscious* Custance tells much more about his life, and his adventures during times when he was slipping into a spell of insanity. He has written much more on the psychology of psychosis as he sees it.

A "Nervous Breakdown"

Robert Dahl's story (*Breakdown*, 1959), which now follows, is instructive largely because he gives a good picture of the terrible time the wife and close friends of an insane man can have when they have to—as he thinks—turn against him, and lose faith in him. Naturally, he resents this keenly, and sometimes, as was the case with Dahl, he bitterly accuses his wife and friends of being his enemies.

Robert Dahl thought his troubles began around January, 1952, but he admits that his moods had been a bit too intense before that. He was "cyclothymic" in that at times he was too enthusiastic, or overbold, or too self-confident, while at other times he was too sad, or too painfully shy.

The usual failure of everyone to recognize the early symp-

toms of a psychosis. When his troubles began, he was working in an office where he had had some disagreements with
his associates. Then he found he could not do any mental
work; he could not even dictate a report of a meeting he
had attended. Accordingly, he decided to resign, but his
friends, unable to believe he was that ill, insisted that he
stay on. But, with every day, Dahl became more and more
depressed and distraught. His memory slipped, and he could
hardly talk to people. He became so weak in the knees that
he went to a physician, but this man failed to see wherein
he was ill and told him to go back to his job.

About that time, Dahl's wife, Marilyn, had a difficult confinement in which she lost her baby. A few days after this,
Dahl decided he just had to get to a hospital. He went so
quickly that he did not wait for his wife to recover. A psychiatrist sent him into a mental hospital where he soon decided to commit suicide. He attempted this by running
head-on into a brick wall. All this did was to give him a
sore head and neck. Along the way his mind was filled with
dull terror. After three months he was sent home.

Discharge from the mental hospital did not mean a cure.
Like so many of these people, when his dismissal came, he
was not yet ready to go back into life. His wife was earning
their living. Robert still could not even carry on a conversation with anyone. He said he could not think of anything to
say. He knew that he couldn't hold any job; he couldn't
even read the newspaper comfortably; he would look at the
paper, but his mind would be somewhere else.

Then, Dahl became tremendously interested in returning
to the Catholic faith into which he had been born. To get
back into the fold he remarried his wife with a Catholic
ceremony. But he failed to receive the great spiritual uplift
he had expected.

Dahl becomes manic. Then, suddenly, Dahl became manic and decided to write a book. As usually happens with
manic persons, he felt like a new man, just full of energy
and ideas. The pages flew through his typewriter, and soon
he was working from fourteen to sixteen hours a day without any strain or fatigue. In "an ecstasy," he wrote several
hundred thousand words. His wife realized that there was

something terribly wrong with him, but she didn't know
what it was. Only his doctor realized that he had become
psychotic again. But when he told Dahl of his great danger,
this only made him angry.

In his mania, Dahl had visions of organizing a great cor-
poration, publishing many books, and becoming tremendously successful. He went to New York and blew in all his
savings in a few days. Then he demanded that his wife
quit her job. He wanted to employ three stenographers to
take down the thoughts which were pouring so rapidly out
of him. He told his friends to quit their jobs and get into
his huge business with him. Naturally, these friends got together and told him that he was a very sick man and ought
to be back in the hospital. As was to be expected, this only
made him angry, and he told his friends that they were insane and hostile to him. He turned angrily also on his wife
and said he never wanted to see her again.

Another hospitalization. But, willy-nilly, soon he had to
go back to a mental hospital. One of the hardest things
about insanity is that a man who so greatly needs help refuses to take it, and only hates his relatives and his best
friends when they have to commit him. He may even be
sure that his doctor, also, has gone crazy or has "sold him
down the river" in order to please some enemies.

Dahl gradually improves. After a while, Dahl's delusions
left him, and he no longer thought he was going to save the
world and make a million dollars. But still he was too deeply
religious—which, of course, was a bad sign. Gradually, he
became less and less bitter toward his devoted wife.

Eventually, Dahl came out, well, and when he wrote his
book, he was regional Director of the Indiana Association
for Mental Health. There he could use his personal knowledge of insanity to help others.

The Story of Several Depressions

The following abstract is of a book which is very instructive
for a number of reasons. It was well written by a newspaper
correspondent.

A marvelous family history. Alonzo Graves (*The Eclipse*

of a Mind, 1942) starts out with a remarkable study of the
poor nervous heredity of his family—actually the best such
study I have ever seen. It shows what I have shown in my
book *Practical Leads to Puzzling Diagnoses: Neuroses That
Run through Families* (Lippincott), namely, that different
troubles come to different members of a family with a nervous curse. Graves's paternal grandfather was a dour man
who, for years, "maintained a grim and unvarying silence."
He and three of his brothers had a vile temper. Graves's
maternal grandfather lost $15,000 in a confidence game, and
later committed suicide. The two grandmothers seem to have
been "normal."

Graves's father was an energetic newspaperman, a mild
manic-depressive who was a bad judge of human character
and of investments. The mother was unstable—a hypochondriac and a difficult person who often went into tantrums of
temper and attacks of hysteria. Sometimes for a while she
would remain silent and almost unconscious. The family
were afraid of her. Some of her sisters were bad-tempered.
Graves's father and mother were always quarreling violently. The father's brother was a drifter who eventually
was lynched in a cattle-stealing adventure. The father's sisters were intelligent, and three of them were unusual characters—one of them a medium. The mother's sibs did well
enough, except that two of them had a tendency to hysteria.

Graves's elder brother, Geoffrey, stuttered. The eldest sister, Laura, was an able schoolteacher, but she married unwisely, and later she twice attempted suicide. A younger
sister, Edna, for years kept going in and out of insanity.

As a child, Alonzo walked and talked in his sleep, and
wet the bed, beyond the usual age. He suffered from
asthma. He says that he was able to read almost as soon as
he could talk—at about the age of three! He was markedly
myopic. He early quit college and went into newspaper
work, in which he continued for most of his days.

Five attacks of insanity. On five occasions he had to go
into a mental hospital. Some of these spells followed a period of great overwork. He tells of one of the first experiences
he had when he was slipping into a psychotic state. "I began to run into serious enhancement of the neurotic symp-

toms. The sensations built up alarmingly; I found myself in a state of tremulousness of nerves, steady insomnia and half panic." There was twitching of some muscles, and a fear of an impending breakdown, also "sensations of a strait-jacket tension about the body, and a kind of fox-tearing-at-the-entrails; and a dimming and spotting of vision." At this time he often vomited his luncheon. Later, he had many headaches. He had a number of affairs with women, and twice married—unhappily.

A unique comparison of the patient's hospital record with his notes. On many pages of his book, Graves puts his hospital record, with its notes made by his psychiatrists in the left-hand column and his running comments in the right-hand column. There is much on how the doctors quizzed him and tried to get him to accept their theories as to the cause of his troubles. Again and again they tried to get him to admit that he was homosexual, but this he denied. Often the doctors tried to prove that his manic-depressive insanity was due—of all things—to an occasional period of sexual continence!

There is nothing in the record to suggest that it ever occurred to anyone, except the patient, that his poor nervous heredity might have had a little to do with his psychotic episodes and those of his two sisters. Actually, Alonzo appears to have been slightly manic for much of his lifetime. It is shown by the great self-centered drive which enabled him to write 722 pages about his troubles. Whenever I receive a letter over thirty pages long from someone who describes his or her symptoms, I know I am dealing with a psychotic person.

An excellent study-book for students of psychiatry. This book can serve as a good text for students of psychiatry who would like to see the daily notes made by physicians in regard to a patient who for years was going in and out of insanity. Beginning on page 554, there is a splendid description of life in a state mental hospital.

Interesting is Graves's statement that, like many psychotic patients, he had a bad habit of talking "too freely to others of personal matters." For instance, he usually told his sexual partners all about his supposed syphilis, which doubtless caused many to pick up quickly and leave; and he would discuss with his business associates his occasional failure in sexual potency. He admitted that in every way he had tended to lean on his wife, and even at times to live off of her. In the last fifth of his book, he analyzes with great frankness and perspicacity his lifelong tendencies to psychosis.

A Major League Player Goes Insane

This is the well-told story of one of baseball's best players, Jim Piersall (*Fear Strikes Out,* 1955), who for months, as he was going insane, did a lot of clowning. He became more and more restless and more and more talkative, until finally he cracked up and had to go into a mental hospital. For some time his wife had seen that he was seriously ill, but she was helpless to stop his mad rush toward a mental breakdown. Remarkable is the fact that Jim remembered nothing after January 15, 1952 (when his mind clouded) until the next August, when he came to his senses in the violent ward of the Westborough State Hospital in Massachusetts. Even more remarkable is the fact that during part of this time, psychotic as he was, he kept playing wonderful baseball.

His poor nervous heredity. Jim had some reasons to go insane because his mother had had several episodes when she had to go into a mental hospital, and his father had a violent and abnormal temper. As one would expect, Jim had had a hard childhood, with poverty, unhappiness, fear, and great worry over his mother. He had good reason to be afraid of his father because of his violent outbursts of anger. Jim's father's father apparently deserted his family, and the wife died while Jim's father was a baby. Jim Piersall apparently inherited his father's temper, but he managed usually to keep it under control.

Jim was always hypomanic and tense. Even when Jim was a lad in High School, he apparently was somewhat manic. He says he could never "unwind at night." From the time when he was fifteen, he woke up every morning with a terrible headache. (The mildly psychotic sometimes have a daily headache.) "I tore from one thing to another. I did everything on the run, and lived such a tight schedule that I left myself only a few hours a night for sleeping." "I spent a lot of time lying down, but I was tense and stiff even then. I tried desperately to unwind. My nerves, stretched like fiddlestrings, were constantly begging for release." "I was running around in a mad circle, using up every reserve of strength God had given me." "But I had to keep hurrying —hurrying nowhere—because I felt that if I didn't hurry, I coudn't keep alive. *I had to get things done.*"

When he began to crack up. One day, on a train, he sat by himself staring out of the window. He was mentally upset, physically uncomfortable, and perspiring so freely that he got soaking wet. Later, he got the distressing delusion that his ball club, the Red Sox, were trying to get rid of him. No one could convince him that they weren't, and when they sent for him to go into training quarters, he didn't want to go. His head was buzzing, and he hadn't had a good night's sleep in weeks. Soon after arriving in Florida for training, he lost his memory. Some seven months later, he had to be put into a mental hospital, and there is where he came to. He had been cured by electroshock treatments. To his great joy, he found that his headaches were gone. He was released from the hopsital on September 9, 1952, and, very fortunately, his team manager took him right back. Fortunately, also, he could play baseball as well as ever he had done. Later, in the summer of 1960, he had another rough time with his nerves.

This story is interesting in that it shows the tenseness that long preceded the nervous breakdown. The clowning was unusual; also, the loss of memory for many months.

Boswell's Depression

It may be of some interest that the famous Boswell was at times depressed. Several entries in his *London Journal*, written when he was twenty-two, to describe the events of nine momentous months of his life, show that there was a depressive strain in him.

On page 253, he said, "Gloomy terrors came upon me,

so much as night approached, that I durst not stay by myself; so I went and had a bed (or rather half a one) from
honest Erskine, which he most kindly gave me." Next day,
"I was still in horror, and so slept this night with him
[Dempster]." The next day "I was awaked as usual, heavy,
confused, and splenetic. Every morning this is the case with
me. Dempster prescribed to me to cut two or three brisk
capers round the room, which I did, and found attended
with most agreeable effects. It expelled the phlegm from
my heart, gave my blood a free circulation, and my spirits a
brisk flow; so that I was all at once made happy."

On page 319 he wrote that he complained to Samuel
Johnson that he was much afflicted with melancholy, which
was hereditary in the Boswell family. Johnson said that he
himself had been greatly distressed with it, and for that
reason had been obliged to fly from study and meditation
to the dissipating variety of life. He advised Boswell to have
constant occupation of mind, to take a great deal of exercise,
and to live moderately; especially to shun drinking at night.
Melancholy people, said he, "are apt to fly to intemperance,
which gives a momentary relief, but sinks the soul much
lower in misery."

When Boswell discovered that Samuel Johnson was also
subject to melancholia, he felt that satisfaction which many
sufferers feel when they find that someone else is suffering
as they are—"and the greater the person our fellow sufferer
is, so much the more good does it do us!"

A Depressed Person Who Had Trouble
from Childhood On

I shall quote only a little from Anna Agnew's *From Under
the Cloud* (1886). What I find most interesting in this
woman's story is her statement that she had always been a
problem to those about her. As a child she was proud, will-
ful, bad-tempered, and often disobedient. She gave her
mother more trouble than all the rest of the family put together. She was often into devilment. Even as a child she
had days of great gloom with a desire to commit suicide.
Like Lara Jefferson, she said that all her life she had felt

near her a terrible shadow: something that was leading her on to insanity.

One night in 1876, while she sat sewing, something "came over her"; something horrible settled down over her. What interests me much is that she says that there came the revelation that this something "had been with me all my life walking by my side, invisible but felt even in my happiest minutes." "It had come and it was insanity."

It appears that in her agony she decided it would be better for her children if they were dead. She thought of killing them because she wanted to save them from inheriting her insanity. I suspect that she did kill or attempt to kill some of the children, because this would explain the fact that for several years she was in a states prison. Only after that was she transferred to a mental hospital. She says she eventually recovered.

CHAPTER 6

Some Persons, When They Become Psychotic, Think of Little besides Religion

Many persons—and even irreligious ones—when they become psychotic, promptly become so obsessed with religion that it is all they can think of or talk about all day. They become so chummy with God that they feel they are visiting with Him all the time. As we have seen, these people also tend to get the idea that the world is coming to an end, and then they will be either a new Noah or the Messiah. Some day, when we get to know more about the workings of the brain, we may know why a derangement of the mechanism so often produces these strange ideas.

The first book I will here describe is a classic by the Reverend Anton Boisen (*The Exploration of the Inner World, a Study of Mental Disorder and Religious Experience,* 1936 and 1952). After having been violently disturbed for short intervals, he recovered and later became probably the second man to be employed as a chaplain to a U.S. mental hospital. Ever since, he has devoted his life to studying, as did William James, the resemblances between psychosis and many of the religious experiences of the world's saints.

Just to illustrate what the mental experiences of a deeply religious person often are, I here put next to the notes on

Boisen's book notes on the autobiography of George Fox, who was one of the world's great religious leaders. I am not saying that Fox was at all times mentally deranged, I just want to show the close resemblances between great religiosity and psychosis which Boisen and James puzzled over.

Next to the abstract of Fox's book, I put one which fits in here perfectly. Why? Because William Cowper, the famous poet, was decidedly manic-depressive during much of his life. There was never any question about that; but in his day there was great argument as to the significance of the fact that for much of his life he could think and talk of only one thing—his great chumminess with God. Some of his friends and biographers felt that his religious monomania was just another manifestation of his psychosis, while other friends and biographers felt somewhat outraged at such an impious statement. What is interesting at this point is that we have the reports of observers who knew the man, and knew that for years he had talked and thought of nothing but religion, much as Fox had done, and yet they were unable to agree on what this meant—a highly commendable piety or a form of mental aberration.

As we saw in Chapter 5, a depression often fills the victim with very distressing convictions of great sinfulness and gives him the idea that God has cut him off and has turned His countenance away from him. Also, when the depression gives way to mania, the person feels unutterable joy, because God has accepted him again and forgiven him his sins. As these people often say, they are so happy over this they want to shout with joy. This fact, so well known to psychiatrists, does not mean, of course, that there aren't thousands of sensible people who are unhappy when they have been sinful, and happy when, perhaps after listening to an evangelist, they feel converted and feel they are back close to God again.

Boisen's Remarkable Book

Boisen's book was written by a highly intelligent, idealistic, and devoted minister of the Gospel who on several occasions went through a tremendous emotional upheaval, the first time with three weeks of violent delirium. The doctors called it catatonic dementia praecox (schizophrenia). After his recovery, Boisen dedicated his life to study and research in psychiatry. Ever since, he has been studying the mental processes of hundreds of insane persons.

One reviewer said, "I have not read a book in many months which has stirred my thinking as has this one. In the field of religion I think it is . . . the most important contribution since the famous 'Varieties' [of Religious Experience] of William James."

What relation is there between insanity and religion? Boisen's thesis is that there is an important relationship between acute mental illness and sudden religious conversion. "Certain types of mental disorder and certain types of religious experience are alike attempts at reorganization of the personality." But here is the all-important difference: "Where the attempt is successful, and some degree of victory is won, it is commonly recognized as a religious experience; where it is unsuccessful . . . it is commonly spoken of as insanity." Unfortunately, in most cases of mental illness in which the patient gets well, he does not entirely solve his problems, and his life does not become great and useful to all mankind, as did the life of St. Paul after his tremendous experience on the Damascus road. There, we have Boisen's thesis in a few sentences.

Because of Boisen's religious and psychiatric training and his several personal experiences with insanity, he knows what he is talking about. He begins his book by saying, "To be plunged as a patient into a hospital for the insane may be a tragedy or it may be an opportunity. For me, it has been an opportunity. It has introduced me to a new world of absorbing interest and profound significance." His disturbance came on suddenly, and it was severe.

The exciting cause appeared to be an inner struggle "arising out of a precocious sexual sensitivity, dating from my fourth year." With the onset of adolescence, the struggle became ever more severe. In his twenty-second year, after a period of black despair, everything seemed to be cleared up by a religious conversion.

Two years later came a relapse into the land of bondage,

and then a desperate struggle to get free. Along the way there was an unhappy love affair which swept him off his feet. This affair he regarded as a cry for salvation, and it led to his entering the Christian ministry. The woman he loved was a fine YWCA worker. She did not accept him and often refused to see him or write him. Then followed nine years of wandering—into rural survey work, into the rural pastorate, and into the YMCA overseas. All this time he was hoping to become reinstated with his girl. In 1920 this reinstatement did occur, but the terrible mental upheaval followed shortly after.

Boisen's experience with acute insanity. After the usual period of insomnia, "there came surging in upon me with overpowering force a terrifying idea about a coming world catastrophe. Although I had never before given serious thought to such a subject, there came flashing into my mind, as though from a source without myself, the idea that this little planet of ours, which has existed for we know not how many millions of years, was about to undergo some sort of metamorphosis."

"Strange and mysterious forces of evil which before I had not had the slightest suspicion were also revealed. I was terrified beyond measure." Naturally, his family was frightened, and Boisen soon found himself in a mental hospital. Then came three weeks of violent delirium the details of which remained indelibly burned into his memory. "There is probably no three-weeks period in all my life that I can recall more clearly." "Then I came out of it much as one awakens out of a bad dream." It is remarkable that in those weeks Boisen lost thirty pounds in weight, but he felt fit. Then he wanted to discuss his experience with people who could help him, but the doctors had no time for such talk. They were not interested. He tried to talk to the ministers of the nearby churches, but they were of no help. They had no knowledge of the problem.

Later, there came another mental storm as severe as the first. This time it lasted ten weeks. Like the first attack, it began suddenly and ended suddenly.

Boisen's search for work in a mental hospital. Boisen concluded that many forms of psychosis are religious rather than medical problems, but he had to work and study for many years before he could get anyone to listen to him. When he left the mental hospital, he started studying with psychiatrists and physicians and theologians. He looked for a chaplaincy in a mental hospital, but at that time there was only one such position known. Eventually, Dr. William A. Bryan of the Worcester State Hospital gave Boisen his opportunity.

Boisen's research into the several forms of insanity. In Worcester, Boisen studied in detail the cases of 173 insane persons, most of them men less than forty years of age. It is remarkable that Boisen found in only seven of the 173 cases any factors in the man's immediate life situation which could have thrown him into the mental disturbance! Almost always the disturbance could be best explained on the basis of some inborn disharmony and conflict which eventually caused an "explosion."

Boisen found that ninety-nine of the 173 patients were of the retiring sort, with few friends and few social contacts. At least 145 of the 173 men had never married, and sixty-two denied ever having had any sexual experience with a woman. One of the surest signs of sanity is a person's ability to love someone of the opposite sex acceptably, with tenderness, generosity, selflessness, and devotion. A large percentage of mildly psychotic persons are so wrapped up in themselves that they never have any interest in anyone else.

Important is Boisen's finding that fifty-six of the 173 persons had made frequent changes in their jobs; they had a poor "work record." Twenty hadn't worked for years. I used to find it hard to get my graduate medical students to see the tremendous value of learning about many a patient's work record. So often, when an assistant would write on the chart that a man's troubles were all due to a gallstone or a heart murmur, I would ask and learn that the fellow had never worked! He had always lived off his mother. Surely, this fact was worth knowing! Surely, it showed a great mental abnormality, and one that all of his doctors should have known about. They could have known then that the man could never be "made over" by the removal of a gallstone.

As Boisen says, the schizophrenic has one decided characteristic, and that is his mental isolation from his fellows. Many of these persons accept society's estimate that they are socially substandard, and the result is often a distressing loss of self-respect. Then many drift, and *do nothing.* Many withdraw into a world of phantasy, and others take to drink and head for Skid Row. A man in this condition may become more and more listless and ineffective and unable to take care of himself, until eventually, he has to be committed.

Boisen wisely felt that if we are ever to know much about mental alienation we must keep talking to the insane until we learn to understand their ideas and their emotions. We must know what is going on in their minds. As Adolf Meyer used to say, "We must discover the sense in the nonsense" of psychotic persons. John Custance tried hard to do this. Boisen said that the insane begin generally with some "eruption of the subconscious which is interpreted as a manifestation of the supernatural." "The impact of such an experience is apt to be terrific. It may destroy the foundations of mental organization, and upset the structure upon which the judgments and reasoning processes are based. We have then that bewildered state which is called schizophrenia. . . . The sufferer finds himself in a strange new world in which previous experience and accepted standards of value do not apply. He sees strange meanings in everything about him."

In fifty-seven of the 173 cases studied, Boisen found remarkable "ideas of an impending world change" with great issues at stake. In fifty-three of the cases, the patient had exalted ideas as to what his role was to be in the newly constituted world. The fate of that new world was to be entirely dependent upon him. Twenty-four persons had this idea of having a great mission to carry out, and twenty-three had ideas about a glorious rebirth. Seven had ideas of a change in their sex like that described by Schreber. Some seventy-three of the patients heard accusing voices which charged them with all sorts of improper behavior. Paranoiacs thought that their minds were being constantly read by the people about them. Some thirty-seven thought that they were being poisoned or drugged, and twenty-nine thought, as Beers did, that they were going to be killed.

Psychiatry and religion. Boisen has an interesting chapter on the psychology of religious leaders, such as Ezekiel, Jeremiah, St. Paul, Fox, Bunyan, and Swedenborg, all of whom had deep religious experiences and obviously felt about these much as did many of Boisen's patients. As I have said, William James often found it impossible to distinguish a mild attack of schizophrenia from a deep religious experience. Boisen has a chapter on the conclusions reached by a number of men who have studied the psychology of religious mysticism.

He admits that among the many patients with whom he has worked, he has not found *anyone* who has emerged from his profound psychic upheaval on a higher moral or mental level than before. "Neither have I myself had a clear record since that first upheaval fifteen years ago. Six years ago I passed through another disturbance, brief but very severe." But Boisen thinks that his psychic storms brought him the right answers to certain important personal questions that were disturbing him.

Boisen said, "The idea which I have since been following with some measure of success was given to me at that time by an Intelligence beyond my own." "It was a terrific life-and-death struggle in which all accepted beliefs and values were overturned, and I did not know what to believe. Many of the ideas that came to me were shocking, and horrifying in the extreme." "Throughout those periods it was my best self that was dominant; something strong and deep and tender and intense, which was, I still believe, more than just myself. My great difficulty now in the period of 'normality' is to remain true to the vision which came to me then.'

In trying to explain what happened, Boisen says, "When you give up everything you have for a certain end, and you then feel called upon to give that up, it is equivalent to giving up your life." "When you think you are giving up all that makes life worth while for you, you don't care much about anything else." Most of the ideas that came to him during his tremendous upheaval were not in line with his previous thinking or experience. Actually, they impressed him greatly just because they were so absolutely different from anything he had ever thought of or heard of before, and because they came surging into his head with such a rush.

Boisen could never find any clear line of demarcation between valid religious experiences and the abnormal conditions and phenomena which to the alienist are evidences of insanity. Saul of Tarsus, George Fox, and others are classed as religious geniuses and not as insane men *"because the experiences through which they passed had a unifying function. That after all is the only test."*

Boisen felt during his crisis that he was in some new and strange world. He did not know who he was. He was first one and then another personality, "other and bigger than himself." He had some delusions of grandeur, about which he later was ashamed.

Boisen and Dr. Albert Schweitzer remind us that even Jesus had some of the convictions met with among the psychotic. As Boisen says, practically all men of outstanding religious genius have looked upon themselves as the unique spokesman of the Lord to the men of their generation. George Fox did, Swedenborg did, the Hebrew prophets did, and many of the men Boisen studied in mental hospitals did. Boisen even goes on frankly and honestly to say that Jesus had so many of these ideas that his relatives thought he was "beside himself." After years of study of this problem, Boisen feels, with Dr. Albert Schweitzer, that "we will never quite understand Him unless we face the fact that He believed that the world was coming to an end, to be replaced by another type of world in which He would be the leader. We should note his feeling of great intimacy with God, and His feeling that He was the spokesman for God; also, we should note His feeling of great power that came from outside of Himself." I doubt if either Boisen or Schweitzer have inferred that Jesus was not sane; I think they have only wondered why it is that a considerable percentage of the insane—and many of them men who never before thought much about religion—should suddenly get many of Jesus's ideas.

Boisen cannot help wondering, also, as William James did, why it is that so many saints and great religious leaders describe their emotional life in the same terms as are used by thousands of insane persons. I greatly respect the Reverend Mr. Boisen for facing this fact. It evidently has not disturbed his faith as a Christian, any more than it has disturbed Schweitzer's faith. Certainly, no one who reads what I have just written should yield to feelings of outrage until he has read and digested William James's great book *The Varieties of Religious Experience*. In that book, he will see that in scores of cases a "saint" describes his or her ecstasies and depressions and feelings of intimacy with God exactly as the insane do.

Much new light on the psychotic person's terrible conviction of sin. Boisen points out that many of the mentally disturbed patients he studied who identified themselves closely with God and thought that they were the most important persons in the world would suddenly speak of themselves as the most miserable of sinners. Boisen perhaps gives us an answer to a question that has been in my mind for 40 years, and that is, why so many deeply religious people get up in meetings and tell of their conviction of hopeless and terrible sinfulness. They keep doing this year after year without ever telling us exactly what their sins were. Now, Boisen says that "to the mentally ill the presence of an unacceptable thought or craving is just as terrible as the actual committing of some forbidden act." Jesus had this idea when He said (Matt. 5:27-28) that "Whosoever looketh on a woman to lust after her hath committed adultery with her already in his heart." This idea has terribly distressed many a good Christian who, being a healthy man, could not help looking with desire on a pretty woman.

Boisen says that an insane person is unable to organize his thoughts and emotions so that he can assimilate his new experiences and make decisions as to what is to be done next (see Henry Martens). "The primary evil in functional mental illness is to be found in the sense of moral failure and isolation." "To have that in one's life which one is afraid to tell for fear of condemnation . . . is isolation, and isolation means death." Many of the insane tell of becoming suicidal when they felt that because of their sinfulness God had turned His face away from them. They felt they were completely cast out by God, and hence unredeemable.

I once learned how vague the idea of sin can be in the mind of an insane man when I asked a psychotic patient who had been going from one urologist to another getting painful examinations which revealed nothing abnormal, why he had been doing it. He said his behavior was an attempt at expiation and reconciliation with God for his supposed infidelity to his wife. When I asked him what he had done, he admitted that he could not remember when or where or with whom he had sinned, but he assumed that he must have done it.

Why all but a very few psychotic persons fail to be the better for their great religious experience. After searching for a cause for the failure of the "prophets on our hospital wards" to go out and reform the world, Boisen concluded that their mistake had lain in their failure to heed the injunction to *walk humbly with their God.* This, the hospital prophets did not do. They were arrogant. They pulled God down to their level. Some patted Him on the back, some argued angrily with Him, and some scolded Him. Some even thought that He was in danger, and they would have to help Him!

Of the 173 patients, twenty-four felt that they had a great prophetic message to deliver to the world, but unfortunately they did not have the strength, wisdom, devotion, and sanity to go out and do as St. Paul did. Even he, great as he was, was so much like a schizoid person that he could not bear the thought of a man's having sexual relations with a woman. If he could have had his way, the world would soon have been depopulated—for lack of new births.

Whatever one may think about Boisen's conclusions, certainly his is one of the world's important books—one which must be read and studied by every psychiatrist, every minister of the Gospel, every philosopher, and every thoughtful man who wants to be well educated.

As my manuscript was being prepared for the printer, the Reverend Mr. Boisen sent me a copy of his latest book *Out of the Depths* (Harper's, 1960). In this very interesting volume he goes into much more detail about his life, his very unhappy love for his Alice, and his struggles with psychosis. The book should be read by all students of psychiatry.

George Fox—A Great Religious Leader

One of the most remarkable of the many religious autobiographies available to us was written by George Fox (*An Autobiography*, 1919), the founder of the Society of Friends. I comment on it here, not so much to emphasize the conviction of psychiatrists that in his youth Fox was manic-depressive, but to emphasize what William James and Anton Boisen have demonstrated—that great religious leaders experienced much the same sensations and convictions that the psychotic have. We need read only a few chapters of Fox's book to see that he was a man with only one interest in life—the preaching of the Gospel as he saw it. All his life he thought and talked religion, and nothing but religion, every day, and all day, and much of each night.

The manic-depressive phases of Fox's early life. In his early years Fox appears to have been manic-depressive, because so typically, at times, he felt entirely deserted by God, and in such despair he could find no comfort in anything. Next, like most depressed and most deeply religious people, he had spells when his melancholia suddenly let up, to be replaced by the great and unutterable joy of reconciliation with his God. As Fox said, "Though my troubles were very great, yet were they not so continual but that I had some intermissions, and I was sometimes brought into such an heavenly joy that I thought I had been in Abraham's bosom." About a later time, when he was again in a depression, he said, "I cannot declare the misery I was in; it was so great and heavy upon me."

Many a time when he was depressed, he did not go to bed, nor could he sleep, but "walked up and down all night out in the fields, praying and crying out to the Lord." Many mildly psychotic persons have this tendency to go on long solitary walks. Soon, Fox was walking about aimlessly throughout England, not knowing what to do. As he said, he thus "continued about a year, in great sorrow and trouble."

The feelings of temptation often complained about by the depressed. Fox tells us that when he was twenty, "Temptations grew more and more, and I was tempted almost to despair; and when Satan could not effect his design upon me that way, he laid snares and baits to draw me to commit some sin, where of he might take advantage to bring me to despair." For some years Fox continued in this condition of great mental distress, "and fain I would have put it from me. I went to many a priest to look for comfort, but found no comfort from them." Again and again the Tempter set upon him, charging him that he had sinned against the Holy Ghost; but Fox said, "I could not tell in what." Here, we have that typical conviction of the depressed and the deeply religious person that he must have been very sinful, but just what he did wrong he can never figure out.

Hallucinations. Occasionally Fox hallucinated; he saw visions and heard voices. "I heard a voice which said, 'There is one, even Christ Jesus, that can speak to thy condition;' and when I heard it, my heart did leap for joy."

At times, Fox would go through a town crying, "Woe to this bloody city." He would do this because there seemed to him "to be a channel of blood running down the streets, and the market-place appeared like a pool of blood." If, today, a psychotic patient were to see such things, his psychiatrist would say he was hallucinating. Sometimes Fox's visions were brilliant, as when "The Lord opened unto me, and let me see a great people in white raiment by a river side, coming to the Lord." Another time he wrote of lying on his bed with "The glory of the Lord round about."

At still other times, Fox would have unusual and peculiar hallucinations. For instance, he said, "I lay down on a grass-plot to slumber, and felt something still about my body: I started up and struck at it in the power of the Lord, and still it was about my body." Another time he said, "The night before I had had a vision of a desperate creature that was coming to destroy me, but I got the victory over it." One is reminded of Jacob's wrestling with the angel at the brook Jabbok.

Fears and paranoia. Fox said he suffered at times from strange fears, as psychotic persons commonly do. Also, just like a paranoid person, he said, "I durst not stay long in a place, being afraid both of professor and profane." On another page of his book, he said, exactly as many a paranoiac does, that the steeple of a church and the chimes were threatening him, and striking at his life. And so he felt the need for keeping more and more to himself.

Trances and hysteria. On at least three occasions Fox went into a prolonged trance. He tells us that as a young man he once went into a trance so remarkable that, for a fortnight, people came from far and wide to see him—"to the admiration of many, who thought I had been dead." After that he was much altered in countenance and person, as if his body had "been new moulded or changed."

Then, his sorrows and troubles began to wear off, and tears of joy dropped from him, so that he could have wept night and day "in humility and brokenness of heart."

On two occasions he was struck blind for a while and was unable to see. Then his vision cleared, as it would have, if he had a spell of hysteria.

Intimacy with God. Like all saints and many psychotic persons, Fox was always in close communion with God; they were often chatting together. Fox knew exactly how the Lord felt about many things. For instance, when Oliver Cromwell had died and was lying in state, Fox was "angered because of the great pother made about the image or effigy, and the soundings of trumpets over his image." "At this my spirit was greatly grieved, *and the Lord, I found, was highly offended!*"

All through his book, Fox keeps telling how God was constantly with him, always talking intimately with him—and often telling him what to do. Fox said that God found him, and he found God. They got together.

Fox forsakes his family and begins his ministry. After several years of indecision, mental turmoil, and alternating depression and elation, Fox found out what God wanted him to do. God told him to go out and preach everywhere, and this he did for as long as he had the strength to travel. The Lord said, "Thou seest how young people go together into vanity; thou must forsake all, young and old; keep out of all, and be as a stranger unto all." So Fox did what the Lord told him to do, and, like Jesus, left his family. For the rest of his life, he appeared to have had no fixed abode. Often he slept in the fields because, when the people in a city had become hostile to him, no inn-keeper dared give him a room. Fox says that about 1648 [when he was twenty-four] in the city of Mansfield, "I was moved to pray, and the Lord's power was so great that the house seemed to be shaken." Even after this, he moved crowds by his great fervor, his enthusiasm, his glowing passion, and the authoritative way in which he spoke.

In order to come closer to God, Fox gave up every other interest and influence in his life. Apparently, like Jesus, St. Paul, and most of the saints, he had absolutely no interest in women. Late in life he married, but he paid little attention to his wife. They separated after the ceremony, and he rarely speaks of having seen her. She appears to have been just a partner in his religious work. For many years she was confined in jail, which fact did not seem to bother him. He does not tell of making any efforts to see her or to try to get her released.

God often told him what to do. God was constantly telling Fox what to do. For instance, often when Fox saw a church, the Lord would say to him, "Thou must go cry against yonder great idol, and against the worshippers therein." That was one of the things that got Fox into endless trouble—his claim that God was to be found outside the churches. Also, he got into serious trouble with priests and ministers because he kept saying he could see no need for them.

As a sample of the minor orders given him by God, Fox said, "Then was I commanded by the Lord to pull off my shoes." So in winter, he took off his shoes and walked around town without them.

Some of Fox's peculiarities. In many ways Fox was fearless and he had an iron will. Time and time again he was arrested and jailed for months; and time and again he was beaten up by crowds. He could have avoided most of his distressing and time-wasting clashes with the law and with mobs if he had only been willing at times to take off his hat, or to take the usual oath of allegiance to his king, or to stop attacking the people in the established churches. Because he was so sure that God was as deeply concerned as he was over little details of his religion, such as that of not doffing his hat, he was willing to rot in an awful pigsty of a jail for a year rather than uncover his head when brought before a judge. Probably no sensible person today would say that this was essential to the practice of any religion.

Fox had piercing eyes, which often bothered people so much that they told him to stop looking at them. With his eyes alone, he could often so dominate men who had come to do him harm that they would slink away.

With all his peculiarities, it is remarkable how practical he could be. He is said to have been a pleasant companion. He had the great ability to found and establish a great religious group. He fought the barbarity of the penal system of his day, and he protested against war and drunkenness. Like many deeply religious people, he fought against the fashionable type of life with its music, plays, feasts, sports, and May-day games. He wanted even young people to be as solemn and averse to fun as he was.

Always Fox felt he was an instrument for the manifestation of God's miraculous power. He took great comfort in the fact that sometimes people who had done him harm came to grief. He thought it was because God had become displeased with them. He was, however, a merciful man, always ready to forgive, and slow to take offense. Occasionally, he fasted, sometimes for ten days.

He wrote many letters to prominent people, telling them to beware and behave better. He would say something like this: "It came upon me about this from the Lord to write a short paper, and send it forth as an exhortation and warning to the Pope, and to all kings and rulers in Europe."

After preaching all over England, Fox took trips through the West Indies, the American Colonies, and parts of Europe, preaching every day to the crowds which gathered everywhere he went. What he said, as we now read his words, may not mean much to many of us, but in his day,.

his message caused thousands of people to be converted to his views.

In his later years, even with his iron constitution, Fox became worn down from constant hard travel, constant exposure to the elements, constant preaching, frequent beatings at the hands of crowds, and years of imprisonment in foul dungeons. As a result, he had to slow down and do most of his preaching by mail.

Summary. According to most standards, Fox was a fine sane man. He had good sense with much kindliness and great honesty, and he was a dedicated man who did much good; but as Boisen would say, if he hadn't become a great religious leader—if he had failed in life—he would have been looked on as just another monomaniac. It must always be a question if a man is entirely sane or well-adjusted when he has only one idea, and when at times he has hallucinations, trances, attacks of hysteria, and paranoid ideas. A psychiatrist might well be puzzled about him when in almost every detail his mental processes were those of many a patient found in a mental hospital. Psychiatrists have felt sure that, in his youth, Fox must have been depressed and psychotic. But, like innumerable mildly psychotic persons, he was—most of the time—a fine, sensible, devoted, kindly, and likable man who did a great work.

The Poet Cowper Was Depressed and Overly Religious

At this point a brief note on the life of William Cowper (*Memoir of the Early Life of William Cowper,* 1817), can be helpful because in his case a severe and typical form of manic-depressive insanity was combined with or alternated with the sort of complete preoccupation with religion which we have found in the case of Fox. As with Fox, for years Cowper thought and talked and wrote only of religion, but he does not appear ever to have bestirred himself to do any preaching. Like Fox, he felt that every day and sometimes all day he was talking to God, "face to face as a man converseth with his friend." Like Fox and others, Cowper had

days when his chumminess with God would suddenly end,
and for a while the two would be estranged.

Like Fox and many others, Cowper suddenly, one day
after a period of depression, felt that he had become converted. As he said, suddenly as he sat at breakfast "the
cloud of horror" passed off, and he felt the glory of God
around about him. He had the well-known sudden change
"from despair to joy." He gave the credit for his cure to
God, and from that time onward, for years his only thought
was of religion. During this time he lost all his friends. One
can easily see, on reading Cowper's letters, that no one
would want to visit him and listen to a long monologue on
the joys of having received salvation.

The inability of biographers to agree. To me, the most interesting point about all this is that Cowper's friends and
biographers could never agree as to the significance of this
outstanding piety. Some saw in it just a phase and a manifestation of his almost lifelong psychosis, while others, more
deeply pious, were outraged at such an interpretation. In
Cowper's day and in certain circles, the more pious a man
was, the more he was respected and looked up to, even
when he became an insufferable bore.

Cowper describes his attempts at suicide. In his youth,
Cowper wrote a description of his mental sufferings, together with a lengthy story of his attempts at suicide. Evidently he was depressed from early boyhood onward. The
manuscript he left, describing his sufferings, was for long
neglected. Some of it is so enlightening it ought to be reprinted and used as a text in college courses on psychiatry.

His early attacks of depression. Speaking of his first deep
depression, Cowper wrote, "I was struck . . . with such a
dejection of spirits as none but they who have felt the same
can have the least conception of. Day and night I was upon
the rack, lying down in horror, and rising up in despair."
Like so many mildly psychotic persons, he says, "I read
without perception." "My first reflections, when I woke in
the morning, were horrible and full of wretchedness." This,
as we have seen, is typical of depressed persons.

Then, like many melancholy persons, he began to feel
very sinful, and for the first time, he wanted reconciliation

with his God. Like Lara Jefferson, when he felt insanity
approaching, he "wished for it earnestly, and looked forward to it with impatient expectation." Soon, "I grew more
sullen and reserved, and fled from all society." He bought a
big bottle of laudanum and for days tried to make himself
drink it, but eventually, he threw it out.

Then, for a while, he was paranoid and thought that people in the street were laughing at him and showing contempt for him. He thought a then-popular song was all
about him. Soon he decided he had committed the unpar-
donable sin, and he had horrors over that. Next, like many
psychotic persons, he developed a "burning in his heart,"
and a feeling as if he were being struck, on his naked brain.
Also, he had some hallucinations. For years after this he was
in the purely religious stage of his psychosis.

In 1773 he sank into another spell of deep melancholy—
a spell that lasted two years. Later, when his brother died,
he went into a depression that lasted five or six years. He
still was all wrapped up in religion.

Mania and more depression. Then, as a biographer said,
Cowper seemed to pass "from the error of doing nothing to
that of doing too much." Obviously, he became manic. He
started to write a great deal. Later, when with his writings
he became famous, he made many friends, and he lost his
constant preoccupation with religion. In 1792, with the
severe illness of his devoted friend and benefactor, Mrs.
Unwin, he again became somewhat depressed. In 1794, he
became badly depressed, and he remained in this state until
he died in 1800.

A Man Who, Like George Fox, Felt Ordered by God to Travel About Preaching

Another autobiographic note which shows how hard it is
often to tell whether a man's visions and "voices" are from
God was that of a man of thirty, who, according to Dr. L.
Forbes Winslow (*Mad Humanity,* 1898, page 317), once
came to a mental hospital, asking for admittance. He said
that for several days and nights he had been wandering
about the streets until he had become exhausted. He said

he was the prophet of the Lord on his way to Jerusalem and that the Holy Spirit had directed him to go there.

Like George Fox, he felt sure he had been anointed by the Lord, and that his mission from the Holy Spirit was to walk incessantly about trying to convert all the people whom he met. He said, "As I passed near to them, I believed the Holy Spirit transferred itself from me to them; so I selected the most crowded thoroughfares in the metropolis for the work of conversion." "Upon the approach of the morning I felt a burning flame around me, and conceived that it was the glory of God sanctifying me for the work I had to perform. But my sensations frequently alarmed me; more than once I was afraid I should go mad, and then I alternately laughed and wept."

Later these ideas left the man; his mind cleared; and his vivid experience came to an end. He knew then that he had been mentally upset.

An Overly Religious Hypochondriac Who Lived about A.D. 150

At this point I introduce a brief abstract of the writings of a certain Aelius Aristides, surnamed Theodorus of Smyrna, a Greek rhetorician and sophist who, about A.D. 150, kept traveling all over the then-known civilized world searching for someone who could cure him of all his discomforts.

His *Sacred Discourses,* in which he described his wide experience with many "cures," should be mentioned here because like the many psychotic persons described by Anton Boisen, he thought he was a great pal of his favorite god —Asclepius—the god of healing. Even more typically psychotic was his idea that he was an equal of the god. It is interesting to see that, 1800 years ago, a mentally sick man thought and wrote exactly as psychotic men do today.

Aelius was evidently a terrible hypochondriac, that is, a man who is convinced that he has some awful disease and spends his life getting treated for it. With huge conceit he felt sure the gods had sent him his many illnesses so that he might grow spiritually and become a great writer. He felt that he had grown in spiritual stature because of his constant association with his friend, the god. He had the delusion that he was as important, also, as was Alexander the Great. Like many a neurotic person today, Aristides kept recording all of his symptoms in a diary; and like many persons whom one can find in the waiting room of any big clinic, he loved to regale his fellow patients with long accounts of his experiences with many quacks and many physicians.

In his book he tells us so much about his dreams that one might speak of him as a forerunner of Freud! Like so many nervous patients today, he eagerly tried out all the diets, drugs, courses of massage, cold or hot baths, mudbaths, and restrictions on living that he could hear of. Some of the treatments were pretty rough, but he tried them all.

He turns away from physicians. Like many neurotic patients today, he eventually turned away from all physicians and took to sleeping in temples where, in his dreams, he would get instructions from the god as to what medicine he should take or what he should do or not do. In temple after temple he was told to abstain from all sorts of things. He even tried treatment by music! Like many persons who today become dependent on their psychoanalyst, Aristides felt upset and without a protector when he was asked to leave a medical temple, and to go out alone into the world.

After some ten years of this search for health, when he was in his forties, he started writing the book about his medical adventures. He died about A.D. 179.

CHAPTER 7

Some Persons with Paralyzing Fears (Phobias)

Remarkable are the accounts given by some psychotic persons of their terrifying and paralyzing phobias. Phobias, of course, are unreasonable fears, and one of the commonest of these is a fear of going away from home. Innumerable people have a fear of getting into a crowd, and others have a terrible fear of close places, or thunder, or dogs, or cats. As will be seen from the two case reports in this chapter, phobias are very hard to cure. The point that impresses me is that many of the persons who suffer much from phobias are poorly adjusted from childhood on. It is this basic peculiarity of the person that can account for the fact, well demonstrated by both Leonard and "Anonymous," that when one phobia clears away, another can soon come to take its place.

The Man Who Was Frightened by a Locomotive

The longest and most detailed treatise I have found on phobias is called *The Locomotive God* (1927) and was written by William Ellery Leonard, Professor of English Literature at the University of Wisconsin. His book is the better for the fact that he was a keen observer with a retentive memory and great skill in writing.

Why "The Locomotive God"? He used the title "The Locomotive God" because, after he found himself unable to go
many yards from his home in Madison, Wisconsin, he spent
years with psychiatrists and accepted the explanation that
all his feelings of terror and insecurity could be traced back
to a time when, at the age of two and a half, he was probably frightened by a locomotive coming into a station.
Through the years, Leonard became more and more convinced of this, and felt that he had a definite memory of the
event. What has impressed me from two readings of Leonard's book is that he seems throughout his lifetime to have
been a borderline psychotic. It is impossible for me to blame
a man's lifelong eccentricity on one fright, especially when,
in his book, he tells of many other "traumatic" episodes in
his childhood and youth.

His heredity. Early in his book, Leonard said that nowhere in his family on either side was there any insanity,
but then he goes on to tell us of a number of relatives who
were decidedly peculiar. Unfortunately, he did not know
what I have shown hundreds of times in my book *Practical
Leads to Puzzling Diagnoses: Neuroses That Run through
Families*—that a poor nervous inheritance, sufficiently bad
to produce mild psychosis in the person before us, can have
shown up in a number of his forebears only as an eccentricity, or impracticality, or oddness, or unmarriageability, or
a violent temper, or a decided fondness for alcohol.

I think we can assume, from what Leonard says about
his sweet, gentle, poverty-stricken minister of a father, that
he was odd enough to have transmitted a poor nervous
inheritance to his son. As Leonard says, his father was a
silent man—"a tragically unpretending man—just like his
own father," who was the sort of man who believed that
Bacon wrote Shakespeare's plays. He was the sort, also,
who at sixty-two, suddenly, without obvious reason, and
without any other occupation or source of income in sight,
decided that his usefulness to the few parishioners in his
little church had come to an end, and hence resigned. In
the last six years of his life he had what was probably a mild
senescent psychosis, with fears and feelings of insecurity

much like those of his son. One of the father's sisters was a queer old maid—"sour, suspicious, and peculiar."

Leonard's mother seems to have been sweet and sane. But he had a sister whom he speaks of as unmarried, and successively a kindergarten teacher, an actress, a social worker, a feature writer, a Christian Scientist, and a spiritualist. She was so odd that to Leonard she was a stranger. There was an "Uncle Oliver" whose younger son was "a problem." William Ellery admits very significantly that he had had his chance to go insane, and he had refused to take it: "I would not escape by that door." How remarkable is this realization that to many persons insanity can be an escape from life's tribulations!

The painful sensitiveness that can go with great artistic gifts. From what Leonard tells us of his family, we can suspect that, along with his great gift for the writing of exquisite poetry—a gift which he must have inherited from someone—he inherited a tremendous hypersensitivity, a strong tendency to panicky fear, and a number of eccentricities which later caused many people to disapprove of him and to cast him out socially. A man can hardly expect to inherit the great artistic gifts that Leonard received at conception without inheriting some other very trying gifts. He himself saw this clearly when he wrote, 'There does remain a connection—a sensitive, imaginative, emotional organization is the pre-requisite for becoming either half a poet or a good phobiac." "I was one who . . . had to pay the price for his temperament, which life does not exact from all."

Leonard was always subject to panics. An important point which I think was not noted clearly enough by Leonard is that from early childhood he had a tendency to go into panics which would send him running home to find security around his mother's skirts. When he first went to school and wet his pants, he went into a panicky state in which he ran for home, expecting a group of school children to come rushing to attack him. Another time, on hearing a band, he ran shrieking home and hid in a closet.

But even that early, like most people suffering from phobias, he knew that there was nothing to be afraid of.

Leonard could remember other panics into which he had gone early in his childhood. The mistake which I think he and his physicians made was to ascribe all the hundreds of panics he had in his life to one early one, which according to analytic theory was probably buried in his unconscious.

His stormy adolescence and young manhood. Leonard's whole big book of 400 pages is filled with details about his emotions—from early childhood on. He probably took many of these details from notes which he says he kept while he was being analyzed. He recalled that, as a young man, "Two or three times in remote and silent twilight, when several miles from the house," he "had experienced momentary moods of the terrors of isolation; of immeasurable distance from home," and had spoken of these feelings as symptoms of "my nervous condition." They were portents of the troubles that were to come.

In his twenties, the earliest manifestations of his phobias were spells of panicky shame, sometimes suddenly attaching themselves for weeks and months to a single individual. "I would have the acutest dread, utterly unmotivated, of facing a given person—always some person with whom I was on the friendliest footing; more often a woman, but often a man, so that I found sex-embarrassment an apparently irrelevant explanation." Sometimes it helped him to hide behind dark glasses. As he says, these troubles were forerunners of a more serious one. He felt the exhaustions were wearing down his resistance. As so commonly happens in these cases, what he called shame phobias disappeared, to be replaced by the "flight-to-shelter" phobias.

He says that after he had finished his university education, he began for the first time since childhood to be at odds with many people, and he admits that, with his temperament what it was, it was a wonder that the men working beside him remained as friendly as they did. He admits he was critical, cocky, and unpleasant. Sometimes he became depressed, irritable, and even hysterical.

His first love affair. Before he completed his education, while still upset nervously, he got into a brief and unhappy love affair. It appears that before he had taken much time to get acquainted with the girl, he proposed to her, and very properly was turned down. With this, a surge of horror and terror came over him, and like a madman he ran to a friend and begged permission to stay near him until midnight. He says that his panic then was much like those that came in later years. They were identical, he thought, with the one he had in his infancy, when he saw the locomotive. As Leonard says, with his abortive love affair he just lost his head and exaggerated everything in a miserable way. For a while he wrecked his schoolwork by mooning over his lost "love."

The fear of an approaching crack-up. To one of his professors he confessed that his mind seemed to be going to pieces, and the professor feared this was true. Others of his teachers decided that he was brilliant but not a safe man to recommend for a position. At this time, Leonard was troubled also by his extreme poverty. He had gone through many months of emotional tension and physical exhaustion. He wrote that he had a sudden and nameless horror of unsheltered isolation and helpless loneliness. Again, there came a feeling of shame, with a dread of meeting his friends. He said he was mixed up in his thinking and perceptions, and he appeared to have some duality of personality. He began to have the curious faculty of mentally converting a half mile or even two blocks from home into a distance with "infinite remoteness." Naturally, he knew it was all silly, but this did not help him. It never does with phobic people.

Then, he began to have trouble with his eyes—trouble which no new glasses would help because it was all up in his tired brain. His eyes ached and ached, and for two years he had much pain in them. He went many nights without sleep. Sometimes, so far as he could tell, he had only five hours' sleep in a week. He was thinking of suicide. He changed his lodgings again and again to escape noises that tortured his raw nerves. He consulted nerve specialists who could find nothing wrong except nervousness and overwork. He had miscellaneous aches all over his body, which is so typical of the person in a mild psychosis. One day these troubles suddenly disappeared, along with the eye troubles. This sudden improvement is very typical of a change to mild mania. Later, he had spells of severe pain in his rectum, such as many psychotic persons have.

Then, frequently, he would be startled out of his initial doze at night by what he called attacks of "consciousness." He would be at the very verge of sleep, and then, suddenly, he would be wide awake "as if consciousness had *burst* up and *flared* forth from its hiding-place within."

Then he got a strange new phobia which attacked him when he was in or on the water. He realized that this was a silly fear, and so he tried hard to master it—but he couldn't. Although a good swimmer, he just could not force himself to swim out to a raft anchored in the lake a hundred feet from shore. "I tried to reach the raft fifty times, but terror would drive me back . . . terror of being *so far* from safety." He also found he couldn't row his boat very far from shore because of the same type of fear. When winter came, he got a fear of skating out a little distance onto a frozen lake.

The coming of his terrible phobia. One day during his professorial years at the University of Wisconsin he took a walk of seven miles with a friend. When they stopped at a tavern for a beer, he began to feel odd—stranger than he had ever felt in his life. He felt he was dying. On the wall of the barroom he thought he saw a "Locomotive God" "leaping out at him across the room." Then a freight train came lumbering past, a half mile away. It whistled, and this reinforced his phobia and added greatly to his terror. He felt all sorts of weird sensations and got queer ideas. His friend left him for a few minutes, and this frightened him all the more. He had some spells which he called "seizures." He hired a buggy and hurried home.

On reaching home, he told his parents he thought he was dying. Next morning he started out on a little walk down the street, but after going a hundred feet from his house, he was compelled to rush back "in horror of being so far away." After that day he could never walk or ride alone or even with others. Many sounds tortured him, much like a chalk crayon's strident squeak when grating on a blackboard.

There were many fears. His central terror was a craving for safety. There was with it a fear of death. Every fear known to timid childhood came back—fear of darkness, of thunderstorms, of dogs, of bodily pains, and of blood, also many fears that only maturity has the knowledge to fabricate —as of imagined diseases. He developed a great fear of razors, of constipation, of poison in his food, of swallowing, and of committing suicide. On several occasions, while expecting death at any moment, he lay on the bed with his father and mother sitting on either side, each with a hand in his and talking to him in low tones. Several times his father had to sleep with him . . . or to sleep near him as he lay "in unresting terror." He could not go downstairs alone at night. Often when he lay down, especially after his noon meal, he suffered from a wildly rapid pulse.

In speaking of his inability to go far from his home, Leonard said that as soon as he would get a certain distance away—a distance varying at different times from yards to miles—he would be overwhelmed with a feeling of insecurity—of terror that he couldn't get back. He was in terror even of getting a seizure of terror. Also, he had some subterrors—fears lest in his panic he would make a public spectacle of himself, or lest he run in front of an automobile, or collapse from nervous exhaustion. Leonard felt that the terror associated with these phobias was as bad as any horror that the human mind is capable of. Along the way, Leonard consulted six or seven psychiatrists and had some psychoanalysis.

All psychiatrists will be interested in Leonard's description of his many futile efforts to fight his phobias. He would say to himself, "I *will* get to such and such a mark—a tree or a house a half mile down the street—by God, I will" [but] "forthwith the Phobia leaped up like a tiger to my throat, and back to the house I flew." "So much for the wisdom of those who have so cheerfully counseled that I kill the phobia with an ax. Let them find me the ax."

Leonard says he re-educated himself so as to get over some of his phobias such as his fear of crowds, of blood from a scratch, or of the shutoff of escape by a closed door. For months, he tried suggestions given during hypnosis, but nothing helped.

Later, *for no clear reason,* he got almost well, so that he could go two miles from his home. He then felt like one raised from the dead. But one snowy day when out walking, he lost the trail; he got panicky, and with this, he promptly relapsed.

His marriage. After reaching Madison, Wisconsin, Leonard married a young woman from a prominent family, but this alliance brought him more sorrow than he had before, because soon he learned that his wife was psychotic and subject to monthly spells of depression. Leonard's experiences with her and her death is described in detail in his book of beautiful sonnets (*Two Lives*, 1933). In that volume he tells of the mental shock he sustained when he learned that his wife's parents, who had said nothing to him about it, were well aware of her serious psychosis, and had apparently been glad to unload onto him their own great responsibility.

Eventually, the wife committed suicide. This was bad enough, but then many of the townspeople jumped to the conclusion that his eccentricities and his occasional efforts to control his wife during her episodes of psychosis had driven her to commit her wild act. What with this accusation and his angry feud with his wife's family, the town split into two camps of the pro-Leonards and the anti-Leonards. The anti-Leonards cut him on the street and attacked him verbally in many ways. Naturally, the shock of his wife's death, plus the feud, nearly drove him insane, and this did not help him with his phobias.

Things got so bad that his superior at the University tried to get rid of him, and his former pastor gave him a good dressing down. With these shocks, his fear of walking out from his house became so acute and his rope got so short that he had to move into an apartment just across the street from the University. He had to go through the process of re-education all over again. Then, "The old demons reclaimed their dominion, and they brought seven others with them." For a year he experienced attacks of acute melancholia, which came usually two or three times a week. They would last from about 11 A.M. to 2 P.M.

A second marriage helped for a while. Later, he became engaged to a young woman who had had enough nervous trouble herself to sympathize with his difficulties. With her, he was able to travel about; he was able to get to Chicago, and two years later, to New York. He even was able to take a trip on a train alone. But, curiously, when he was in New York, he hadn't the courage to run up to Boston to see his parents.

He married the woman, but unfortunately, in the next twelve years he learned that even the comfort of having a helpful wife with him could not bring complete relief from his phobias. Each summer for three years he was able to go forty miles away for a vacation, but even then the old panic could easily be brought back. Unfortunately, his second marriage eventually broke up.

Why blame one fright for a lifetime of suffering? While I won't question the possibility that, in his early childhood, Leonard was frightened by a railroad engine, I still feel that the sort of child he was—a child born to grow up into an odd and eccentric and mildly psychotic poet—could easily have been badly frightened by anything. Why blame all of a man's lifelong mental disturbances on just one of his innumerable fears? Why not say that the fears were just the natural results of a peculiar temperament with which the man was born? In my early childhood, I was badly frightened several times—as when I was attacked and tossed in the air by a range cow, or when I was picked up and thrown off a wharf into deep water by an old sailor who thought that that was the best way to teach a boy to swim —but these frights had no effect on me, even the next day.

I should think it would be discouraging to psychiatrists to note that although much psychoanalyzing was supposed to have brought out into the light the cause of Leonard's phobias, this did not do him any good. He still could not go a hundred feet from his house!

There is no question that usually phobias are very hard to cure. Perhaps they would not be if the person suffering from them had enough will power. I am reminded of a magnificent but very skittish horse that I used to ride in my youth. He had one bad habit of getting badly frightened when he saw a piece of newspaper lying on the road. I broke him of this phobia by making him walk back and forth over the paper until he quit snuffling at it and jumping sideways from it.

Another Book on Phobias by "Anonymous"— A Phobic Man

I do not know why "Anonymous" (*The Autobiography of a Suicide,* 1934), spoke of himself as a suicide unless because he had made of his life a living death. I cannot classify him as either schizophrenic or manic-depressive, so I will call him just a phobic. In his early years he was an able writer, an able newspaperman, and a fine orator. In his middle life, he became so phobic that he lost one good position after another, and became a nervous wreck, fearful of almost everything. This book belongs on the shelf alongside *The Locomotive God.* Interestingly, Anonymous explains his agoraphobia (fear of open spaces) in much the same words as were used by William Ellery Leonard.

It is interesting to note that, in the first half of the book, the man writes well, and his description of his life and activities is fairly sequential. In the latter half of the book, he writes much as a schizophrenic would do, with no clear coherence. He jumps around from one happening to another. Typically, he doesn't explain why or when his wife and children left him. However, to someone studying psychiatry this very lack of sequence and method and arrangement in writing can be highly instructive; it is so typical of the disconnected mental processes of many a psychotic person.

A severe agoraphobia. On the first page, the man, like many a manic-depressive, blames all his troubles on his own misdeeds, particularly in the field of adultery. He says that many affairs with women had made him "the beaten, grovelling creature that I am today." He tells how he, who once was a sort of gypsy, roaming over half the states of the union, now sits at a window and stares disconsolately at the people who pass by. He cannot go more than a few yards from his prison. He complains that he has a jailer—"a woman who now scorns the thing she once loved, and gloats over my horrible soul-sapping predicament. She is

my mental crutch; without her, I feel I would go insane
or die of shock."

An unsatisfactory marriage. The man married early, when
he was in his twenties. He apparently had been fond of
the woman, but as so often happens when a girl becomes
pregnant and must be married in a hurry, love disappeared,
and happiness went out the window. Evidently the marriage
was unsatisfactory also to the wife, because on several occasions she left the man. Also, during a certain vacation,
she arranged it so that another woman would take her
place in bed! What happened was that, with the idea of
winning back his wife's love, the man took her to a summer
camp where there was only one large bed. The wife insisted
on having her friend Eunice go along with them; and worse
yet, she insisted that the three sleep in the bed together.
Soon it happened that every morning, while the wife was
getting breakfast downstairs, the man was committing
adultery.

The disastrous results of not being able to sin cheerfully.
Soon after this episode with Eunice, his nervous and phobic
troubles started. One of his big troubles according to his
account was that he never learned to sin joyously and without regret! After a bit of adultery, he always had the horrors. "An overpowering fear seized me, and made me a worm
of the earth. I had had relations with a woman who was not
my wife. I had sinned with another woman. I thought that
God would strike me dead. I felt like a lost soul, like a sheep
that had wandered away from the fold to be devoured by
wolves, and I resolved to keep away from this foul woman."
But as the "foul woman" said to him with apparent justification, "Your wife doesn't give a hoot in hell about you any-
way." So he eloped with the woman who evidently was
promiscuous, because, as he says, for a while he "shared her
meagre hall-room accommodations with this man and that!"

Then, nervous disaster came: ". . . this horrible memory
has been my own assassin; it has struck at my soul, and
snuffed out the light within my brain. And only I can ever
know the horror of this destruction; only I can ever know
the loss it has caused me. Indeed, I feel that it is an ogre
that has robbed not only me but the whole world. I am, I

believe, a gifted human; I have within me, if my power to feel does not elude me, talent and genius which would have yielded me a place among the immortals. Tied as I am, I cannot achieve this coveted niche. But what is to prevent me from telling my brother and sister humans all over the world the story of my life, my hopes, and my defeat?"

"Here, then, is the story of a man's life and soul, told without evasion or restraint." "It was scarcely a year later that I found myself feeling like a haunted, hunted thing, afraid to live, and afraid to die." "I had been guilty of a vile deed, and I must some day stand trial before the God who had given me life."

The supposed causes of his phobias. As with most of these odd persons who get psychoanalyzed, he tries to blame all of his troubles on some early sexual traumas. He says the first came when he was four and was seduced repeatedly by a little nymphomaniac, aged twelve! One wonders if a boy of four could be induced to have sexual intercourse, but I feel inclined to believe the man because he is so frank and shameless about all other details of his sexual life. He says, "I did not know it then, but this experience was to control most of my actions in all of the years to come. It was to make me feel that I must possess every woman I ever met; it was to drive me to prison, to the insane asylum, and then, at last, to these relentless chains."

Later in his book he tells of another time when, as a child, he started to attempt sexual intercourse with a little girl. Someone approaching scared him away. Although there had been no penetration, for weeks afterward the boy went in constant fear of the police. He thought they were after him, and hence "lived like a hunted animal." Some readers may wonder if children have sexual intercourse, but many adults say that they had it, perhaps repeatedly, after the age of six.

In later life, Anonymous wanted to blame all of his troubles on these episodes, and on his misdemeanors with Eunice, but this explanation does not seem plausible. It seems far more likely that he was born with a tremendous tendency to worry about many things—real and unreal. He

probably inherited his tendency to worry insanely just as
he inherited his ability to write poetry and his ability to
hold an audience spellbound with his oratory.

A series of severe phobias. When the man began to have
phobias, his first trouble was his inability to sign his name
without experiencing intense pain, together with a feeling
of approaching insanity. Curiously, he could sign a letter to
someone who lived ten or more miles away, but he could
not sign if the letter was to go to someone less than nine
miles away! He couldn't figure out why this phobia had
come to him. A brilliant psychoanalyst told him it was due
to mother fixation and the fear of castration. But as with
William Ellery Leonard, knowing the cause did not enable
him to get rid of the trouble.

With the help of another psychoanalyst he thought he
could remember a time when he was in a baby carriage,
and a boy ran off with a pretzel his mother had given him.
He screamed for his mother, and she came running. Because this was said to have happened in the shadow of a
church steeple, for years afterward, church steeples were
supposed to have bothered him. Of course, disciples of
Freud told him that it was a phallic symbol, and so he
wondered if his unconscious was confusing the loss of the
pretzel with the loss of a phallus. An able disciple of Freud
felt that this loss of a pretzel in the shadow of "a phallus"
must mean fear of castration, and this must be the explanation of the years of unhappiness.

After some time, the man developed a phobia which
made it almost impossible for him to cross a bridge, even
in a motorcar or a bus. This was explained as being due
to a time in childhood when he had fallen off his mother's
ironing board! It is true that in his childhood he had a rough
time with a drunken, good-for-nothing stepfather, but it is
impossible to say how much harm this environment did him.

For much of his life, he always had some terrible thing
to worry about. Eventually, he developed the paralyzing
"fear of the loss of shelter" exactly like that which ruined
the life of William Ellery Leonard.

As Anonymous says so wisely, how can a physician expect to learn much about fear from psychiatrists or psy-

chologists unless they themselves have experienced terrible fear and horror? We can learn most from the people who have suffered greatly. One of our author's first great fears was that he would lose his job and never find another. In his mind's eye he kept seeing his wife and children dying of starvation. This fear came to him even when he had a good job in a publishing firm. "Every day a nightmare to me; every night a slimy thing of horror and dread. How would I ever again get my hands on some money?" "I was always thinking about money, money, money." He lost all interest in life. Even when he was at the theater, he couldn't notice the music or the play because he was thinking about money and starvation. Sleep brought him no rest. Then he began to think of suicide as the only way out. Soon he had pain which he thought was in his heart, and so, again, he feared death.

Suddenly, without the slightest warning, he developed a need for constant companionship. When on a trolley or bus, he had to talk to the man next to him. For a while he even paid a man just to go around with him. He grew so nervous, he had to give up his job. Later, he went back to his writing for a Wall Street magazine. But again there came an old fear, a horrible fear, of premature burial. He spent his days and nights thinking up ways in which he could avoid being buried alive.

Then, for reasons he couldn't understand, he became convinced he was going to be put in prison. "The thought of suffering in prison became so real to me that I found myself plunging headlong into the abyss of insanity." But he decided, "better the jail than death," even though he kept imagining himself sitting on the electric chair. Soon he learned that "the supply of horrors is inexhaustible. As soon as one fear is banished, another one arises." It did him no good when he lost his terrible fear of being buried alive because, then, he became obsessed with the idea that if a man is dead when he is buried, he must be born again— to face hell-fire. With this, his terror over hell-fire became so great that he could hardly stand it. As he said, "To the phobic person, the flames are real. They rage day and night; they occupy a man's thoughts as soon as he rises in the

morning, and they keep him in terror until he retires at
night. They keep him awake until weakness renders him
unconscious, and at dawn they waken and torture him until
he sees fit to rise. They even creep into his dreams."

Then, fortunately, he was able to get back to his job, and
under the influence of work his phobias, for a time, were
dissipated. About then he tried having an affair with a
young woman—but this did not work well. He also tried
going back to his wife, but after twelve weeks, that venture
failed.

He becomes enslaved by a woman. Then, he fell in love
with a woman and felt that, with her, he would be so
happy he would never have another phobia. She was fourteen years older than he, but he felt she was the woman of
whom he had dreamed all his days. But soon, with her, a
terrible phobia made an absolute prisoner of him. After
a night in which he became almost paralyzed with horror
at finding himself alone out in the open, he concluded, "I
could never be alone, not even for a moment; in all of my
waking and sleeping hours; I had to have my fast-decaying
ego buoyed up by human companionship. I could not walk
or ride alone; I could not even sit alone or venture unaccom-
panied to the front gate."

What made it all the harder, he felt that the woman who
held him in bondage was taking pleasure in her conquest
of him and was rejoicing in a fiendish and diabolical way.
"I had sought a sweetheart, a woman who would understand me, and I had found instead a heartless task-master,
a female Simon Legree. She told me what to do, and made
certain that I did it. She plagued me and then laughed at
me, because I could not run away." "Tortured day and night,
I planned an escape." In his desperation he fled into a state
mental hospital, but after three weeks he was let out.

In his writing, he shows how a man can be decidedly psychotic and, at the same time, so sane that he can be earning
his living outside a mental hospital. He remained "a ham-
pered, tortured human, contemplating suicide," but he felt
that things might have been worse. At least, he was no
longer in the State Hospital. He went back to the woman
and again became her miserable slave—"a mindless mario-

nette, who had to live at the mercy of this tyrannical grand-mother." As he said, "for me there is no escape, no hope but death. I am compelled to do this woman's bidding, and to pray that she lives on to torture me. My phobia is such that the very thought of her disappearance or death sets my heart fluttering like that of a frightened bird, and almost catapults me into the realm of insanity." Then, to make matters worse, he found that even when one of the pupils in the woman's boarding school went into town, he would be frightened and utterly miserable until he or she came back.

Later, he apparently got so much better that he could run away and go back to be chief editorial writer of two weekly newspapers. This work, naturally, brought him great joy. But then, suddenly, came another devastating phobia. He discovered that he couldn't allow any of his manuscripts to leave his house. So he had to resign his fine editorial post. And then there returned his "loss of shelter" complex. One day, it seemed as if someone had said to him, "If you don't hurry home, you'll die right here and now." After that, for two years, he could not venture beyond the nearest street corner. "I have tried to, but always I have been driven back. Always there is that indescribable feeling of horror, that awful dread of sudden death." He ends the book with the statement that for long he had had to live within a circle with a radius of two hundred feet.

The physician must not treat just a phobia—but a sick man. As I said above, my impression is strong that this man was born with great gifts, but also with the curse of a strong tendency to psychosis. His sex life obviously was badly mixed up. He was very sensual, and as he said, several times his chasing after a woman had led to his downfall! But, if he had been born with better sense, he would not have gotten mixed up with so many unsuitable women. The book is valuable in that it shows so clearly that phobias can suddenly go, but when one goes, another can come. When a man was born to be a phobic, any old fear will do to keep him in chains. This fact should now be remembered by all psychotherapists when they feel like trying to treat one single fear. Perhaps some day we physicians will know that these persons have a defective spot in the brain, and that this is why they remain for most of their days full of fear. Against this idea is the fact that both Anonymous and Leonard had times when, without any explanation, they would get well and go back to work.

The Autobiography of David—

Another very instructive story of a gifted, handsome, and charming British newspaper editor—a man who all his life had great difficulty in crossing wide spaces—is *The Autobiography of David—*. Curiously, he could seldom *walk* across an open area, but he could *drive* across in a car. The fact that, on several occasions, he had to be put in a mental hospital shows how close a paralyzing agoraphobia can be to insanity. The man also had at times a strong compulsion to expose himself to women. This terrified him because, if he yielded to his impulse, he could be arrested and disgraced. Unskillful psychotherapy upset him greatly and made him much worse.

CHAPTER 8

Some Persons Who Heard Voices and Saw Strange Sights (Hallucinations)

In this chapter I have brought together a few stories of men and women whose insanity showed itself mainly, or entirely, in the form of hallucinations.

A Woman Who Suddenly Heard Voices

The Maniac (by E. Thelmar, 1909) is a classic in that it describes vividly the remarkable hallucinations of hearing that started a woman out, rather suddenly, on an attack of psychosis. She says she can report the conversations she had with the "voices" almost as exactly as if she had taken them down in shorthand.

At the time her illness started, she was an unmarried journalist, over thirty, working for a London magazine, and living alone in a rented room. Apparently she had long been a bit eccentric. She was somewhat of a spiritualist and said that she could see auras around some people's heads.

On a certain Wednesday afternoon one September, after much worry over a legal problem she had gone home dead tired and "too miserable for words or for tears." She "longed to be quit of it all," and to be "quit of her physical body." That day she had kept at work only with great difficulty. All her fatigue seemed concentrated in her head. "My brain

175

seemed like a cog-wheel that had stuck"; she had to push
it to keep it going. Because of these feelings, she had asked
for a week's leave. By Friday, she had eaten very little, and
whatever she had tried to swallow had seemed to stick in
her throat.

The hallucinations begin. That night, after she had gone
to bed, she heard a man's voice "proceeding apparently from
the arm-chair by the fire-place, asking 'Are you awake?'"
She answered, "Yes, wide awake. Who are you?" As she
says, if she had been in her right mind, she would have been
much frightened, but actually she was in such a psychotic
state that she cheerfully kept chatting with the man as he
kept asking her about a book which she had written. For a
while, she tried to find out who he was, but eventually she
dropped off to sleep.

The next morning she woke feeling well. She remembered
the conversation of the previous evening, but still it seemed
to her an ordinary occurrence. In fact, she had rather enjoyed the experience! That night, again, as soon as she
blew out the light, the same voice began talking to her. It
asked, "Darling, are you afraid?" "No," she answered, "I'm
not in the least afraid; why should I be afraid? But who
are you?" Again, she spent some time conversing with the
voice until she said good night and went to sleep. Next
morning, while having breakfast, she heard music, and
again "the voice."

She realizes she is going mad. That day she could do
nothing at the office. The next morning at home she listened
to two men's voices disputing. Then, a voice told her to
change and put on all clean clothes, then to kneel down and
pray. Later he said, "Strip naked," and she did! Then a
voice told her that a fiend had gotten inside her body, and
that he had seduced her so that she would bear a fiend-
child. This sent her into a frenzy, and she began to call
upon God for help. She felt a fury and a despair. Later,
thousands of mad voices commenced yelling at her, and she
realized she was going mad.

With this, she went to the home of a friend who let her
stay the night. As soon as she laid her head on the pillow,
a voice began saying that the demon who had seduced her

was coming. Soon this fiend kept saying, "As long as you keep awake and resist me with the force of your will I cannot touch you, but immediately you fall asleep you will be in my power!" And so, for hours, she and her friend "sat up in bed, praying to God and defying the fiend."

At last the fiend said, "Keep awake if you choose, or do what you choose— You cannot keep awake always; if you do you will go mad. So in any case you are lost." Then the original man's voice chimed in and discussed matters. Soon "shriek after shriek rent the air, until my blood felt curdled with horror." "I was fully aware that I had gone mad, and this knowledge was a mental agony such as no one can imagine."

Then she began to wonder to what asylum she had better go and give herself up. Then the man's voice said to her, "Take a dagger and go and kill that woman who has made you mad." There was much more of this sort of conversation, and as a result, the victim never closed an eye the entire night through. Curiously, at times she wasn't frightened, and was even amused at the efforts of the fiends to get at her.

Then she thought she had better try going to her sister's home; perhaps with this change of scene, she could escape being put into an asylum. But a friend managed to get her to a doctor's where she felt she could prove that she was sane. Soon, her brother and a Mrs. W. took charge of her and got a doctor and a nurse. By this time, she was constantly hallucinating, and evidently was confused about everything.

Then, one evening, "I suddenly awoke to normal consciousness—I mean consciousness of my real, bodily surroundings—and found myself standing with two nurses. I remembered all that had been occurring, and I felt so weak and ill I could scarcely sit up. I could not comprehend what it was that had happened to me (I had again ceased to understand that I was mad)."

The futility of psychotherapy. Again, she became confused and began to hallucinate. Later, when she had recovered, her doctor told her that time and again during her period of insanity, he had reasoned with her and had told

her that her ideas were nonsense, but, as she says, "What
he seemed unable to grasp was that neither his words, his
presence, nor his reasonings ever penetrated to my consciousness at all!" She felt that any doctor who expects to
influence "a lunatic" by reasoning with her is a lunatic himself! He hasn't sense enough to know that the patient is literally "out of her mind"—she isn't there!

One night she woke and saw her doctor and the two
nurses. She felt so strange; it seemed as if she was in a body
not her own! She thought—"*Now,* who am I?" But soon she
drifted back into a world of hallucination. One day when
she woke she was sure she was in her coffin. A week or so
later, she became lucid enough to recognize her brother
and to talk with him. Another time she was sure she had
been annihilated. She thought her existence had been "ex-
tinguished as suddenly and utterly and completely as the
flame of a candle, when it is blown out. That was the precise
sensation." She felt she had suddenly and utterly ceased
to be.

Later, the fiends came back to torture her. For a while,
she kept hearing music. Sometimes when she thought the
nurses were fiends she spat in their faces. She tried to avoid
taking her medicine because she thought it was poison.

A remarkable explanation of insanity and what it is like.
As the woman recovered, she had a remarkable thought
which throws great light on the nature of insanity. She reminds us, first, what a relief we all experience when we
wake from a terrible nightmare to find that it was only a
dream. Well, if someone wants to know what it feels like
to be insane, just let him imagine how it would feel to wake
from a horrible nightmare to find that *it was real.* That's
what madness is like. Then is when the patient is frantic
with terror.

In spite of some improvement, the voices went on bothering the woman every day. Then came another curious
sound; it was loud and like the chirping of a bird. She says
that throughout her attack of madness, she "never relaxed
for a moment her efforts to understand what was the meaning of, and reason for" everything that was happening to
her. "Then on November 6, suddenly, the noises which

had been going on ceaselessly—many of them like the roar of an express-train speeding through a tunnel"—suddenly ceased. And from that moment she was sane again. The spell of acute madness had lasted from September 29 to November 6.

The sudden return to complete sanity. As many a formerly insane person keeps saying, during the attack she could reason well enough, but all her senses were deceiving her. The senses of hearing, sight, touch, smell—every one "furnished me with false data for my reasonings, and made all logic futile." "Bewildered as I was when mad, I really was almost equally bewildered on becoming sane!" She maintained, from her experience, that "a lunatic's reason remains with him intact whenever he is at all conscious. What a lunatic loses is not his *reason,* but his *consciousness.*" He *goes out of his mind.* In the end, she felt, as many of the ex-insane do, that she had emerged from her attack unscathed; she was her old self again.

In this connection, I was much impressed a while ago reading about an educated man who for twelve years had been a typical "bench case." He had sat in a mental hospital paying no attention to anyone or anything, and saying never a word. Then he had a pneumonia, and when he recovered, he sent for his family and again was his old fine and intelligent self. Evidently, during those many years, his largely unused mind had not deteriorated; it had just been turned off, like a faucet.

Today, with the help of all our new knowledge of the several drugs which can make a man psychotic for some hours or a day or two, we physicians are wondering if those brief episodes of acute insanity which some people have could be due to some disturbance in the chemistry of the brain, or of the whole body.

Maupassant's Insanity

In his short story "The Horla," Maupassant, the great French writer of short stories, apparently described the hallucinations which filled him with horror as he was going insane. Some persons have questioned the genuineness of this story, but Frances Steegmuller (*A Lion in the Path*, Random House) says that before he wrote the story, Maupassant told Paul Bourget, "Every time I come home I see my double. I open my door and I see him sitting in my arm-chair. I know it is an hallucination even while experiencing it. Curious: if I didn't have a little common sense, I'd be afraid."

At times he complained of great melancholy, a vague fear, and a feeling of approaching danger. He had terrible nightmares, and soon he saw that some day his reason would disintegrate.

Frances Steegmuller wrote also that in the *Lettres d'un fou,* which was published in February, 1885, there was a crude version of "The Horla." Maupassant's story "La Main écorchée" is one of a number of morbid stories written about 1875, when he is said to have developed nervous syphilis. He was "certified" the first time in 1877, after two years of treatment. In 1891, Edmond de Goncourt wrote that he had heard that Maupassant was suffering from delusions of grandeur such as are typical of brain syphilis. Soon after this he had to go into a mental hospital where he got the progressive type of paralysis which is typical of paresis, or syphilis of the brain.

But Maupassant was probably also born to be neurotic. His mother was always sickly and was said to have suffered from major hysteria. She may have been manic-depressive. His brother Hervé went insane and died in a mental hospital, perhaps also with nervous syphilis.

When Guy was fifteen, his mother told Flaubert that the lad's "nerves were not strong." He was a "hypochondriac" who wrote gloomy letters. His hair was falling out, which suggests that he already had syphilis.

In "The Horla," Maupassant tells of a most distressing type of hallucination, horrible enough to justify the sufferer in demanding that someone sit up with him all night! On a certain day after a slight attack of fever, he felt low-spirited. Each morning after his walk, he would feel wretched.

On May 16 he wrote, "I am ill; I am feverish; I have continually that horrible sensation of some impending danger; that apprehension of some coming misfortune, or of approaching death: that presentiment which is, no doubt, an attack of some illness which is still unknown." "I try to read, but I do not understand the words, and can scarcely distinguish the letters. Then I walk up and down my drawing-room, oppressed by a feeling of confused and irresistible fear —fear of sleep, and fear of my bed."

On going to his room, he double-locked and bolted his door. He was afraid of he knew not what. Up to that time he had never been afraid of anything. Then he would go to bed and wait for sleep as a man might wait for an executioner. He waited with dread, with his heart beating, his legs trembling, and his body shivering beneath the bed-clothes. When sleep came, it brought a nightmare. "I feel that somebody is coming close to me, is looking at me, touching me, is getting onto my bed, is kneeling on my chest, is taking my neck between his hands and squeezing it in order to strangle me." "And then suddenly I wake, trembling, and bathed in perspiration."

While walking through a forest, suddenly it would seem to him that he was being followed—that someone was walking at his heels, close, close to him—near enough to touch him. Perhaps all of us in our childhood have been able to imagine this situation. Coleridge described it perfectly. In *The Ancient Mariner* (part vii) he wrote

> Like one, that on a lonesome road
> Doth walk in fear and dread,
> And having once turned round walks on,
> And turns no more his head;
> Because he knows, a frightful fiend
> Doth close behind him tread.

With all this, Maupassant could get no rest and his nights "devoured his days." He wondered if he had lost his reason. He went on to describe the worst of the horrors that kept distressing him night after night. What frightened him so terribly was that during the night the level of the water in the bottle beside his bed would be lowered, suggesting that someone in the room had had a drink. He became so frightened by this observation that he would sit up until daylight, afraid to go back to bed. And still each night the water bottle appeared to be emptied by unseen hands. As a result of this, Maupassant kept saying, "I am going mad."

Days later, he wrote, "This time I am not mad. I have seen . . . I have seen . . . I can doubt no longer . . . I have seen it!" "I was walking at two o'clock among my rose-trees in the full sunlight. As I stopped to look at a Géant de Bataille, which had three splendid blossoms, I distinctly saw the stalk of one of the roses near me bend, as if an invisible hand had bent it, and then broken it, as if the hand had picked it! Then the flower raised itself, following the course which a hand would have described in carrying it toward a mouth, and it remained suspended in the transparent air, all alone and motionless, a terrible red spot, three yards from my eyes. In desperation I rushed at it to take it! I found nothing; it had disappeared. Then I was seized with a furious rage against myself, because a reasonable and serious man should not have such hallucinations. But was it a hallucination?"

"I am certain now, that there exists close to me an invisible being that lives on milk and water, that can touch objects, take them, and change their places." "It lives as I do, under my roof." "I have seen mad people, and I have known some who have been intelligent, lucid, even clear-sighted in every concern of life, except on one point. They spoke clearly, readily, profoundly on everything, when suddenly their mind struck upon the shoals of their madness, and broke to pieces there, and scattered and foundered in that furious and terrible sea, full of rolling waves, fogs and squalls, which is called madness."

"I spent a terrible evening yesterday. *He* does not show himself any more, but I feel that he is near me; watching me, looking at me, penetrating me, dominating me; and more redoubtable when he hides himself thus than if he were to manifest his constant and invisible presence by supernatural phenomena."

Maupassant then lost courage and self-control, and the power even to set his will in motion. He felt lost and dependent on others. He felt that someone possessed his soul and dominated it. Someone was ordering all his acts and all his thoughts.

Later, he woke one night and saw the page of a book which was lying open upon his table turn over. Later, another page lifted up and fell down on the others, as if a finger had turned it over. He said, "My arm chair was empty; it appeared empty, but I knew that *He* was there, sitting in my place, and that he was reading." "He is the Horla—he has come!"

The Horla was in him and was becoming his soul; he would have to kill him! Several times Maupassant tried to jump at the Horla and strangle him, but each time he got away. Once he was certain that *He* was reading over his shoulder, that he was there, touching his ear. Finally, in his attempt to conquer the Horla, Maupassant says he set fire to his house and ran. The house burned down, but apparently the Horla got away. Then Maupassant felt there could be only one escape for him and that would be through suicide. "Then—I must kill myself!"

According to Ernest Boyd (*Guy de Maupassant, a Biographical Study*, Knopf, 1926), in 1892 Guy tried to commit suicide by cutting his throat. After some time spent in a mental hospital, he died on July 6, 1893.

A Good Description of Hallucinations

A certain D. Davidson, an Englishman who wrote in 1912 (*Remembrances of a Religio-Maniac*), described some hallucinations which had bothered him off and on for some time. He was twice committed; the first time when he was about twenty-one, and the second time when he was about thirty-three. Each time he had to remain in a mental hospital for only a few months. As he says, wasn't it curious that a man like him who, when sane, had had no interest in religion, when insane, should have had his mind completely taken up with religious matters! Why should this remarkable change take place in the insane?

Davidson was the eldest of twelve children, and apparently his people were well off. He tells us that long before Freud stressed the importance of childhood impressions, John Locke had discussed the subject.

Early tendencies to psychosis. It is worth noting that even as a child Davidson had some strange experiences that showed him that something was wrong with him. Before he was ten, he was often rebuked because of his tendency to cry like a girl. And even that early, he had a feeling that some day he would go insane. In his teens, he was morose, lazy, late for appointments, and inclined to bad habits. One day he heard a voice say, "If you do this you will never [again] see your father." Sometimes he would think he was having a long conversation with someone, only to realize later that he had been alone and that he had been talking to himself—or hallucinating.

On an ocean trip he felt a great impulse to jump overboard. Shortly after reaching Australia, he thought he had had a long chat with someone and then found that no one was there. It took him a while before he could be sure that these talks were hallucinations. Sometimes people remarked that for a while he had acted peculiarly and for no reason at all had been rude to the persons with him. With this, he would realize that his mind had not been working right.

Occasionally, there came over him a compulsion to grab someone—as did the Ancient Mariner—and describe to him all of the badness and the idleness of his life. Usually, the person seized did not care to listen and wanted only to get away. Davidson would have loved the sessions of the Buchmanites of today, some of whom like to get up in meeting and describe all their evil deeds to the assembled crowd.

His first step over the edge into psychosis. One day, Davidson insisted on taking his brother to a doctor, but soon the doctor decided that it was Davidson who was the sick man—and actually he was mentally ill. Then, one evening, for a minute, he saw what looked like the black shadow of the devil flying over him. Later, he began to hear voices calling his name. Next thing he knew, he walked up to a man who hadn't done anything to him and struck him in the face. That evening, while passing a physician's home, he put his fist through the window of the consulting room, because he had heard the doctor was irreligious. Soon after this, Davidson was cursing people and promising great disasters ahead—much as the prophets of Israel did.

In a mental hospital. On arrival in a mental hospital,

Davidson wondered if he "was God Himself, and not a man." At times he was made miserable by the sight of creatures that were half man and half beast. These hallucinations remind one of the curious beasts that one finds pictured on the walls of ancient Mesopotamian palaces. Perhaps those were conceived by religious visionaries who had hallucinated. As Professor Badé said in his great book *The Old Testament in the Light of Today* (Houghton Mifflin, 1915), the ancients could think of their god one minute as a man, the next minute as someone with feminine characteristics, and the next minute as something part man and part animal or bird.

Every so often in the hospital, Davidson gained the overpowering impression that the great spirit of God was directly overhead or all about him, and so he took off his shoes and socks and walked around in his bare feet, as Fox sometimes did. He felt that he was on holy ground.

Davidson goes home to England and goes insane again. After a while, Davidson was released from the asylum and allowed to go home to England. There, "like most lunatics, I blamed everything and everybody, except myself, for my past mistakes and present predicament, and I kept harping upon this."

Later, while manic, he wrote, "I became conscious of a distinct difference in myself. I felt light-hearted and happy." As other manic persons have said, during this period of elation his mind was clearer, and his perception keener than at any other time in his life. But then the hallucinations returned, and he saw something that looked like a small animal walking around in his library. Like Luther, he was tempted to throw an inkpot at it. Later, from his state of mania, he dropped down into a state of depression in which he was overcome with the sense of his unutterable sinfulness and the irrevocable harm he had done. He began to hear voices, and soon he felt that he was identified with God. Later, as was the case with George Fox, as soon as a religious service was over, he felt bursting to get up and speak.

Another hospitalization. A little later he got the delusion "that everyone in the world was dead, except myself." He decided he had better put his house in order quickly, before the final catastrophe could come. And then he had to be taken again to a mental hospital where he kept constantly hallucinating. Much of his book is taken up with a magnificent description of this experience. In the hospital, like George Fox, Davidson talked on only one subject, which was religion. He "felt that he was in the hands of tremendous powers that could cause things to come to pass." Once he was amused at his own delusion; but it was not long before another took its place. This shows how an insane man can realize that he is mentally confused.

Paranoia appears. Shortly after this, Davidson became paranoiac, and as he said, "I began to suffer from hideous and unworthy suspicions regarding members of my own family." "I wrote letters which I now greatly regret writing, and I see now that doctors [in mental hospitals] have good reason for examining patients' outgoing letters."

After his release, he was still too religious. After some months, the man was set at liberty, but obviously he was still too deeply concerned with religion. Religion was all he thought of or talked about from morning to night. Davidson felt that "God in His mercy wished me to recover and do something definite for Him." Unfortunately, we have no evidence to show that Davidson ever did anything wonderful for God and religion; and so, according to Anton Boisen's criterion, his religious experience was only a manifestation of insanity.

A Remarkable Case of "Hearing Voices" in Which the Man Says He Remained Sane

The case here described is taken from a series found in the book *Mad Humanity* (1898) by Dr. L. Forbes Winslow (page 300).

The patient, a man, wrote that "whilst taking a walk one evening . . . about five years since, I heard the sound of voices near me, speaking of me. I looked in every direction, but could not discover any one. I walked away, but still the voices pursued me. I mixed with the thickest of the throng in the metropolis; the voices still continued to haunt me, and the words then uttered were: 'Who is he? do you know who he is?' The response was, 'He is Satan's own.' " "These words seemed continuously to proceed from the persons I passed."

The victim of this hallucination kept walking around town hoping that the voices would leave him; but they didn't. And yet, he felt that, in spite of these hallucinations, he was perfectly sane. For a long time he heard the voices, constantly, until he was exhausted.

Hoping that he might get free from this annoyance, twice he traveled about Europe, but this did not help. "I could plainly distinguish seven voices, two of which struck me as the voices of females." These "voices remained with me many months, when three left me, and four continued to torment me for a couple of years." After that, two remained, but with the years, they gradually became less and less annoying.

The probability was that he had a small area in his brain that was diseased in such a way that it kept sending out the voices. Dr. Wilder Penfield of the great Neurological Institute in Montreal once told of such a case in which a man kept hearing someone named Charlie talking. Dr. Penfield opened the man's skull under local anesthesia and saw an area of brain that looked abnormal. When he stimulated this electrically, the man said, "Why, there's Charlie!"

Summary. I do not know of any better way of learning what hallucinations are like than to read the accounts here abstracted. These writers give the reader a good idea of what it feels like to go mad. Very interesting are the statements of some of them that at times they were not frightened by the voices they heard. Sometimes they realized that these voices were not real, and were arising in a disturbed brain. We find this same lack of fear commented on by Lara Jefferson, when she tells of seeing little imps.

Interesting is the "Maniac's" statement that on occasions she knew that she had gone mad, and this distressed her greatly. As Lara Jefferson and others have pointed out, part of the brain seems to go mad, while another part remains sane, and looks on disapprovingly. The sane part may struggle to straighten out the insane part, and sometimes it succeeds. One sees this division in the brain in some alcoholics who, while very drunk and misbehaving, will have sense enough to admit to the bystanders that they are drunk.

Another curious feature of the psychosis of these halluci- nating people was their tendency to have brief intervals when they were lucid and able to talk sensibly. I have ob- served this many times in a big city hospital, where an al- coholic one moment would be out of his head and scream- ing that he was fighting snakes, and the next minute would be chatting with me very normally.

Interestingly, Maupassant was terrified by his conviction that there was a demon in his room drinking the water in the carafe by his bed. One can easily see why with this the man's mind should have been filled with horror.

I am impressed by the fact that in the cases of some of the disturbed persons who have written up their experience, the main difficulty or even the sole difficulty, was a tend- ency to hallucinate. In Davidson's case, he had other trou- bles such as depressions, paranoia, and too much religion. How different was the situation in the last case described in which the man seemed perfectly sane except for the hearing of voices. In years to come some of these persons will probably be cured by a brain surgeon who will cut out a bit of diseased tissue.

CHAPTER 9

Paranoiacs Who Thought That Enemies Were after Them

Paranoia is that form of mental disease in which the patient thinks people—and perhaps vague forces of evil—are plotting against him. Many purely accidental happenings are assumed by him to be threats against his safety. He thinks people are sensing his thoughts, or they are beaming radar at him. Perhaps he hallucinates, and then he hears voices jeering at him. Many persons who are accepted as normal by their fellows are paranoid, which means "like a paranoiac." They have only a few of the symptoms. They are suspicious people. Many have a single-track mind. There is a variety of schizophrenia in which the person is paranoid. A paranoid man may tell me his mother was, like him, so suspicious that, when he was a child, she would never let even one of his playmates into her house. He may tell me that he has no pleasure from his teen-age children because, whenever one of them shows him any affection, he immediately thinks, "What is she planning to get out of me now?"

The best description I know of the problems of a paranoiac is to be found in the autobiographies of August Strindberg (see Chapter 3). Another remarkable story of a man who confesses in his book to having had most of the symptoms of a paranoiac is that of Dr. Donald McI. Johnson (see Chapter 14). Some paranoid men are so sure that they are right and are so determined to do something or other that they become leaders of causes or heads of large corporations. Several who have come to me as patients were "sad-sack" millionaires. Occasionally, a man will come into my office who is a dangerous paranoiac likely some day to kill someone. For instance, a man told me that the country was full of "gehockers"—people who cleared their throat in a noisy way *just to annoy him*. He said they were an organized group who kept two or three persons always following him about and nearly driving him crazy. He had bought a gun and some day he was going to shoot one of his tormentors! Another man like this whom I knew actually shot and killed a stranger passing by on the street. When asked why he had done this, he said the man was a member of a national group organized for the purpose of committing sodomy with him!

A Professor Who Thought People Were Constantly Jeering at Him

The *Letters of a Lunatic* by G. F. Adler (1854), would be amusing if the story told were not so sad. A professor of languages, while writing a book to show that he was perfectly sane, succeeded only in showing that he was a paranoiac who, for some time, had been making a nuisance of himself around the college in which he was teaching. It shows clearly the mental processes of a man who is sure that people are talking about him, jeering at him, and trying to annoy or harm him. Any casual statement which he heard might be construed by him as a veiled insult directed at him. Because he thought—doubtless quite erroneously—that something said by his superior, the Reverend Isaac Ferris, was a sneer directed at him, he wrote a long letter about it, demanding an apology. It is probable that many of the insults and jibes that Professor Adler kept thinking he heard were really hallucinations of hearing.

The paranoiac often appeals to city officials for protection. Adler's behavior was typical when he wrote a letter to the mayor of the City of New York asking for protection against the many persons "who were deliberately annoying him by making a lot of noise in rooms next to his office at the school, and in the street near his apartment." He kept hearing "such cries as 'Go on! Stop! Out of the institution with that man!'" Adler heard cries of "Kill him!—besides multitudes of vulgar chuckles, screams and other horrid vociferations . . . until at times I felt as if I could support the vexation no longer."

The unwisdom of writing a letter about someone who is misbehaving. President Ferris was foolish enough to write a letter to one of Adler's best friends, saying that during the winter the man had been showing so many signs of a disordered mind that he had lost his value as a teacher. Ferris thought Adler's friends ought to get him away for a while for a rest. As so commonly happens in these cases, someone promptly purloined the letter and took it to Adler. Naturally, he was outraged and went about showing the communication to everyone.

Adler has to be committed. Soon he had to be committed, but, as he said, he couldn't possibly have been insane because, during the months in which he was in the hospital, he was finishing and seeing through the press a highly technical book on which he was working. Adler maintained that his symptoms of unusual excitement were the *result* of the outrages perpetrated on him. Probably, if he had gotten a writ of habeas corpus and had come up before a jury, he could quickly have convinced them that he was as sane as the judge.

He leaves town, and his persecutors follow! Typical of all paranoiacs was his discovery, when he moved from one university to another, that his persecutors had followed him! "They followed me at every step. The scum of New York . . . were hired, in well-organized gangs, to drop mysterious allusions, and to offer me insults in the street." "A body of proselyting religionists were busy in their endeavors to make me a submissive tool of some ecclesiastical party." Adler complained also that the menials in his college had been induced to be insolent to him. There were "mysterious *desk-slammings* in the council-room, and equally significant and intimidating *door-slammings!*"

The danger that a paranoiac will kill someone. From what

Adler says, one can easily see why his associates at the university became fearful even that he might attack or shoot them. As I have said, many a paranoiac of this type, when he has felt himself hounded and badgered beyond human endurance, and when his disordered brain keeps telling him that people have been jeering at him, buys a gun and shoots someone. One can easily see why the paranoiac sometimes feels driven to do this.

I remember a brilliant research chemist who, one day, asked to see the head of the laboratories. The chief said, "Why, yes; show him in; he has been doing such fine work I was planning to send for him and give him a promotion." When the man came in, he said to his chief, "See here; I have had all the annoyance from you that I can stand; if you don't stop changing the labels on the bottles in my lab, I am going to kill you!"

The Story of a Man Full of Paranoid Fears

In Paul Hackett's book *The Cardboard Giants* (1952), one can learn much about the fears and mental upsets that can assail a paranoid man. As his wife tells us in her book *The Cliff's Edge* (1954)—written after her husband was discharged from a mental hospital—he was mentally disturbed in his early years even before she married him. When they were engaged, he told her he was subject to such violent swings of mood that he wondered if he was being fair in asking her to marry him.

His decided paranoia. After the honeymoon, on their moving into their first apartment, she proudly placed their name on a card in the space opposite their button in the entrance hall. Imagine her surprise and distress and wonderment when, on his coming home and seeing what she had done, he angrily removed the card and said, "Never do that again." To his way of thinking, her action had made it possible for persons who might be planning to injure them to learn where they lived.

Like many paranoiacs, Paul liked to move quickly and silently out of one city and into another so that he could give his supposed enemies the slip. (See Strindberg's story.)

Paul felt that he was constantly being watched and spied on. Typically, one night when, on a trip, he and Marie had gone to a hotel, suddenly Paul whispered that they would have to get out of there quickly—"the place was bad." And so they sat up half the night in a cold railroad station!

Early in his book, Paul said, "I tried to remember when I first knew that the world was controlled by this evil force, the Mind. It may have been when I was little." He often felt that some day the evil force would surely destroy him and his loved ones.

His early tendency to crime. Paul says in his book that when he met his wife, "I told her that I dealt in stolen cars, and she just asked me why, and I didn't know why. I told her of the Army, and my head injury, and the voices I sometimes heard in the night, and I wondered why I told her these things which I told to no one else." Marie found out later that he had been living a double life—partly in study and in business, and partly in association with underworld characters. As she says in her book, it was a shock to her when she discovered that her Paul was spending hours in dimly lit bars—talking with criminals and engaging in conspiracies with them.

It was some time before Marie could bring all the several facts together into focus in her mind—his wide swings in mood, his tendency to criminality, his leaving school, his terrible headaches, and his habit of sleeping with a gun beside his bed. As she tells us, she probably should have sensed earlier than she did that he was mentally ill, but there were long periods of time in which he was well. Then, suddenly, he would do some strange or wrong thing, and she would say to herself that it just couldn't be true; and yet, inside, she would have the sickening knowledge that it was true. Obviously, he was mentally disturbed.

His inner conflicts. Eventually, Paul himself came to see that his curious streak of criminality had been related to some need he had to rebel against authority—some urgency to prove he was above the law, some foreshadowing of his later delusions of grandeur. Looking back on his life, he could see the unfolding of his sickness, with one half of him leaning toward crime and the other half directed by a conscience which forbade him to do any wrong. No wonder that eventually the inner struggle tore him to pieces.

After he had cracked up, he could recall hundreds of incidents which had been forerunners of his mental sickness—incidents which he and his wife had puzzled over. First, there were little flashes of suspicion or secretiveness, or big explosions of temper; or, after business failures, periods of depression.

To show the sort of devil-may-care temper Hackett had: one evening when a taxi driver had refused to take him home because, as he said, he was tired and hungry and wanted a rest and something to eat, Hackett waited until the man was out of sight and then drove home in the fellow's cab! He left the taxi on the street with some money for his fare! He was not sane enough to realize how much trouble he could have gotten into if the police had caught him.

Once, Marie was distressed because, when her Paul woke in the morning, he was confused, and apparently so disoriented that he had to struggle to remember who he was and where he was. Typically, he looked at her for a long time and then looked at himself in a mirror and examined everything in the room. Later, he said that his mind seemed to be "melting," and he didn't want to forget his wife.

When a man going insane can no longer fight it off. Eventually came a day when, like so many of the people who are slowly becoming psychotic, he felt he could no longer fight for his sanity and hang onto it. Then, as often happens, he lost his ability to sleep, and this led to his breakdown.

Like so many mildly psychotic persons, he had always had such a tendency to cut himself off from people that he had no friends. Fortunately, he was able deeply to love his wife and his children, and this love remained unclouded even during the time when he was badly upset in the hospital. Once he said, "I love you, Marie, and when I defeat the forces of evil, you'll be proud. I'll free mankind from evil, and you'll be proud of me."

Several facts suggest an epileptic equivalent. There are many points in Hackett's story that suggest that, together with his paranoia, there might have been an epileptic element. First is his statement that he and his people were often angry and violent. As he said, "I come from angry people. We are born angry and never get over it." What a remarkable statement that is! As we shall see later, one of the man's greatest troubles came from this fact that he lived with a constant smouldering anger and rage within him. Because of this, he had constantly to be careful not to lash out at people. Sometimes he did.

Once he said, "I could feel the fury mount in little surges, like a pressure rising: waves of anger. There was no one to strike at." One can easily see why people with these feelings of rage sometimes hurt someone, or even kill a stranger. Marie was much impressed one day by the statement of a man who had been working with her husband. He said that although he was fond of Paul, he had parted company with him because he was afraid that some day, in one of his rages, Paul would murder him!

As a child, Paul got along well enough and did well in school. But he tells us that at the age of four he already had times when his mind was working queerly. He felt as if he were seeing something he had seen in a previous existence—what the French psychiatrists call the *déjà vu impression*. This is a well-known symptom of a certain type of psychic epilepsy.

Again suggestive of an epileptic component in Hackett's trouble is the fact that his son John once had severe "fever convulsions." In perhaps half of such cases, the child, when fully grown, shows further signs of epilepsy. As I showed in my book *Practical Leads to Puzzling Diagnoses: Neuroses That Run through Families* (Lippincott, 1958) in one generation of a family there may be psychoses, or alcoholism, and in the next generation there may be epilepsy, perhaps in a mild and not easily recognized form. If I had been consulted by Hackett, with his violent temper and inner rages, the first thing I would have done would have been to get electroencephalograms made, to see if in them there were signs of epilepsy. Unfortunately, it is only recently that we physicians have been learning to think of a latent epilepsy in cases like Hackett's. Paul had good reason to fear, as he did, that one of his children might inherit his tendency to psychosis.

Hackett's inability to realize why he was kept hospitalized. In Hackett's book he tells of his life in a mental hospital. There, he was almost always clear in his head, and always well-behaved. He was so sensible that it was hard for him to see why he should be detained. But the doctors kept trying to explain to him that he was a very sick man, and that it was much safer for him and for his family that he remain locked up and taking treatment. That they were correct and wise was shown by the fact that once, when he had been allowed to go home for a night, his wife found him up and walking in the darkness—confused, and coming at her with a *carving knife in his hand*. Very fortunately, he became lucid just in time to avoid a tragedy. Another time like this, when he mistook Marie for an enemy, he struck her in the face. This occurrence frightened him so that he went right back into the hospital.

Interestingly, one of Paul's fellow inmates who had been around the mental hospital a long time told him it would be easy for him to get out: all he would have to do would be to tell the psychiatrists that his delusions were all gone. But Paul was too honest to do this.

Typical to show how people like Paul think was the text of the letter which he once wanted to mail. It read, "I, Paul Hackett, have discovered the cosmic force ruling the world is an evil force. What men call God does not exist, only a force of evil called a Mind." There was more along these lines.

Fury. I always marvel at the violence of the hates that fill the minds of many psychotic people. Hackett tells how he "lay in bed with a fury." "Through the long night, the anger ran and flowed through my mind, swelled every second by the memory of some uprooted insult or long buried resentment. Worst of all, whatever substance within me that retained hope for myself was being wasted away by the fury of the self-hate." One wonders why *self*-hate?

Even when Hackett was approaching the time when he would be dismissed from the hospital, he kept "varying between moods of anger, depression, and well-wishing." When a social worker came to help him with his problems of leaving the hospital, for no reason he insulted her. Finally, after about a year, he was dismissed, much improved.

In her book, his wife tells how, after his discharge, it was almost impossible for him to get a job. Finally, after much tramping of the streets, he got a job as a grave digger!

Good-By, My Son

Good-by, My Son (1960), by Arthur Woolson, is a splendid book to show the difficulties a parent can run into when his much-loved son, a previously very attractive young man, becomes convinced that gangsters are closing in to kill him. The great lesson of the book is that much very expensive psychotherapy did not help greatly, if it helped at all. The young man only decided that his father and some of the psychiatrists had joined up with the murderous gangsters.

Eventually, the son went to sea and dropped out of sight, which perhaps showed that, with all his delusions, he had more sense than anyone else concerned! The net result was that the father, an able advertising man, went so deeply into debt he had to try to sell his house and his car.

Summary. Obviously, some paranoiacs are very dangerous persons, and many a psychiatrist has had very unpleasant experiences with these people. A number of my friends in the medical profession have been killed by them. Usually, there is little anyone can do in the way of talking the paranoiac out of his delusion. One must not question what the patient says—only his *interpretation* of what he observed. If a physician argues with him, all the man does is to decide that the doctor has joined his persecutors.

Anyone who would like to study the mental processes of an able man (a physician and a member of the British House of Commons) who for years has kept trying to convince his friends that international gangsters are poisoning him, should read the book by Dr. Donald McI. Johnson (see Chapter 14).

As I have said, some paranoiacs and most paranoids can "pass," out in the world, and can keep out of trouble. A few, like Paul Hackett, have enough complicating problems of minor psychosis that they lose all of their friends, one after the other, or they lose their job, or they have to be committed for a while, or they start suing people right and left, or for one reason or another they are sent to jail.

Many who read this may now suddenly remember some old friend who, years ago, was so touchy or suspicious that one day he took grave offense, when no offense was meant or thought of. Old people, after they have had perhaps a few "little strokes" will sometimes become so paranoid they will not trust a formerly much-loved son or daughter.

Because paranoia is often a manifestation of schizophrenia, sometimes the treatment has to consist mainly of insulin shocks.

CHAPTER 10

Mental Distresses of Epileptics

Few people, and as yet few even of us physicians, realize how often an epileptic is troubled far more by an irascible temperament and a mind full of antagonisms and hates than by his rare seizures. Many an epileptic has no seizures at all, all he has is a great difficulty in adjusting to life, in living peaceably with his friends, and in holding a job. Often he has terrible nightmares, distressing fears, and queer "tizzies" in which he feels as if something awful were about to happen to him.

It is now being discovered that many delinquent youngsters have typically epileptic electroencephalograms (the records of the tiny electric currents constantly being formed in the brain), and it is almost certain that some day, when these currents are more often recorded in police departments, it will be found that some two thirds of the men and women who have committed crimes of violence have an epileptic type of stormy record with what are called "seizure discharges." Then we will understand why the person had such a violent and uncontrollable temper. Usually in such cases when I ask the family, I find that some of the forebears also had a violent and dangerous temper, and perhaps some had had in their youth an occasional blackout.

The Mental Life of an Epileptic

A Ray of Darkness, written by Mrs. Margiad Evans (1943), is one of the most valuable books a physician can have, because it throws so much light on the often stormy temperament of the person born with a tendency to epilepsy. This knowledge is so needed today when the man in the street, the epileptic, and even most of us physicians think of epilepsy as just seizures. It is immensely more than that; in fact, most of the epileptics I see in my office either have never had a seizure, or they have had only a few in their lifetime, or they have had only a few "fever convulsions" in infancy. In many cases, they complain only of nervousness, and occasional "tizzies." Many consult a physician because of difficulties in adjusting to life—difficulties such as those encountered by Van Gogh in *Dear Theo,* or by Dostoevsky, or Hackett (see Chapter 9).

Mrs. Evans's unusual temperament. Mrs. Evans tells us that she had her first blackout and convulsion at the age of forty-two, but from childhood on, she had had an uncomfortable temperament. From what she says, it seems obvious that she was born with an abnormal nervous system. She was an unhappy child, who developed so slowly that she did not read until she was nine. At the age of three, she was already having the terrible nightmares which make nights hideous for so many epileptics.

By the time she was eleven she knew that something was very wrong with her mental processes. There was "a part of her psychic life which was not hers!" Sometimes she "heard voices." From childhood on she felt that she was being deprived of something she much wanted but could not put into words. She felt that people did not return the love she gave them.

A violent temper. As a child, Mrs. Evans had the violent rages and feelings of hatred that so many epileptics describe. Many tell of unreasoning and distressing impulses to attack people. A few tell of times when they *did* attack someone but later had no memory of the episode. Many of the men say that they know they must never get into an acrimonious debate in a bar, because it could so easily lead them into a murderous attack on their opponent. Most epileptic fathers say they have learned they must never spank a child, because they might not know when to stop. As Mrs. Evans said in another book—her *Autobiography*—"I felt a fury against I don't know what, and sometimes any little thing could send me into a rage."

The fears of the epileptic. Many an epileptic suffers from terrible fears and feelings of horror; and already, as a child, Mrs. Evans was feeling "stampedes of panic." Later, after her first big convulsion, these feelings of fear became so distressing as to be almost unbearable.

The solitariness of the epileptic. Early in life Mrs. Evans felt the epileptic's frequent desire to be left alone. She speaks of "the joys of loneliness," and she says so eloquently, "A person may be so used to living alone that another creature on a hilltop a mile away jostles him!" Often she hated to have anyone talking to her. Many an epileptic cannot marry, if only because he could not bear to live with anyone in the same apartment with him.

Interruptions in consciousness. Mrs. Evans tells about those curious gaps in consciousness that some epileptics have. For instance, once when she was a child, her breathing stopped for a minute and then started up again. She said, "I cannot recall [a time] when I was without moments of separation from my consciousness—moments when I was conscious and unconscious at the same time." "This is epilepsy itself, though in its minor form." "It caused no pain; it lasted a few seconds; I saw and heard and moved while it happened. I have often crossed a room, and while not losing sight or bearings, have not known *how* I crossed it. The sequence of consciousness was but little broken by it."

Seriously, she speaks of going on at times "guided by *the consciousness left over,* rather than the consciousness of the moment." These strange spells became more frequent, and as she grew older, they lasted longer. For a second, she sensed "oblivion of mind, and cessation of sight." These brief interruptions of consciousness will be described by many an epileptic if his physician has the knowledge and curiosity to ask about them.

As an epileptic physician once said to me, "A normal person is conscious during every moment of his waking hours, but I am not; every so often I am 'out' for a few seconds." An epileptic woman explained it to me this way: she said, "When in the beauty parlor I am sitting with my head under a drier, every so often it seems as if the blower had been turned off for a few seconds; my consciousness is discontinuous."

In the cases of children, many such spells, of course, are equivalents of *petit mal,* the minor form of epilepsy. In this form the child is silent for a few seconds and his eyes may turn upward.

The presentiment of great danger ahead. Interesting is Mrs. Evans's statement that for some three years before her first big convulsion, a part of her had sensed that something wrong, dangerous, and *different* was about to happen to her. "Gradually a most disagreeable and threatening sort of restlessness spoiled all my happiness, and took away my peace. It is hard to describe, but it was as though I couldn't stop *hurrying.*" "As soon as I began a thing I longed for it to be over." Then, "concentration began to slip: and in my writing I, who had always written so thoughtfully and so slowly that words and phrases were like a birth, began to race over the pages without stopping." Evidently, she had become somewhat manic because she describes the typical ability to write easily. Also, for the first time in her life, lyric poems of some beauty began to come from her pen. Before that she says she had never written any outstanding poetry. Curiously, then, "The thought of death, to my hurried, anxious mind, was lovely and soothing." At that time she had severe headaches and much giddiness. "My head felt awry; it was is if my brain was askew or weighted at one side."

She had a feeling, also, that any day she might split into "two figures of me." "It took me a whole year of suffering and possibly a dozen major fits, to disentangle myself from the terror of mental disorder." "Has not every one of us a mental image of himself which he watches ceaselessly, which he must watch, and which must not, for his health's and sanity's sake, deviate from the self seen by everybody else?" "*Epileptics must cling to themselves—for they are likely any moment to become something else!*"

In the winter of 1949-1950, Mrs. Evans probably had a seizure during her sleep, as many other epileptics have done.

"I could not have gone quite out, or there would have been no mind to record the memory." "I seemed to remember a time in the night when my muscles had gone rigid, my teeth locked, and I was shaken by a kind of ghastly iron palsy. My arms seemed to lift, my head to jerk and my face to be covered with a grimace."

Her first big blackout. On the night of May 11, 1950, as she was sitting at home, alone, writing, she looked at the clock and noted that it was ten minutes past eleven. "The next thing [I knew] I was still looking up at the clock, and the hands stood at five and twenty minutes past midnight. I had fallen through Time, Continuity, and Being. My first thought was, not that the clock had gone wrong, but that I had been asleep. Then I discovered I was lying on the floor on my back, my head against the rungs of a rocking-chair." She was lucky that she hadn't fallen into the fireplace. After this spell, she says, "The brain held and let go, held and let go." She wasn't sure who she was, or where her bed was. Then, terrified, she found that her clothes were wet with her urine.

For several days following this seizure she had a curious sensation that "if I turned my head quickly, something— some unusual—some significant shape seemed just to avoid me, just to run out of the corner of my eye." Once she saw a bluish halo around a dog. She wrote, "The terror has deeply affected me emotionally and mentally. I know I am changed. I am more dependent on others." Her feeling of security was gone. At times her breathing would stop, and a "minute" later it would come on again. She never knew what moment she might fall.

The consultant she saw assured her that since epilepsy "is not hereditary," the child she had borne shortly before the fit would be safe. In her book, she does not speak of her heredity, but, as I said above, the fact that her mental processes were always odd shows that she was almost certainly born to be an epileptic.

The horror of epilepsy. Mrs. Evans went on to tell of the horrors that many epileptics feel. She said that if her attacks had been frequent, she could easily have gone insane, "for within each seizure is embedded an embryonic second of such terror that body and mind recoil from any association with it."

One night when alone in her house with her baby upstairs asleep, "Suddenly there was present in me the ghastly thought that, outside my consciousness, I had mounted the stairs, gone into my baby's nursery, and killed her; and that I had only to go up to find her dead." Several women epileptics have told me of this great fear they had, that they might kill a child.

The great value of Mrs. Evans's book. What I hope is that Mrs. Evans's book will some day convince people that there is immensely more to epilepsy than an occasional blackout or seizure. Few even of us doctors know that an epileptic can easily have spells of mania, or depression, or paranoia. Sometimes he takes to drink with the hope of getting some relief from his mental distress. But it is dangerous for him to drink, because sometimes, after even a few beers, he will go berserk.

In their great work *Epilepsy and Related Disorders,* William G. Lennox and his daughter Margaret A. Lennox say (page 711) that Margiad Evans had a gliomatous brain tumor which in fourteen years caused her death. I still am convinced from Mrs. Evans's story that she started out in life with an epileptic type of personality. I have seen many cases in which people in an epileptic family eventually were found to have a brain tumor. I have family records which suggest that an inherited defect which in some members of a family produced a small epileptogenic area in others produced a tumor.

Dostoevsky and His Nervous Troubles

Marc Slonim, in his *The Three Loves of Dostoevsky* (1955), quotes much material from the great writer's books which is autobiographic and tells us a great deal about the psychology of a person who, all his life, suffered from epilepsy. I have found this material very helpful and instructive, showing, as it does, the essential violence of temperament of some epileptics. His father was even worse off than Fyodor. He was a terrible man, violent and cruel—so cruel to his serfs that eventually they turned on him and beat him to death. One of this man's sons—Nicholas (Fyodor's brother)—was a drunkard. Alcoholism was probably his share of his father's curse.

For much of his life, Fyodor was morose, sad, highly irritable, hypersensitive, full of oddities and superstitions: irascible, haughty, and "close to a mad-man." He was a strange person who was hard to live with. On many days, he was unsociable, and then no one could get a kind word out of him. Often he was nasty, and insulting even to guests in his house. He did not know how to behave in company, and in his youth he was much embarrassed in the society of well-bred women.

His first epileptic seizures. In his youth he had many spells of "poor health," but just what the symptoms were, we do not know. He had "nervous spasms" which may well have been mild manifestations of his epilepsy. It seems clear that early in life he began to have seizures. Occasionally, he could be gay, witty, animated, sociable, and amusing, and at such times he might behave like a manic person. At other times he went down into the depths of melancholia. Also, like many epileptics, he had spells of "mystic horror"—a horror so awful that he could not describe it. Fortunately, he did not take to drink. He suffered from a great fear of being buried alive. At times he was highly excitable sexually. Following a spasm of fright, he might go into a spell of hypochondriasis and lethargy, accompanied by weakness and impotence. Then, in order to forget himself, he loved to go to the gambling table.

He said that when he was twenty-four, his "life was grim, disorderly, and lonely to the verge of savagery." He admitted that occasionally, he would plunge into "a dark subterranean pool of vile depravity." He would become hysterical and fearful, and perhaps end up in a convulsion. After such a spell he would have days of melancholy and lethargy when he could do nothing. Often he had some of the terrible nightmares of epileptics. Writing in 1854, he spoke of his "inexpressible and interminable suffering." He spoke also of spells he had which "*resembled* epilepsy."

He made a poor husband. Naturally, he and his first wife

—who also was "difficult"—had a hard time trying to get along together. He broke up with her and then also with a second wife. Although often full of violent lusts for women, like many a psychotic person, he apparently was unable ever to show anyone real love or affection or tenderness. "Before a seizure, his melancholy and irritation would increase, and he would become so morose and quarrelsome that he would scream at people. He frequently heard voices, and then visions would sweep past him, or he would experience a poignant, unbearable blissfulness."

At last he got a very forgiving wife. After his first two tragic marriages, he found happiness with Anna, a remarkable person. It is hard to understand how she could have loved him with such forbearance. But, even with her, he was always paranoid and suspicious, and often ill-natured and hot-tempered. He took great offense over trifles. If Anna hadn't been a saint, she could never have put up with him and his raging fits of jealousy. He was always making scenes and shouting at the top of his voice at someone. He had a petty self-pride, together with an inferiority complex, based on the fact that he was so often boorish, and even with company, grouchy as a bear. Like a few epileptics I have known, when he got excited, he would get chills and fever.

In him, the passion for gambling rivaled his passion for sexual intercourse. Often, even when far away from home, he would gamble away every cent he had. Like most epileptics, he knew enough never to lay a finger on his children. If he had ever started spanking one, he might have beaten him to death. When paranoid, he would be filled with ideas of persecution.

Again, we learn from Dostoevsky—as from Mrs. Evans and Van Gogh—that there is immensely more to epilepsy than seizures.

Dear Theo

This collection of letters from the painter Vincent Van Gogh to his brother Theo is one of the great autobiographies of the world (1937). It is the often-beautiful story of a very sensitive and mentally harassed man who craved the love and understanding of only one person in the world—his brother. Vincent had one governing passion—a great desire to paint, and to paint so beautifully that the souls of people would be touched. Each day for years he strained every nerve in his weak, tired, and undernourished body to become a great painter. He *did* become a great painter, but hardly anyone recognized this fact during his lifetime. Hardly a one of his paintings was salable until long after his death. He was so honest that no matter if he was starving, he would not paint a picture in a style chosen just to make it sell.

Difficulties in getting along with people. Vincent admitted that he was a difficult man to get along with. As a child he was a problem—unruly, difficult, stubborn, bad-tempered, and rough—like many of the children who are carriers of epilepsy. He grew up to be suspicious, proud, impatient, abrupt, and with a hot temper that in a moment could flare into an uncontrollable fury. Naturally, he had few friends; and when he *did* make one, something soon caused the man to refuse ever to speak to him again. We can easily imagine what had happened. As the Hansons, his biographers, say in *Passionate Pilgrim* (1955), a chance word of slight criticism, and he would react fiercely, as if he were insane— shouting insults in his sudden, overpowering rage. He was so unreasonable that even when someone *praised* a drawing, he tore it up! He couldn't get along with even his relatives, and hence he never tried to live with his parents or even with the brother whom he loved as well as he ever could love anyone. Even with Theo, he was often unpleasant and critical. Often he accused Theo of not trying to sell his paintings.

As we have learned from Mrs. Evans, an inability to get along with people is often the main problem of an epileptic (eventually, as we shall see, Vincent had some seizures). He said once, "I am a man of passions, capable of, and subject to, doing more or less foolish things, of which I happen to repent, more or less, afterwards. Now and then I speak and act too quickly, when it would have been better if I had waited patiently."

Once he wrote Theo that he wished that people would

only take him as he was. One of his former friends accused
him of having a vicious character and desired to have no
more to do with him. Vincent said, "I think it no fault of
mine that many people take me to be a disagreeable character. I am often terribly melancholy, irritable, hungry for
sympathy; and when I do not get it I try to act indifferently
and speak harshly; often I even throw oil on the flames."
"I am too terribly sensitive, physically as well as morally."
"It is often painful and difficult for me to mingle with people,
or to speak with them." This is typical of both epileptics and
schizophrenics; and some psychiatrists might prefer to call
Vincent a schizophrenic. The important point, as I said
earlier in this book, is that many a person who looks and
often acts and thinks like a schizophrenic can at times be
typically depressed, and at times can have seizures like an
epileptic. Probably by far the most logical and practical
way of classifying a mentally disturbed person would be to
say that he was so many per cent schizophrenic and so many
per cent manic-depressive, paranoid, epileptoid, hysterical,
overly religious, or confused.

He was slow to find his lifework. When Vincent was
thirty, he still hadn't gotten anywhere. Perhaps because his
father was a minister, for years he had much wanted to be
a religious worker. He said, "Theo, if only I might succeed
in this. If only that heavy depression that comes because
everything I undertake fails . . . if only this might be taken
from me."

Once he wrote, "My only anxiety is: How can I be of
use in the world?" He hated to take just *any* job, just in
order to get enough money with which to live and eat.

Eventually, he wrote Theo that he was frantic to paint
pictures. At last, he had found what he wanted to do. But
he had absolutely no money. As he said so truly, "Poverty
prevents growth." Several of his near relatives were rich,
but none cared to help him. He was a dirty ragamuffin of
whom they were ashamed.

Spells of depression. In a number of his letters he spoke
of his painful despondency and his efforts to fight it. At
times he became feverish from worry and nervousness and
depression. He said that on such days he felt as if he were

lying bound head and foot and helpless at the bottom of a deep dark well—certainly a vivid description!

His brother supported him. All through the years from 1873 to 1890, Theo supported Vincent, sending him from 100 to 250 francs a month. Vincent was so frantic to keep painting that often he'd live on only a crust of bread a day so that he could buy more paints and canvases and pay a model to pose. He spoke of always trying to portray truly what he saw. As he said, if he did that, then he would some day "arrive." "I feel, Theo, that there is a power within me, and I do what I can to bring it out and free it."

Sometimes he felt he was as rich as Croesus, "because, I have found in my work something to which I can devote myself with heart and soul, and which gives inspiration and zest to life." From time to time he took courage because he saw that each year his technic improved.

Often, his reaching out to his brother for love was beautiful. As he said, "Yes, Theo, you need not spare me if it is only a question of money; if as a friend and brother you keep a little sympathy for the work, salable or unsalable; if only I may keep your sympathy in this respect, I care very little for the rest." In dozens of letters Vincent spoke of his distress to think he had to be constantly asking for money. A hundred times he would write something like this: "My money ran out on Thursday, and I have lived for four days on nothing but twenty-three cups of coffee, with bread for which I still owe." He knew he was a terrible burden on Theo.

In one letter, he remarked to Theo that even between *them* there was a strong "barricade." He mused over the fact "that for ten years we have been so little together." As one reads Vincent's letters, one wonders why he chose to live in cities far from his beloved brother. Perhaps he sensed that if he tried to live near Theo he would soon be fighting with him.

The coming of mania and epilepsy. Around the end of 1889, when Vincent was thirty-six, he began to tell Theo of spells in which his head felt tired, or in which he would become hopelessly absent-minded and incapable of doing much. He felt that he was getting old. Also, he feared that his work might drive him to madness. One day Theo received a telegram saying that in a spell of maniacal excitement and high fever Vincent had cut off a piece of his left ear and had taken it as a gift to a woman in a brothel. He had then been taken to a hospital, bleeding, anemic, and unconscious. Apparently, it was an acute and violent attack, such as some epileptics have, because next day his brain was clear. But he still felt weak, uneasy, and frightened. As he wrote, "For a moment I am not yet mad." Occasionally, he drank too much, but alcoholism was not his problem.

Later, he wrote to his brother that "the unbearable hallucinations have ceased." But he said that, so far as he was concerned, the doctors might as well shut him up in a madhouse. With all his illness, and even when he was in the mental hospital, he kept on painting. As he said, "If we painters are a bit mad, what of it?"

In February, 1890, Vincent became paranoid and imagined that people wanted to poison him. He wrote, "As far as I can judge, I am not, properly speaking, a madman." "You will see by the pictures I send that I am still working well." Later, he said, "There have been moods of indescribable mental anguish." "What comforts me a little is that I am beginning to consider madness as a disease like any other, and will accept the thing as such." "During the crises I thought that everything I imagined was real." On some days he couldn't write because he wasn't clear enough in his head. "The anguish and suffering are no joke." He kept hoping that he would get over his epileptic spells. One day he wrote, "At present this *horror of life* is less strong, and the melancholy less acute."

But Vincent went on having spell after spell. He dreaded the possibility that, with some attack, he would lose his power to paint. At times, like many epileptics, he had horrible nightmares. Also, his old fits of severe depression came back. But with it all, he kept painting. At times, he was mentally deranged, and at other times, the doctor thought his mind was perfectly clear.

Then the good news came that one of his pictures had sold for 400 francs, and this cheered him. Later, however, he wrote, "I feel done for." "My own work, I am risking my life for it, and my reason has half-foundered." Shortly afterwards, in 1890, he gave up the long fight; he shot himself in the stomach, and a few days later he died. Theo was badly upset, and six months later he had a stroke and died.

Johanna Van Gogh saves Vincent's paintings and his letters. Despite the fact that Theo's wife, Johanna Van Gogh, was busy working to support herself and her infant son, she spent years fighting to gain recognition for Vincent's genius, and she kept arranging, translating, and editing his letters so that they could be published. She had to leave out much that was abusive and offensive. She had such faith in the paintings that she would not sell one until they were recognized the world over as masterpieces.

Summary. As I said before, if we will listen with an open mind to what epileptics—and especially those many epileptics without seizures—have to tell us about their many sufferings and difficulties in adjustment to living, we will see how much more there is to epilepsy than seizures.

Also, it is becoming more evident each year that perhaps more than half of the many children and teen-agers who are difficult at home and at school, or who have reading problems, or who have become delinquent have abnormal electroencephalograms, many of which resemble those of epileptics.

Many epileptics or parents of epileptics become much distressed when they hear of these findings: they gain the impression that they are being attacked and slandered. I can sympathize deeply with them in their sorrow, but I feel it essential that all people hear of these great advances in our knowledge of epilepsy. Why? Because, in so many cases, a boy who for years was looked on as just stupid or bad or criminal now turns out to be a sick boy—an epileptic without seizures—a boy who needs treatment and not punishment. Often when these facts emerge, the parents are tremendously relieved, and they are even more relieved when, with a daily dose of dexedrine or perhaps dilantin, the boy immediately begins to do much better at school and at home.

CHAPTER 11

The Mental Troubles of Some Alcoholics

In my library I have two shelves full of books by people who drank until they went to pieces nervously. Several had to have themselves committed for many months in order to get sobered up. Because I plan to publish abstracts of many of these autobiographies in another book, I am including here only a few of the stories these men and women have told.

These volumes have great value because they tell us so much about the mental processes which often cause an able man to ruin his life by drinking. I have found in my practice evidence that in many families alcoholism is inherited, apparently as an equivalent of psychosis. Oftentimes I meet with what I call a *primarily* alcoholic family in which there are a number of psychotic nondrinkers.

Many people will probably object to my speaking of the *inheritance* of alcoholism; they may say that in alcoholic families some of the members must have acquired their habit by imitation. I can sometimes disprove this by showing that perhaps two hard-drinking uncles or an alcoholic grandfather lived so far away from the alcoholic nephews or grandsons that there was no possibility of transmitting the curse by bad example. Often, also, I can show that the person who seemed to have transmitted the nervous curse which led to alcoholism was never an alcoholic; he was depressed or epileptic or highly eccentric. In my book *Prac-*

tical Leads to Puzzling Diagnoses (1958), I describe many such families in which in one generation there were alcoholics and in the next, psychotic persons.

Some of my patients who seemed to have inherited a thirst for hard drink told me that at times a tension would build up and up in their brain until they just *had* to start drinking. As we shall see, a good definition of an alcoholic is a person who cannot trust himself to take one drink without going on and getting drunk, even when he very much wants to stay sober and *should* stay sober for all-important business reasons. Another definition is a man who has so lost control over his drinking that he often goes ahead and gets drunk when he doesn't want to.

William Seabrook expressed this very well when he wrote of the years in which, on a week end, with a bunch of cronies, he would deliberately get tight; and then, for a month or two, he would just as deliberately stay sober, perhaps so as to finish a book. But then came a time when he found he no longer had any control, and he would get drunk when he didn't want to, and perhaps when he much needed to finish some writing to make a deadline. Jack London tells us in his autobiography, *John Barleycorn,* how he knew he was entering a new and very dangerous stage in his drinking when one day he wanted, not to take a drink, but to get drunk.

As I have read the several books written by alcoholics who spent months or years on Skid Row, I have been impressed by the fact that eventually came a day when they decided to go back to a decent life—and did. The question is, how did they happen to do this? My impression is that, during the man's worst spells of drinking, he was not sane. Perhaps he was depressed. And when the depression passed, he was able to go back to his normal life. Some of the alcoholics do speak of their having been not sane.

I think it highly significant that in alcoholic families, I have usually found a number of psychotic or eccentric or escapist members. To show what I mean, there comes to my mind the case of a fine, able business woman of forty who told me that, in her spells of depression—each lasting perhaps two weeks—she would crave alcohol and would wish that she could drink herself into unconsciousness. But her refinement kept her from doing this. One day, her brilliant uncle, who had drunk himself out of a fine career as a banker, confessed that he had the same brief spells of depression his niece had; the only difference was that he would give in and go on a bender. My father knew a nice young woman who had an alcoholic father. Every so often, when a great thirst would come upon her, she would lock herself up in a hotel room and drink her fill of cheap whiskey.

A Man Who Once Lived on Skid Row Is Now Curing Hundreds of Alcoholics

Perhaps the most hopeful of all the books written by ex-alcoholics is called *No Hiding Place* (1957). It was written by Beth Day in collaboration with Vincent Tracy. Tracy was born into a good family and received a college education. But from the first, there was something odd about his nervous system. In 1925, when he was fourteen, he took his first drink, and liked it so well that he kept on—taking alcohol to make him feel gay, to drown out a nagging conscience, to ease his restlessness and his boredom, and to enable him to escape from anything that was unpleasant.

Like so many persons with a tendency to alcoholism, Tracy felt a kinship more with the outcasts of society than with the educated people among whom he had been brought up. He was at ease with the misfits and often uncomfortable with his mother and her friends.

Because he was a handsome lad, with considerable charm, women soon began to seduce him, and before long he was living a dissolute life. Shortly after leaving college, a drinking bout left him in his first "blackout"—a blackout in which he couldn't remember even who he was. Soon after this, he had his first nervous breakdown. Then, for a time, he quit drinking and worked up to a splendid position as assistant to one of the top executives in a large department store. But after a while, again he got to drinking so heavily that, occasionally, he couldn't show up for work.

Then, except for one slip, Vincent remained on the wagon

for over three years. But he was unhappy; he had the feeling that "life was passing him by." He became increasingly tense, nervous, discouraged, and doubtful about his future. He went back to drinking because he was "unable to face up to the responsibilities of life." For the next year or so, he managed to keep his drinking under some control, but then it got entirely out of hand.

Then he met an able woman who worked alongside him in the store. He fell in love with her, but even his love couldn't keep him from drinking. Hating loneliness, he often would walk the streets all night rather than go to his apartment. His biggest problem was finding something to do at night after all the clubs and bars had closed. He seldom wanted to sleep, and when he went to bed he could not relax. His legs cramped, and he sweated heavily. When he did drop off into fitful sleep, he would awake shivering in a pool of sweat. He would get out of bed, pull off the sodden sheets, wrap himself in a blanket, and try to sleep again.

For months, Vincent fought off his desire to drink in the mornings, but finally he gave in. Then he went on a trip and was drunk the whole time. He ran through $1,500 in three days. Later, he tried desperately to cut down on the amount of his drinking, but he failed. He had lost control.

One morning, like so many drunks who black out, he was startled to wake and find himself in a strange bed, in a strange room. A strange middle-aged blonde was lying naked in the bed with him. He couldn't remember ever having seen her before. Without waking her, he slipped out of the bed, dressed, and sneaked out of the apartment. Naturally, he couldn't remember if he had been intimate with the woman.

Every so often he'd go to church and sign the pledge, but that didn't do any good. He went to two psychiatrists, one after the other, but they didn't help. Then, one night Vincent suddenly woke to the fact that he was drinking in the club car of the Twentieth Century Limited. He had no memory of how he had gotten on the train, and he had no reason to be on it! Later, he took some Keeley cures. He also tried AA, but even those devoted people could not help him.

On some twenty-seven occasions he had to go into a hospital—"to get dried out." He'd go in when for ten days or more he hadn't slept or eaten and was close to DT's.

Vincent hits bottom. Finally, his mother, his kindly brother, and many of his best friends all washed their hands of him; and then he knew that alcohol really had him down. No longer did it do any good to get sobered up. Each time he would go right back to drinking again.

Eventually, Vincent's money was gone, and so he had to live largely in Grand Central Station. From there he went to the Bowery, where he remained for eighteen months. One night he went out on the Brooklyn Bridge to commit suicide, but he couldn't make up his mind to go over the edge.

At last, he was just a bum without any decent clothes. He had pawned everything he had, including his coat. Like most Skid Row men, he'd get a little work each day as a porter or a dishwasher, or he would go panhandling.

A second time Vincent decided to kill himself. Out he went on the bridge, but again, he didn't jump. He went into a bar for a drink, but then, "Suddenly, for the first time in over a year, he wondered, 'What am I doing here?'. . ." He left his drink on the bar and walked out. He went to a church and prayed as he hadn't been able to pray for years. As he repeated the Lord's Prayer, it suddenly occurred to him, had he ever forgiven anyone their trespasses against him? Had he ever thought of anyone besides himself? Perhaps that was what was wrong with him.

Why had he been drinking? During all of his years of drinking, his constant question had been, "Why do I drink?" And no one had given him a satisfactory answer. Now, he began to get some answers. And suddenly he decided that "despite the wreckage of the past ten years, since he had his intellect intact, he could still reverse the course of his life." At last he saw "that he was sicker *morally* than he had ever been *physically.*" He decided to go for help to a hospital run by an ex-alcoholic named Edward J. McGoldrick, Jr., who had become very successful in treating alcoholics. This man helped him greatly.

The night Vincent left the Bowery, he had realized that

he was his problem. He realized that his "will was weak from lack of use. He had always chosen only what he wanted to do." Vincent, then, wondered how a man could strengthen his will, and he decided that, every day, he would have to do at least three things that were inconvenient or distasteful. Perhaps, with such exercise, he would acquire the strength of will with which to stop drinking.

In the hospital, he started right off helping to nurse other patients and to visit with them, when he would rather have been doing something for himself. That was a beginning at least. Later, he started going to visit patients in the psychopathic wards of King's County Hospital. He hated this, but he forced himself to do it.

He realized "he had always seen life through the distortion of self-pity and resentments, and he had used alcohol to get away from what he saw. Now he must learn to look at life honestly as it was. Also, he had to face the man he was, and tear out the old, destructive patterns of thought that had kept him from objectivity.

Once, when he was working at the department store, a friend had said to him, "Why don't you try coming down off that pedestal you've got yourself on, Vincent, and take a look at the guy who came down?" And Vincent had been furious at this. Now he saw that the man had asked something important.

At last, Vincent realized that he was fighting for his life. He saw how nasty he had been with his mother and his brother when he was constantly trying to get large sums of money out of them. He saw how he had abused the love of the woman who had worked beside him in the department store, and how he had almost broken her heart. He saw these misdeeds which were bad enough to make him writhe and squirm with shame. In his drinking days, he had always thought of himself as just overly sensitive, kind, and generous, but now he saw he was a "moral bankrupt—a bum, an emotional slob with a stinking ego."

A false pride. Vincent thought that the clue to his failure as a man had been his false pride. He had thought that he was too good to stand up to the pressures and problems that face all men. He had taken the good that the world had

offered him, but not the bad. He had tolerated in himself
"selfishness, impatience, dishonesty, and a lack of charity
toward others." If he was ever going to stop drinking for
good and all, "he must first get rid of the mental vices that
supported it, and supplant them with their opposites, the
virtues that would give him the strength he would need.
He would need humility, patience, tolerance and charity."

How to conquer drinking. Vincent decided that the only
way to conquer would be "to want something more than
he wanted alcohol. And the only thing he could want that
would be powerful enough to win him away from drink
would be a desire to qualify as a morally responsible human
being." The program would require guts, and where does
a man go for guts? "To his God." Soon Vincent saw that
"his eventual life's work would be helping other alcoholics."
"He'd always known his chief interest was people." One of
his problems had been that business and the making of
money had not interested him enough.

But first, before he could start trying to cure others, he
would have to prove that he was cured himself, So he went
to work in a humble job and gradually worked up until,
again, he had a decent suit of clothes and a clean shirt. Soon
he began to pick drunks up out of the gutter and to help
them. He knew how, because he had so recently been a
bum. When the drunks knew this, they listened to what he
had to say.

In December, 1948, he married the woman who had once
worked beside him, and before long, the two had a place in
New York City where they were treating alcoholics. There,
Vincent decided that "The root of it all lies in the human
will." "So long as a man has a shred of intellect left, he can
make a choice if he so wills." He placed the responsibility
on the moral deficiency of the drinker.

Vincent soon decided he must have a place in the country—a lovely place, because "a drinker freezes up and rejects
therapy in an institutional atmosphere." "A man must re-
move himself from his life to take a long view."

When Vincent left New York City in 1951, he had treated
over two hundred alcoholics, forty per cent of them women.

Out of this group, less than ten per cent had failed to learn to live without alcohol.

Vincent gets a big place to house his patients. Vincent moved to an estate near the village of Coeyman's Hollow, near Albany. At "Tracy Farms" there are no barred windows, the patients are all on their honor. Vincent's guests are his helpers. "If they did not help each other, I could not manage to get along."

As Tracy said, "We don't just get people to quit drinking. It is an entire way of life that we are teaching. What we try to find is the cause for the drinking. When it is realized that drinking comes from the failure to face up to our responsibilities as moral human beings . . . then it is easier not to drink than to drink. *The same will that wills you to drink can will you not to drink.*"

Vincent spends much time with his patients in "bull sessions." The only trouble is that often the guests "want to talk from one to four in the morning!" Vincent uses in his talks much good Irish humor and a lot of bantering. The people finally laugh at themselves and at each other. They talk over their past experiences.

Vincent is often impressed by the harm that wealthy people do when they too greatly shelter their children. The lives of these children then become so empty that they turn to alcohol. The socialites are Vincent's most difficult problems. Their lives have been based so largely on personal gratification that they can neither give nor receive love. Also, they are too full of snobberies.

Tracy's own experience with alcoholism and his God-given talent for handling people of all levels has enabled him to cut quickly through the fraudulences and excuses of both the highborn and the lowborn drinkers. He will not stand any "guff" or dishonesty from any of his guests. He can bawl a man out and show him just what sort of a skunk he is trying to be. "It is a revelation to many a socialite to learn that the poor man has exactly the same drinking problems as he has. When the poor drunk and the rich drunk discover this, tolerance develops on both sides."

Sometimes Vincent gets as a patient a man who confesses that he married a wealthy woman for her money; he says he sold his soul for a dollar bill, and ever since he has been paying a thousand cents on the dollar.

Vincent found that many of the women in society get to drinking heavily because they never had a job, a career, or a duty to fulfill. They had nothing to live for. As Tracy often points out to the socialites, to be honest with oneself requires humility, and humility and snobbery just cannot go together.

The people Vincent likes best to treat are what he calls "real pros," men like himself who got down to the point where they saw that unless they quit drinking they had only two choices left—death or commitment to a mental hospital. "You can talk straight to guys like that."

Secrets of his success. To date, Vincent has treated over a thousand people, most of them formerly considered hopeless. They have come to him from all over the world. These people say that the most important element of Tracy's success with them are the talks he gives each day. He does not plan these addresses; he just gets up and says what is in his heart.

Tracy says to alcoholics, just as the AA people do: "First you have got to convince yourself that you need help; that you want to quit drinking permanently, and that you are ready to help yourself." "You have to be intellectually honest. Remember that any fool can sober up." The problem is to stay sober for life.

It is always easiest for a heavy drinker to blame his trouble on his glands or on the way his parents treated him when he was a child. What he has got to realize is that he has a *moral* deficiency. He must see that "he has willed his own disaster."

Vincent agrees that when an alcoholic takes one drink, he *has to* take a second and then a third. No alcoholic can drink in moderation. But no one compelled him to take that first whiskey. "That was intentional on his part. That was willed. And this is the point to remember: *what you will to do, you can will not to do!*" Nothing can stop you from drinking except you. Convince yourself that alcohol does not give courage and it does not help to settle problems.

Many drinkers are "A walking volcano of resentments—

against the world," their job, their family, everything that they cannot face. "You habitually lay the blame for your actions on everyone except yourself."

A good definition of an alcoholic. As Tracy says, a man is sadly in need of help if he has to take a drink in the morning; if he loses time from work; if he gets the shakes; if his personality changes from drinking; if his health fails; if he gets restless and has trouble sleeping; if his initiative, ambition, or efficiency has decreased; if he has less perseverance, less self-control; if he drinks to get up courage or to relieve feelings of inadequacy; if he gets to lying about his drinking; if he gets careless about his personal appearance or his language; or if his drinking causes him to seek out an inferior environment.

Two convincing lessons. How vivid is that statement of Vincent's that "If a guy came to your door, and you knew that every time he came he would rape your wife and beat your kids, you wouldn't let him in, would you?" Sometimes Vincent would put two glasses before him, one filled with sulphuric acid and the other with whiskey, and he would wonder why a man has no trouble leaving alone the acid, while he cannot resist drinking the whiskey, yet they can both be highly destructive of his health and happiness.

Tracy suggests to his guests that, as he does each day, so they too should do three things that they would prefer not to do—things that are inconvenient or difficult or distasteful. He says to his guests, "If you are satisfied with your way of life, you don't belong here. If you don't have the guts to do something for yourself, then pack up and leave. I need your bed for someone I can help." "All you need to beat the booze is honesty and guts, and you get them from the grace of God, not from me."

Problems that arise after the "cure." As Tracy says, the worst problems come when people who have been straightened out at "The Farms" go back home. Often, there, they run into blundering on the part of the family and friends. There will be a wife's lack of faith in the man; and of course she has many good reasons for not believing in him. And there are the many people who will try hard to get the man off the wagon. They are so terribly cruel. They should all know that if he takes one drink he will be lost again; he'll surely go on a bender. For instance: Tracy knows a man who, after having been on the wagon for eleven years, was induced to take a drink. With this, he started drinking so heavily that he soon died of acute alcoholism.

Often a man's wife does many things that tend to drive her husband back into the gutter. She nags and she scolds. As Vincent says to wives, never threaten your husband with divorce, or cutting off his money, or his sex privileges, and never attempt to extract a promise from him. Never attempt to discusss his problems with him while he is drinking.

A prayer. Vincent suggests that his patients use each day the prayer of St. Francis: "Lord, make me an instrument of Thy peace. Where there is hatred, let me sow love; where there is injury, pardon; where there is doubt, faith; where there is despair, hope; where there is darkness, light; and where there is sadness, joy."

Vincent clings to the idea that no alcoholic is entirely hopeless unless, perhaps, he has gone insane.

Another Alcoholic Tells Much about His Psychology

One of the best autobiographies to show why some men drink heavily was written by Harold Maine (*If a Man Be Mad,* 1947). His description of his mental processes is excellent. Often, when sober, he kept counting the days until he could have one of his monthly debauches. He spoke of the need for breaking through "the armor of loneliness." He said he was fighting a losing battle, and trying to reconcile his dream world with the world of actualities. He felt safe only when life made few demands on him. He said so truly that "the tragedy of many men is that they are trying to fulfill the needs of a lost child while occupying the body of a man."

As so often happens with alcoholics, a fine able woman was glad to marry him. She wanted to protect him and help him. They were married while he was drunk! He said he could be very drunk without its showing. Later, when he found himself unable to escape from his wife by distance and indifference, he escaped through drink. But still she kept getting him out of jails and kept nursing him through hangovers. He admits he never took marriage seriously: "it was a temporary camp by the side of the road, where I would quickly grow restless. I knew that if I stayed in one place, guilts would gather like filth around a camping-site. Permanence was a threat to reality and my sanity." Like hundreds of other alcoholics and hypomanic persons, he felt a great need to wander. "The guilts and debts that accrued had to be dropped over each day's horizon or I was sunk."

Soon, the Pacific island on which he was living had become a prison, and Virginia had become his keeper. For a while, remorse and an effort to make up to Virginia for the evil he had done to her held him to life. "Virginia's patience was heroic but futile. Love changed to a tired responsibility. Like all wives of drunks, she said she would leave him were it not for her fear that he would then end up in the gutter. She just could not escape from her feeling of responsibility for the man, even after her love for him was gone. For a while his will power got so weak that he could not make much of an effort even to get away from her!

Then came to Maine a remarkable idea: he became fearful that if he were to stop drinking he would become a very dull and uninteresting fellow! Probably there is many an alcoholic and many a beachcomber who has justified his behavior in life by saying that if he were to go on the wagon he would end up as an average person. Curiously, these human misfits have the delusion that they are very interesting fellows who have "all the fun" as they travel about over the face of the earth. They feel a great contempt for those stodgy fellows who live out their life in one spot, going each day to the same office, coming home each night on the same 5:30 train, to the same wife, educating some children, and accumulating some stocks and bonds.

Later, Maine wrote something that is probably very revealing about the psychology of some alcoholics and "queer birds" who cannot adjust to life. He said that from his army days onward, he had never felt comfortable in a group. Whenever he found himself with more than three people, he promptly felt on the defensive; he kept watching the others to see how he should act. When he tried to enter into the conversation, "inside of me was the beaten menial, uncertain and insecure." What a revealing statement that is! So many schizoid girls give a similar answer when one asks them why they won't go out for an evening with a man. Their excuse is, "I wouldn't know what to say," or, "I would be afraid."

Then Maine left his wife, and just as she feared, he soon drank himself into a mental hospital. Much as it did to Lara Jefferson, it seemed to him that one sometimes had to accept madness in order to be comfortable. He even began to worry about having to leave the hospital—the only safe place he had ever found. He dreaded to go back into the outside world, into which he could not fit. He could not accept its responsibilities and duties and needs to "stay put." Like Seabrook, he enjoyed his stay in a mental hospital because there he was mothered and told what to do.

Maine was soon examined by a lunacy commission, made up of politicians, who, as he feared, said that they could not keep him. So far as he could see, they had no concern over the fact that he was in no shape to go back into the world. The only one who could or would take him in was Virginia, but he was not appreciative of her help. I have always marveled at the tremendous devotion that for years many wives of alcoholics show them. Maine tells us that his Virginia, because of her love for him, had "tossed over everything—family, position, friends, and even her child by a former marriage."

Soon they began to bicker, and Virginia began to wait for and dread the day when he would start drinking again. As he admits, without Virginia, life for him would have been empty and meaningless. "I needed a guiding force; I could no longer trust myself alone." And yet, with all his need of her, he kept wanting to get rid of her. When, eventually, she left, he immediately went on a grand drunk. He said he could stand his own company only so long as it took him to reach oblivion.

Then he sobered up long enough to marry a beautiful and lovely woman named Jean, whom he had known when he was a boy. "We were in each other's arms minutes after we met, clinging together like two lost children." "It was, I think, the child in her that turned to me, another child." "Neither of us was a whole person; each existed as if in the other." But soon he was at the bottle again, and Jean tried to commit suicide.

Maine then went to a psychiatrist, who as usual tried to get him to confess to something or other, perhaps some childhood trauma, "neither of them knew what." Maine was blamed by the doctor for not promptly coming through with the expected secret information.

Then, Maine tried staying sober for a while, but in doing this he found that he had become something that he had never been before—an irritable man. "I found myself brooding and resenting, and I heard the first signs of bitterness in my speech. I didn't like it, but there it was. Perhaps drink was the price I paid for always being an amiable person." Jean agreed that in some ways she liked him better when he was drinking!

Life became happier with his sweet wife and his good friends, and for a while he saw clearly that if he were to get drunk again he would lose everything that was worthwhile for him in life. It would bring a sort of terrible death. And so he stayed sober for fifteen months. But then came what so often ruins an ex-alcoholic, and this is a great disappointment. The novel on which he had worked so hard was rejected by the publisher. He "cringed like an exposed embezzler," and went right back to the bottle.

He tried AA, but did not cooperate, so he soon wound up in Bellevue Hospital. He realized that when drinking he was psychotic, as so many other alcoholics are. He said, "Scratch the surface of any alcoholic and you are likely to find a mildly psychotic person." How I wish all alcoholics could read and accept this statement!

Maine once wrote that he should never have gotten married. He knew that he wasn't entitled to a home or to more than a bare subsistence until he had paid people back the many sums that he had borrowed or stolen. He realized that in order to be a real man he had first to extricate himself from the maze of the past "one miserable slow step at a time."

Back he went to AA. He had insomnia by night and the jitters by day. Soon he began to get delirium tremens and to see snakes. Whether what happened next was a nightmare or an hallucination makes little difference; "I seemed to be in my cell, thoroughly aware of where I was, but a host of madmen, imbeciles and monsters strayed into my vision." Maine made a good point when he said that the person who is hallucinating often sees some real thing like a shadow, but interprets it wrongly, and thinks it is, perhaps, a black cat.

His stepfather, in telling Maine's new psychiatrist about his youth, said that he had never been normal; his mother had always protected him from discipline. He could always "get around" her. As a child, he stole change from her purse; he played hookey from school, and he consorted with tough boys. He always hated everything in the community that stood for decency, law, order, and respect. His stepfather went on to say, "He is the most plausible liar I have ever known." Obviously, in many ways, he was like a psychopathic delinquent.

Then Maine decided that the best job in the world for him would be that of an attendant in a mental hospital, where he would be among men like himself. He would feel easy because these people could not demand normalcy of him. Food and shelter he would have and some pocket money. For a while he did well, but then he got in wrong with the management and was fired.

An Able but Alcoholic Editor Has Himself Committed

A good description of life in a mental hospital was left us by a newspaper editor who, when he saw that he was killing himself with drink, had himself committed. Because after a few days his mind was clear, he was able to give us a good picture of the life around him. He called it *Behind the Door of Delusion* by Inmate Ward-8 (1932).

He said that some of the older attendants and some of the older patients could tell quickly which of the incoming persons would give trouble and which would be well-behaved. In this particular hospital, brutal attendants were quickly discharged, and hence the editor never witnessed any case of intentional brutality.

However, the superintendent was needlessly cruel in that he did not permit the patients to have books or magazines. As a result, they had to sit silently all day, looking into space. They were deprived, also, of tobacco, which would have given great comfort to all of the smokers and chewers. The way the people were treated in this hospital was likely to deprive a sane man of his reason.

The food was terrible, and badly cooked. I, who once lived for a year in a graft-ridden county hospital, have ever since marveled at the magnificent incompetence of a so-called cook who can succeed in making almost every food taste awful. In one state hospital, an incoming superintendent showed that when a good cook was obtained and good food was supplied, it paid the state well because many of the patients quickly got well enough to be sent home!

The patients observed by the editor were partially sane. Most of the men on the ward could talk rationally for a few minutes, but then they would drift off into a discussion of their pet delusion or obsession. Their reasoning and judgment were twisted; they couldn't think in straight lines, and their conclusions were often grotesquely illogical.

The women are hard to handle. The editor said that, as a rule, women in a mental hospital are much more disgusting, profane, and obscene than are the men. Many keep screaming at the tops of their voices. They are more troublesome to the attendants and are more dangerous to handle. Many have no shame left. They insist on going around naked, and urinating where they stand! We all know that alcoholic intoxication often removes inhibitions, but few of us realize that insanity can completely erase them. The women require the closest watching and the sternest handling. The men generally do what a nurse tells them to do, but the women are often obstreperous.

Fear. Very important is the editor's conclusion that, in the minds of every one of the insane persons with whom he had chatted, there was one emotion which overshadowed and outweighed all others, and this was *fear;* fear which no effort of their will could overcome or dislodge—"unreasoning fear, often vague and formless, but hopelessly controlling and impelling."

The curious psychology of alcoholism. Very instructive is the editor's statement that even when he was paying a big sum every month to the owner of a private hospital to keep him from drinking, he kept bribing the employees of the place to bring him whiskey! What a remarkable picture we have there of the mental processes of an alcoholic!

The physical demand for alcohol. As the editor said, the various "cures" can eradicate the physical desire for alcohol within a few days; but they cannot possibly reach into the brain and extract the recurrent craving any more than medicines given by mouth can cure insanity. The editor went on to say that in his case these craving paroxysms occurred at regular intervals, three weeks apart, and lasted for several days. If not quieted with liquor, these cravings brought spells of physical and mental illness. The mouth drooled saliva, the stomach and intestines seemed cramped, and the man became so bilious and nauseated that he went into a shaky, nervous funk. In the hospital, with the passage of months, these spells quit coming, and the editor was discharged "cured." Unfortunately, a year after he left the hospital and finished his book, he died of cancer.

An Able Alcoholic Who Kept Running Away from Life

In two interesting books, William Seabrook, the able writer, told much about the psychology of the sort of man who ends up as a hopeless alcoholic (*Asylum*, 1935; *No Hiding Place*, 1942). He tells us that his father was odd and unusual in that one day he gave up a promising career as a lawyer to become a poor minister of the Gospel in a village. This is the sort of running away that William was to keep doing all his life. William's father's father and William's father's grandfather each had a violent temper. William's father's brother, Clarence, was an eccentric. William's father's father, though a strong advocate of temperance, always carried with him a bottle of whiskey—"for medicinal purposes"—and kept taking a swallow at frequent intervals.

William's father's mother was an odd, interesting person who took opium. Like William, she found a normal ordinary life unbearable. She was fey. When William was a child, she used to take him out into the woods where she would get him to "participate in her imageries and daydreams." William used to love to escape into "that other dream world" with his Grandma Piny. She rescued him "from depressions in which my child life had become unbearable." He describes some of the visions which he saw with his grandmother. On William's mother's side there were four maiden great-aunts, only one of whom ever married. One, he thought, was feeble-minded.

His family and neighbors said that William was a "queer mopey little boy."

William's first fugue. Very interesting to me is the fact that the first of William's many fugues, or runnings away from life, came when he was a boy. He says one day he was amazed to hear himself saying, "Mama, I feel sick. I feel awful." So he was put to bed. The doctor came and gave some pills and a tonic. William tells us that really there was nothing wrong with him, but he stayed in bed from October until May. He did this with no particular reason; he would have been happier playing around outside.

In school he daydreamed a lot, and although, as his teacher said, he could have been at the top of the class, he was generally at the bottom. In the eyes of his teacher, he was "no good and useless." Also, for most of his last year in college his "mind was absent." He spent most of his time whittling. Fortunately, he got interested in shorthand and became skillful in it.

Later, William got a good job with a railroad, but soon, because he didn't like it, he ran away. Next, he became a reporter on a paper; and eventually he worked up to where he was city editor, but he didn't like that; he didn't like *anything* that needed attention to details. So he ran away, and for much of a year lived as a tramp in Europe.

He came back to America and again worked up until he was a feature writer on a big newspaper. Next, he married a lovely girl from a wealthy family and became a partner in

a very profitable advertising company. But, again, he felt
he had to run away.

When William did this he broke the hearts of his partners
and his wife, but he said he just had to go. He went to
Europe and worked for the Allies. On his return, his wealthy
father-in-law gave him and his wife a big farm. But he soon
gave this up and went to work on a newspaper in New
York. There he got to drinking heavily.

Then he learned the trick of making large sums of money
writing for a magazine. But he soon had another fugue. He
quit going to the office, and day after day he just played
chess with a man who also had run away from responsibility. For months they did no work. Then they suddenly quit
the chess and went back to the office. Again, Seabrook did
very well as a writer, and again, he ran away, this time to
join a group of Arabs in the desert.

Then he went to Haiti, where he became a great friend
of a black witchwoman. He came back and wrote "The
Magic Island" which was a best seller. Next, he went to
Central Africa where he lived with cannibals and ate some
human flesh. From Africa he went to Europe where, for
some time, he kept drinking himself sodden. For two years
he drank a fifth of whiskey every day.

He had to be committed. He got so bad that he came
back to New York and had himself committed to a mental
hospital. His experience there is written up in his book
Asylum. In the preface Seabrook tells how he had reached
the point where he knew he was killing himself, and he did
not want to die. He knew he had lost all control over himself, and he wanted to be saved from his weakness.

The definition of an alcoholic—a man who has lost control.
The remarkable point which Seabrook several times emphasized in his books—and it is very important—is that for
years a man can drink a lot and can keep getting tight in-
tentionally and yet not ruin himself. As he said, he knew
plenty of good citizens—businessmen, artists, and writers
—who not only went in heavily for highballs and cocktails,
but got drunk when they chose; but with all this, year after
year, they kept their health and balance; they did their
work, and some turned out good writing.

As Seabrook maintained, it isn't just drinking that makes a drunkard. He had been drinking for years, "enthusiastically, and with pleasure," *when he had wanted to.* Then something snapped, and *he lost control.* He began to have to drink when he didn't want to, and he couldn't stop when he wanted to and much needed to. Also, drinking no longer gave him any pleasure.

The people in the mental hospital were living as children again. Interesting is Seabrook's conviction that, like him, most of the people in his ward in the mental hospital had lost control over themselves, and hence they had to be treated like children. The mental hospital "seemed to me to be a kindergarten or a nursery." The nurse took care of the inmates and always told them what to do—from morning to night.

"We were handled as children, as *irresponsible* children who didn't know what was good for us, and therefore had to be told. It was a 'mama knows best' . . . atmosphere, protective and generally kindly, but backed up with 'mama will spank' when children became unmanageable, and just had to be dragged kicking to bed without their suppers." As Seabrook went on to say, everything was decided for them; they were put to bed and made to get up. "I remember the haven it was . . . almost wish sometimes I were back there."

Seabrook returns to drinking. Dr. Paschall, Seabrook's psychiatrist, told him that knowing the truth in regard to his motivation didn't necessarily mean he was cured, or free. In Dr. Paschall's opinion, the popular notion that complexes can be gotten rid of merely by trotting them out into the daylight "is all poppycock." This certainly was true in Seabrook's case. Even when he thought he knew the secret of his messed-up life, he was not well. Soon after he left the hospital, he started drinking heavily again. As he said, "I was drinking again in the mornings when *I didn't want to drink,* not for pleasure, but in the desperate false hope that I might write a page or two that wasn't wooden; and presently because I no longer dared to face the typewriter." Although he lived to write other books, he eventually ended it all by taking his own life.

The Alcoholic Adventures of a "Bohemian" Writer

In a book called *Brainstorm* (1944), Mr. Carlton Brown tells about the adventure of Mike, an alcoholic fast-living writer. According to the book, when Mike recovered from his breakdown, he got Carlton Brown to help him in putting the account together. Theirs is one of the best descriptions I have seen of the type of life that many an alcoholic writer lives with his erratic friends in the night spots of a big city. Such a life is calculated to wreck the nerves of anyone. Why shouldn't a man crack up when he misuses his brain so terribly—when he feeds it on little besides alcohol and coffee and tobacco—when for months he gives it little rest by day or by night, and when, on many an evening, instead of going to bed, he goes to a night club to listen to a jazz orchestra blaring away as loudly as possible?

A poor nervous inheritance. Mike would appear to have had a poor nervous inheritance—just the sort that could have made him what he was, or at least could have started him out on the sort of life that eventually caused his downfall. His father, whom he calls Bill, was a "wild" young man who also was a writer, and also drank, smoked, gambled, and was rather proud of his lack of respect for the conventionalities. From early life Bill had tended to be sexually loose. For a while he made money, but later, he went broke and had to keep sponging off his friends. Whatever the reader may want to think about heredity, Mike was just the sort of son we would have expected Bill to have. Also, Mike's sister soon wound up as an alcoholic, and she died young. When told by her doctor to choose between a sensible life and death by drinking, she chose death.

Suggestive of a poor nervous inheritance was Mike's tendency in his youth to suffer from terrifying nightmares and to wet the bed after the age of four.

A stormy married life. In the spring of 1940, just before Mike went insane (when he was twenty-seven), he was an editorial assistant on a magazine, and before that he had been a free-lance writer. Early in life, he became sexually promiscuous, and like his sister he soon began to drink too much. When twenty-one, and while drunk, he got married to a girl he had been sleeping with. For the next seven years, he and his wife spent much of their time either bickering or fighting noisily.

For a while, Mike, like many other psychotic persons, blamed everyone but himself for his troubles, but eventually he came to see that the fault was mainly his. Because of their alcoholism and their improvidence, he and his wife lived from hand to mouth. When he got a check for an article, they had to "celebrate," and usually by next morning, they were broke again. Mike got to drinking heavily every day, and as a result, his mind soon became so dull that it was hard for him to do his stint of writing.

When one is going insane. Once he said, "I cannot fix the exact point at which I began to act strangely, because I did not know that I was acting strangely. One month, one week, one day, I held a pretty good job, and led a fairly reasonable existence, and then one week or one day, I was on my way out of the everyday world and into one that I didn't recognize as being my own creation until after it had dissolved again."

About this time his wife left him—apparently for good— and he didn't much mind this. But, with her departure, he started drinking even more heavily than had been usual for him.

Goofy thoughts. One day when he realized he was getting goofy, he asked his secretary to write out something he had dictated on the cylinder, and here it is. It is worth quoting as showing the disorganization of a mind. It resembles what Seabrook once dictated.

"This is where the over and under matter begins on this cylinder. This is where the over and over and over and over matter begins on this cylinder. Take a memo to Joe Anti. Stop it, stop it, stop it, Joe. You've got us all desperately overcrowded up against the wall. Joe Anti by the way is not to be confused with Buster of the same name. I wish you to transcribe all of this over and under matter with great care and precision. Put it in a sealed envelope and stop it. Stuff it into my incoming and outgoing basket. And finally, take a memo, take a momo, a booko, a backo, a tickle-tackle, a fish, a flash, a pistache, a pinko, a panko, a finkle-fankle. This is all urgent and immaterial. This is all URGENT and immaterial. Signed, Cordially and detestably."

Many a time in my office, a schizophrenic has answered my questions in much this irrelevant sort of way. There was no good sequence in his speech, which showed me how disorganized his mental functions were.

When hallucinations began. Mike went on to say, "One night, shortly after my wife had left, I had what may have been a mild attack of delirium tremens. I awoke shaking violently, with a feverish chill and an intense feeling of fear. Some unspeakably evil, gnomish little green figures, resembling the demons of Hieronymus Bosch, danced in the dark before my open eyes, as clearly as though they were cut out of luminescent celluloid and dangled on strings. They soon disappeared, but the sense of terror remained. Trembling, and cold with sweat, I fought against a sudden strong compulsion to jump out of the open window at the foot of the bed."

Later, after this fright, he got to drinking again, and then, in order to keep going, he would take with his liquor large amounts of coffee, or large amounts of Benzedrine; also, some spirits of ammonia, some bromides, and occasionally a marihuana cigarette!

Mania comes. Then he began to get manic, "My imagination, miraculously freed from its bonds of inhibition, adapted actuality to its own fanciful mood." "At the height of my elation, my body became light and agile, responding instantly to my bidding; my motions were effortless and perfectly co-ordinated." "Sounds, sights, tastes, touches, smells, seemed to pour into me directly, to flood my being with their distilled essence."

"I was amazed at the way phrases came to me spontaneously." "Ideas seemed to be coming to me faster and better than ever, but I carried few of them through to a successful conclusion, and the things I wrote did not stand up under later, sane examination. I 'expressed myself' to the utmost, turbulently, emotionally, without intellectual discipline." "When I came to look on myself as a versatile genius, poet, promoter, Byronic lover, and all-talented Messiah, I found quite a few ardent disciples."

Mike's life through the years. The bulk of the book contains a detailed description of Mike's disorganized life—and particularly the life he led while he was slipping into his psychosis. Living insanely as he did, fighting constantly with his wife, and having tremendous emotional storms with her, even an iron man would probably have cracked up. Practically every day he was drinking heavily, and in the evening he was out with friends. He tells of a series of nights "given over to complete insomnia, which I mistook for a manifestation of the great draughts of energy and inspiration that were coming to me from on High." About this time he began to get great religious ideas, and the conviction that he was going to be the Messiah in a Second Coming.

Why does a man with a good brain wreck it? Many readers may wonder why a man like Mike, with so good a brain, lived in such a crazy way; they may wonder why he didn't work steadily on his newspaper or in the publishing house until he had been promoted into a good job with a good salary. He said once, "But I hadn't wanted security and a safe, dull job." Several alcoholics have expressed contempt for the man who lives sensibly—who stays faithful to one wife—who builds a home and pays for it, and who becomes a respectable member of the community. People like Mike think they have all the fun, and they think they are much more sensible than is the man who settles down. The wastrel says the settled-down man is a lap dog while he is a timber-wolf!

Mike has to be locked up. Then one day in 1940, Mike went definitely off his head. He got into a row with some police officers who, sensing that he was not sane, sent him to Bellevue. From there he was sent to a state hospital. For a while, he thought of getting a writ of habeas corpus that would "spring" him out, but he saw that he wasn't yet ready to live sensibly on the outside, and hence it was better for him to remain where he was. As he said, he was pretty sure he could go before a jury and convince twelve men that he was perfectly sane, but then he would find himself faced with the problem of living without a job, without an income, and without any ability to work—all of which shows how well a man in a mental hospital can reason.

Interesting is Mike's statement that when he was chatting with an alcoholic who hoped soon to get discharged from the hospital, the fellow said, "You know the first thing I'll do when I get out? I'll get myself a quart of rye and a girl." This is typical.

After two months in the hospital, Mike was dismissed, apparently sane; but for the next six or seven months he went from his state of religious mania into a deep depression, which brought him close to suicide.

After hospitalization, what? Mike found when he got back to his mother's apartment that, though he was sober, he was depressed and in no condition to face the world. When he started writing again, he found it hard to finish anything. But gradually he recovered, and we are left to infer that he got well.

Summary. I think that, after reading this chapter, everyone will agree that the only way in which to understand why many men drink themselves into the gutter is to listen to the explanations they give. Some of the more intelligent of these men, like Tracy, spent years trying to figure out what their motivation was.

To me, it is clear that all of these men and women were born with a certain weakness of character or defect in personality which caused them to be so uncomfortable that they craved help from a drug. A number of them, like Maine, say that they always felt inadequate, or shy, or unable to be sociable when in a crowd. Only after taking three drinks could they lose their inhibitions, their fears, their shyness, or their touch-me-not-ness.

As we have seen, some men drink in order to anesthetize themselves, and to forget their inadequacies and their repeated failures in life. Many take to the bottle the minute anything goes wrong in their life, like the salesman who is sure to get drunk the day he fails to get that big order he was after. Some, like William Seabrook, drink to help them run away from life and the routine that bores them. Others drink because every so often an overpowering physical distress comes upon them.

Everyone with a tendency to alcoholism ought to read Tracy's book because he can give so much hope to anyone who will do what Tracy demands of the people who come to him for help: they must quit kidding themselves; they must become absolutely honest; they must give up trying to blame everyone but themselves; they must start rebuilding themselves from the ground up; and to strengthen their flabby will, they must do each day three things they do not want to do.

Very important are two ideas: one, that a social drinker is an alcoholic the day he has lost control, so that he gets drunk some day when he very much wants not to; and that an alcoholic is a man who, when he takes one drink, cannot stop, but has to go on into a debauch.

To me, it is so hopeful to read that every so often a man who for months or years was on Skid Row climbs back again to a life of decency and success.

CHAPTER 12

Some People Whose Mental Disease
Was Hard to Classify

In many cases it is hard to say from a person's symptoms how his mental disease should be classified. Some men, for a while, just lose their good business sense and their ability to do their work. They may not be able to settle down to anything or get started on any job—even a small one. Some cannot even read a book. Other persons, in a lifetime, will have only one or two brief episodes of depression or mental confusion or wild excitement (see Anton Boisen, Chapter 6). Probably, in many of these cases, the nature of the disease could have been easily classified if the psychiatrist had had some way of knowing that the patient had always been schizoid, or even schizophrenic—overly shy, unsociable, uncommunicative, retiring, "touch-me-not," and without any ability to show affection, or even interest in anyone. I know a janitor's assistant in my office building who is as typical a schizophrenic as I ever saw, much like those who stand silent and immobile all day in a mental hospital. This janitor never looks at anyone and never says a word to anyone unless he has to. He is fortunate in that he can earn his living in a job in which he can work most of the day all by himself.

As we shall see, Jane Hillyer had symptoms of both schizophrenia and manic-depressive psychosis. Jayson's story is

238

also puzzling, with its mixture of symptoms. It is hard to say what type of insanity the kindly Scotchman from Glasgow had. He had only two violent episodes in a lifetime. In many ways, Arthur Symons behaved as an odd, hypersensitive, eccentric, and schizoid man; and yet he so conquered his touch-me-not-ness that he became a sensual lover of women. Colonel Joyce had one acute maniacal episode.

Actually, often it matters little what we call a man's insanity; most of what we want to know is, how can we help him? Is he likely to get well? If so, how long will it take?

An Excellent Description of a Spell of Insanity

In her book, *Reluctantly Told* (1926), Jane Hillyer tells how her father, an able musician who had worked for years against great odds, cracked up and committed suicide. I have been told by friends of the family that Miss Hillyer had a cousin who committed suicide; and as she says, she had an elder brother who was hovering on the edge of a nervous breakdown.

Great fatigue and a desire to end it all. Miss Hillyer begins her book by telling of her tremendous feelings of guilt over her father's suicide. She feared that on one occasion she had hurt him deeply and hence had had something to do with causing him to take his life. Then she attempted suicide, but fortunately, she did not take enough of the drug. "I had to come back. I was trapped into living again. There was no use in trying any more. Death and life seemed equally impossible to achieve in any vital way."

She went on then to say that she could always tell how tired she was by her hands. If it was an effort for her to open them, she was only "pretty tired," but if she could hardly lift them from the desk or found it difficult to pick up a pen, she was so tired that she knew she had better "go easy." Getting her hair fixed in the morning was an interminable job—her arms ached so, and she hurt all over.

She was sent on a vacation, but as usually happens with psychotic persons, she could not sleep; she lay wide-eyed all through the hot summer nights. "The *thing* was beside me, over me, around me." Then, so typically, she found herself reading the same paragraph over and over again but getting nothing out of it. As I must keep saying throughout this book, this is one of the first great danger signals, which means mental trouble ahead. Finally, she got so she couldn't even think. She would start a train of ideas which would end nowhere—"lost in a tangle of cross-associations."

Insanity came. Then a terror gripped her. She looked in a mirror and knew that the person she saw was mad. "*I* was mad." "I seemed dual: struggling against the truth, crying out against fate, pleading, praying; and at the same time, cool and almost surgical in my analysis of the situation. I probed to find the cause; I reckoned the factor of fatigue, long-continued fever, strain, tension; I checked my recent behaviour, and the accompanying drives and emotions. Yes, they explained it all."

Then the horror came, with the thought that she would be shut up. Actually, she soon was sent to a private sanatorium where she was shocked to find that the doors were locked. What she had so feared had happened. Soon, "mental inaccessibility" closed in on her. When the nurses were sweet to her, she recoiled from them angrily and with hate. "I would not try to make connections or to retain those already made. I deliberately cut my moorings." "Though I heard when people spoke, why answer? They were not for me nor I for them." This type of behavior came intermittently, but with increasing frequency. "More and more I began to object to the intrusion of those about me, and to resist. I did not want to go for a walk with my kind and capable little nurse. I did not want to sit on the lawn. I did not want to get up and dress in the morning. Why should I? What was there to dress for? I wanted nothing they had to offer me. Why didn't they let me alone?" This is the best description I have seen of the refusal of a psychotic and usually a schizophrenic person to accept any friendly advances.

She didn't even want to get well, which was logical in a way, because she felt there was no place in the world for her. Accordingly, in the hospital she refused her medicine; and as a result, the nurses held her and poured it down her throat. This made her exceedingly angry and resentful.

She said, if the nurses had assumed she was a beast, then she *would be one*. But still there were periods of complete lucidity. "I hated these almost as much as the times of confusion, because then I had to remember."

Her life in the hospital. With all the nervous upset, she developed a severe diabetes—which suggests that the tremendous storm in the mind caused serious damage to important cells in the pancreas. I have seen two cases of this type, one in which a severe diabetes appeared a few days after the woman discovered that her husband had been unfaithful, and the other in which a sensitive and very able man lost his only son.

Interesting is Miss Hillyer's statement that for a time in the hospital she was like an infant who has to learn what sounds and other sensations mean. As she said, "Sounds came to my ears. They meant little besides just noise. I was unable to translate them into the milkman's cart, the doctor's machine, or the ice-cream freezer: they were just so many vibrations hitting my ear drum."

She said that even when she seemed to be badly confused, "I could think of abstract things clearly; I could picture affairs at home; remember melodies, and visualize musical scores more accurately than I had been able to for days; but my immediate environment was blurred."

Later, she picked up a book and found it was readily comprehensible. "My heart gave a leap; I was better. But, later again, back came lethargy and despair, and complete passivity." Following this she had an upsurge into mania, and later a plunge into depression. "Hours and days followed when the world around me hardly existed, save in brief flashes. I have no definite recollection of anything, only a sense of feverish restlessness and discomfort, and certain brief fantastic obsessions." Later, came a "complete snuffing out of my individuality."

The bad effect on her of untruths. As so commonly happens in these cases, when a family with moderate means sends their loved one to a private hospital, the heavy expense soon exhausts them financially. Then they have to send the patient to a state hospital. I always feel like saying to such a family, "If you will soon have to send the patient

to a state hospital, why not do it *before* you go broke?"
When this crisis came, Miss Hillyer's people made the grave
mistake of easing matters for themselves by having the girl
told that she was being taken home. Naturally, when she
found that her relatives had lied to her and had had her
locked up in another hospital, she was very angry and rebellious and uncooperative. As she said later, if only they
had known how to handle an insane person, they could
have helped her so much more and perhaps might have
saved her from months of suffering. Their behavior when
moving her had a most damaging effect on her in two
ways. First, for many months she could not be prevailed
upon to trust anyone, and often she broke into open revolt;
second, they had greatly widened the gulf between her and
the world of reality. "I would have bitten off my tongue
before I would have asked these people who *lied*, for the
simplest bit of information."

In a new hospital. In the new hospital, a woman psychiatrist came twice a day, and Miss Hillyer liked her and
wanted to respond to her but for a while could not let go.
She remained as cold and hard as possible. She said that
insanity can stress some features of a personality, while it
blanks others out, "so that *the patient's feel of himself* is
new, nagging, and disturbing in the extreme." For a while
she had a terrible fear that some of her friends might come
to see her. She feared the effort she would have to make in
talking to them and adjusting to them. For much of the
time she lay in a sort of stupor. As a result, for a while, she
was kept in the "Hopeless Ward."

During this time, it helped her greatly to become convinced that her kindly woman physician had never had
anything to do with the lie that had been told her. Miss
Hillyer was impressed by the fact that the doctor always
answered questions immediately and without any hesita-
tion, like a person who is telling the truth.

Anyone who has to deal with the insane should remember that they are particularly keen when it comes to recognizing the honesty or dishonesty or the good or evil intentions of the person to whom they are talking. For instance,
Miss Hillyer was much helped one day when a nice woman

on the housekeeping staff came into her room. When she found that this woman had nothing to do with either the managerial or the medical staff, she looked on her as a neutral, disinterested person and talked to her freely.

Years later, Miss Hillyer said, "If I could have been given just solitude and fresh air and a sense of freedom, much might have been accomplished." This is why it is so good today that in mental hospitals as many wards as possible are being left unlocked.

After a year or so, the woman's delusions faded out, but she was still confused. She was sure that in some of the people around the hospital she recognized her dead mother, or her aunt or her uncle. Fortunately, about this time she met a fellow patient she liked, a woman of education and refinement, who while a bit disturbed, was still well-behaved and gracious. As is the case with so many psychotic persons, it was only when this able woman went out and tried to adjust to the world that she failed in certain ways. Again and again she had gone home, only to have to return—confused and baffled—from her attempts to meet life on the outside.

This brings up one of the greatest problems of superintendents of mental hospitals—the problem of deciding when a patient should be allowed to go home. When is a patient "cured"? In thousands of cases, the patient seems sane enough while protected in the hospital, but the day he or she goes out, the family finds that the illness is not quite cured. A man patient may go on a bender, or a woman may get into an awful row with her people.

Improvement, but a great loss of strength. Fortunately, after three years, Miss Hillyer was well enough to be transferred to one of the cottages on the hospital grounds. There she felt much better. She improved much when she was allowed to go out into the garden and to enjoy the flowers. And yet, even while in the cottage, she had a period of depression during which she sat all day and said nothing. She was still so weak that she spent a large part of her time on a couch in a sort of half stupor. She had then what I call a "Charles Darwin's Asthenia." In this state, a half hour's chatting with people was enough to make it necessary that she lie down for the rest of the day. On visiting days, a brief talk with a relative could completely exhaust her. "Even the doctor's coming was at times fatiguing, simply because it was a bit *unusual*." Everyone should know that one of the early signs of a mild psychosis is the person's inability to stand up to the strain of any event which is out of the usual.

Then Miss Hillyer discovered the hospital library, and reading there soon helped her. Later, when she was put in charge of this library, she really showed signs of getting well. For the first time since her illness, she became concerned about her personal appearance. She brushed and arranged her hair and asked for a neater dress.

But, curiously, with all this improvement, there still was a danger that she might commit suicide. Psychiatrists know that depressed people are most likely to take their own lives, when they are recovering. Then perhaps they get the strength and determination to tackle the job of doing away with themselves. One day, Jane managed to get hold of a few tablets of bichloride of mercury. She took them, but fortunately, the dose was not big enough to kill her.

About this time she began to write a good deal, and then she discovered she could write verse. Gradually, during the next few months, she got better; and then she saw that she was growing away from the other patients. She saw that she no longer was one of them; and they saw the change in her. With her new freedom in the hospital grounds, one of her greatest joys was to be able to go through unlocked doors. Fortunately, as with many other patients, the unlocking of the doors did not tempt her to take "French leave."

She goes home. Then, after five years, came the great day when she was allowed to go home; and again her greatest joy was the open door. She wasn't locked in. Her most difficult problem was that of meeting old friends. As she said, "I was not embarrassed or constrained in any way; just easily tired by them." "Solitude, long deep draughts of it, was a complete necessity for months." "My reactions were entirely different. Things that I would never have noticed before now cut into me like a knife; sounds, smells, mechanical adjustments, telephones, street cars."

One of the first things she had to do was to adjust to people's attitudes toward her hospital experience. She knew, of course, that the attitude of many would be one of recoil. To them, it would seem a disgrace—a thing to speak of only in whispers.

Soon after coming home Jane fortunately was given a job in the music school in which she formerly had taught. She worked half a day, which was all she could stand. "Usually I went home, lay on my bed in a softly lighted room with the door shut, and I wept. I was perfectly happy and calm. Nothing worried me. I even had the good sense not to be humiliated by tears; I knew they meant nothing but fatigue and weariness, and I remembered the wise remark of William James to the effect that: 'The Lord may forgive us our sins, but our nervous system never does.'"

With it all she came to see that the regaining of equilibrium was to be a matter of months, not weeks; possibly years. She had lost her old habits of work, and she found that concentration was possible only through a supreme effort of the will—an effort that left her weak and exhausted. She so needed a *complete* rest, that she felt that if she could only die for a week, then she might pick up and carry on. There still was great need for solving a number of the problems which remained in her mind.

Help from a good doctor. About this time she was fortunate in finding a psychologist who helped her tremendously. She found that "the convalescent is not able to make his own personal adjustments and handle his own case; the responsibility is too utterly crushing." The doctor who helped her had to get her to fight a number of phobias. He worked largely on what he called the "principle of the purple omnibus." "If," he said, "a horse has been frightened by a purple omnibus . . . there is just one thing to do—lead him past purple omnibuses again and again until he is at last used to them. You are like that horse." "And," as she says, "I was."

Again and again the doctor made her recall her distressing memories of childhood and to face them until they didn't hurt her any more. She had to go back over many of the experiences in the hospital until she no longer feared them. In the end, the relief "was indescribable."

Another point which, I think, is very important was that as she struggled to help her gifted musical students in the school she would forget her distresses and her disturbing thoughts, and then she would feel well. She said, "Nothing so establishes a sense of sanity as trivial, seemingly unimportant touches with all sorts of people." Then she found she must have play. "That brings sanity, too." Along the way, she had to pile up a mass of reserve energy.

A Man Who Cracked Up after the Loss of All His Money in 1929

In the book *Mania* (1937), Lawrence M. Jayson tells of his spell of hospitalization after lifeguards had fished him out of the ocean where he had tried to drown himself. A year later, he felt he just had to tell people what goes on in a mental hospital. He admits that many readers may wonder how he could remember so clearly details of events which took place months before, but, like all of the other people who wrote up their experience in a mental hospital, he said that everything had remained as vivid as though it had happened yesterday. "Even when I seemed torn completely from reality, my mind was making an indelible record of all occurrences, easily recast when my reason was restored."

The beginnings of the trouble. Jayson tells how, after the crash of 1929, he had been unable to sleep. Night and day he was driven by thoughts of how he might find new sources of business that would help him to recoup his fortunes. His head got to aching; he felt distraught, bewildered, tense, and "driven."

As he was slipping into insanity, his doctor only laughed at his fears and urged him to get away for a few days in the country. Jayson said he had tried this, and, typically, it hadn't helped. He had even gone out and worked hard with lumberjacks, but always his head had kept pounding with the old worries about business. Then he was stricken with a great sense of guilt. He returned home "more depressed than ever before—haggard, tighter inside, and more self-accusatory."

This sending of a man on a vacation is so typical of what we doctors and many lay people do to the man who is going insane. It may help a man with a fatigue state but not a man with a psychosis. When a month's good vacation does nothing for a nervous man or woman, this means usually that the disease is a dangerous psychosis, and not the mild neurosis it was thought to be.

Then, one day, while sitting in a chair on the boardwalk at Coney Island, a voice said to him, "Jayson, you are worthless; you've never been any good." "There is the ocean. You might just as well drown yourself. Just walk in, and keep walking." So that is what he immediately did. The next thing he knew, he was being revived, and later he found himself in a county hospital.

Fights due to misunderstandings. Soon, he got into a fight with the attendant who was talking to him, and as a result he was tied to his bed. Like Beers, when his brother came to see him, he couldn't believe the visitor was his brother —he thought he was an enemy, dressed up to resemble his brother. When friends came, he laughed to think how quickly he could see through their little deception. Then the man who looked like his brother said, "We're going to take you for a little ride, Larry." This was unfortunate because Jayson immediately thought of a gangster's type of "ride" from which one does not return alive. So again he got ready to fight and eventually landed in a strait jacket.

On arrival at a mental hospital, he got the idea that his enemies were going to roast him alive, and hence it is no wonder that he struggled fiercely to get free. This is so typical of what happens with the insane. They fight because they are so convinced that something terrible is going to be done to them. Any normal man, if he felt the same way, would doubtless put up the same type of fight.

Because of Jayson's pugnacity and great restlessness, he was put into a tub of warm water and kept there until he relaxed. Later, he had more fights when he refused to eat. He quit eating because he thought they were putting germs in his food. The attendants fed him by tube, and he fought that. For a while he refused to speak to anyone. This was because he could not understand what people were saying. Later, he became convinced that he had died and was in hell. "My enemies had killed me without my knowing."

Then Jayson got a little better and asked for a pencil and paper so that he could write to his unknown persecutors. He wanted to explain to them why he was unworthy and good-for-nothing. Later, when he was taken to a bowling alley in the hospital and asked if he'd like to play, he "knew" that if he touched a ball he would become a devil; and so, naturally, he wouldn't play. This is a good example of why mental patients are so uncooperative and so "ornery." They have what they think are good reasons for what they do or don't do.

Jayson got better. Later, he began to get clearer mentally and to come more into contact with the world about him. "No longer sure I was in hell, no longer completely wrapped up in a world of my own making, I was forced . . . to begin wondering where I was and why I was there." With this change, the doctor moved him to a quieter ward. Always this happens in mental hospitals; as soon as possible, the patient who has calmed down and has become cooperative is moved into a ward where he will have a much freer life, with more privileges and saner people about him.

Later, when his brother came, this time Larry responded with some affection. "He was the first person I had seen for months in whom I had felt any interest." But still he was suspicious and cautious, and would not say anything so long as an attendant was around. As his brother talked to him, he kept wondering "if this man could be trusted." As Clifford Beers had done, Jayson tried a trick to see if this man, who looked like his brother, really was he. Fortunately, Jayson eventually became satisfied on this point.

His horror on finding out that he was in an "insane asylum." The next sign of improving health was his willingness to be friendly. Soon he got chummy with a number of the men. Later, he began to read, and this was a good sign. When he came to realize that he was in a mental hospital, he "was filled with piercing anguish and shame." He wondered how it could be that his roommate, Joe, "who was

the best guy in the world," could be insane. Then he turned
to three of his companions and asked, "Does it mean we're
all in here to stay?" "The horror of that thought overwhelmed me. Hopelessly I buried my face in my hands."
Later, he calmed down and adjusted to the situation, and
filled his days with card-playing, reading, talking, and occasional walks.

A *court hearing*. Jayson was then taken into court for the
usual sanity hearing before a jury, and a guardian was ap-
pointed to look after his interests. He became sick with
despair. He felt sure he was as sane as any of the jury, and
so he felt he had been betrayed and let down by all his
friends. He imagined they had been animated by a desire
to get his money. But then, showing how sane an insane
man can be, he remembered that with the 1929 crash in the
stock market, he had lost everything. He had no money, and
so his "suspicions began to fall like a house of cards." Eventually, he became sane enough to see that the men in court
had acted for his good.

Shortly after this, he was taken to the Villa, a part of the
hospital that looked like a club, with carpets on the floors,
paintings on the walls, and curtains on the windows. But he
still was sad because there were bars on the windows and
locks on the doors. It was explained to him that the doctors
and the attendants watch the patients, and when they see
that one of them is getting interested in things outside of
himself, they know that he is getting well. Soon Jayson
noted that in the Villa the inmates were *normal*, except perhaps for one single quirk. If one didn't discover this quirk,
one would never suspect anything wrong with the man.

Here, Jayson got hungry; he ate voraciously and rapidly
gained weight. This was a good sign. Unfortunately, on
occasions a patient in the Villa would become obstreperous
and would have to be put back in the ward whence he had
come. At night there was entertainment for the patients,
but "those from the back halls," who had been "dragged in,"
"showed no interest at all in what was going on. They kept
their heads down, a million miles away, muttering through
their closed lips, completely indifferent." In the bulk of the
book, Jayson tells much about his fellow inmates and their

doings. The friendliness of one patient for another often had a good effect. People who had been feeling terribly lonely began to realize that they weren't quite alone.

Jayson was allowed to go home for a visit. Then a great day came when the doctors allowed Jayson to go out by himself. He went to New York and dropped in at his office. He got back to the hospital safely, but he had discovered that he wasn't yet strong enough to face the world. Later, his brother came and drove him home for his first visit with his family. He got along perfectly with his brother, but not so well with his other relatives and some of his friends. With them, "for a moment that same feeling of terror and isolation engulfed me." The friends and relatives showed Jayson some affection, but their desperate attempt to make him feel at ease worked in reverse. Soon he was wishing that some of them—particularly the friends—would either clear out or let him escape. Jayson then decided that dinner with his pals in the Villa was much more fun. Why? Because there, no one was solicitous about him; everyone treated him as an equal, and that was what he wanted.

Life in the Villa was by now very congenial to Jayson, and actually, he preferred it to living at home! So many people who have done well in a mental hospital feel this way. As Lois Vidal found, home can be a very poor place for the person who is mentally upset. Relatives can get to scolding the invalid who, they think, ought to be ashamed of himself!

The long period of convalescence. For a while Jayson thought that he had become quite sane, as shown by the fact that he had gone after some business and had gotten it. But there still was such a constant turmoil within him, and so decided a degree of elation (mania) that he knew he wasn't yet well-balanced. Later, he abruptly changed from elation to melancholy, and this showed him he wouldn't be safe until he could get rid of the "constant fight for and against something inside of him." Also, in his business, he wasn't yet sure of himself. More and more he enjoyed the relaxation of life in the Villa. Every day he played golf in the hospital grounds. He even lost his old desire to leave the hospital. Actually, it was another year before he was released. He felt then that at last he had sense and balance and strength enough not to go back into his old frenzied rush in business; he felt he was a graduate of a university that had taught him well. He felt that its lessons had been salutary and would be enduring.

A Kindly Scotchman Who Went Insane

Some years ago, Dr. Frieda Fromm-Reichmann found a copy of a rare book, published in Glasgow in 1860 (Anonymous, *The Philosophy of Insanity*). It interested her so much she had it reprinted. The anonymous author saw clearly into many of the problems of insanity. For instance, he said that a "fit of insanity does not necessarily injure permanently either the feelings or the intelligence of the person." Also, he felt sure "that the difference between the mentally healthy and the mentally disturbed is one of quantity only." Perhaps many psychiatrists today would agree with him.

Our Scotchman believed much in an hereditary predisposition to insanity. As he said, such a predisposition would explain why one person under tremendous psychic strain stays sane, while another, under slight strain, or without any obvious strain, goes under and becomes psychotic. Also, "A man may be quite rational upon almost every point save one, and on that he may be a dangerous lunatic. And his lunacy may have its root in the most humane and praiseworthy feelings of his nature." "There is nothing more wicked than virtue out of its wits, nothing more cruel than humanity run mad." The author felt sure that it is useless to try to argue an insane man out of his delusions. He thought it better to leave him alone to the curative influences of time.

A modern mental hospital a hundred years ago. It is interesting to read that way back in 1860 Dr. Mackintosh, who was superintendent of the Gartnavel Royal Lunatic Asylum in Scotland, was giving his patients concerts and dances, and he was getting journalists to come and describe what went on, for publication in their several papers. The doctor wanted to familiarize the public with practices in well-run mental hospitals so as to lessen people's dread of them. He wanted people to know that in many cases their loved one soon recovers and goes home.

The ex-patient wrote, "Lunatics in general are a harmless class; there is seldom much about them to fear. For months, I have slept every night surrounded by them, and without any feeling of fear I could do so still. No doubt it is a dreadful disease, but not so universally dreadful as is generally thought." As he went on to say, "So long as a man is able to provide for himself and his family (if he has one) and offers no violence to himself or others, however false and absurd his ideas may be and however eccentric his actions, he should not be treated as a lunatic."

Problems of the criminally insane. "In criminal cases it will remain forever impossible to tell to what extent a maniac should be held responsible, for no one, not even the unfortunate person himself, can tell whether the power to resist or the power which impelled him to commit the criminal action, if fairly pitted against each other, would have been strongest." "This apparently unnatural conduct does, in some cases, arise from motives which, could we trace them, would command pity, veneration, and love. An insane husband may turn from, and refuse to acknowledge his wife and children, and yet a mad regard for their safety may be the only motive which compels him to commit this seemingly unnatural act. He may believe with an intensity of belief which no man who has been always sane can ever imagine, that to acknowledge them as his would cause their eternal destruction; and from motives equally affectionate and holy he may imbrue his hands in their blood. There is a fearful page in the book of human nature, unread by him who judges an insane man by his actions."

"It is a fearful thing for a man to be mad and to be conscious that he is so. I am convinced that a thought of an intensely exciting nature passing through a brain in this state, or through one very easily excited naturally, can [cause the man to] kill as quickly as a shock of electricity from a thunder cloud." Several times, "while recovering from an attack of mania," "I have been struck down as utterly senseless by a thought as I would have been by a blow."

A sudden impulse to kill a loved one. After much over-work and then inability to sleep, the Scotchman went mad. Then, "One night, after a number of weeks of fearful suffer-ing, as I was lying in bed tossing, sleepless and despairing, a most horrible impulse seized upon me, an impulse im-pelling me to destroy one who of all living beings, most deserved my love. I buried myself under the bedclothes and struggled with the hellish impulse till the bed shook. It still gained strength. I sprang up, clung to the bedpost and sunk my teeth, in the agony of despair, into the hard wood. It was uncontrollable. I shut my eyes, bowed down my head for fear that I should see her, and rushed out of the house." Like Lara Jefferson, "Barefooted, with no covering save a nightshirt," the Scotchman ran through the streets to the Police Officers and implored them to lock him up. Later, "the paroxysm had passed, and gasping, panting for death in any form, I accompanied them home, steeped to the lips in despair."

The motives that actuate an insane person. The author tells why, for a long time in the mental hospital, he wouldn't eat. The trouble was that he had a little sickly boy, and after he (the father) was taken to the asylum, night and day he had the hallucination that he could hear "the weep-ing and wailing of that child." "It rang around me, and the cry, 'I'm hungry, father, I'm hungry' scorched my heart like fire." While he thought the child was starving, he could not bear to eat a mouthful.

So many people who go to visit a relative in a mental hospital are terribly distressed because the patient won't speak to them. But, as our author says, when his wife visited him, he might easily have refused her admittance because he had a tremendous fear that if he spoke to her, this might cause her to be killed. This thought so distressed him that for a while his actions were dominated by it. As he went on to say, a patient gets so many ideas in his head which are absolutely wrong, as, for instance, when for weeks he was sure that his children were somewhere in the mental hospi-tal with him—somewhere down under the floor. He could hear their voices screaming for help. As he said, that will

give some idea of the mental tortures that assail the mind
of an insane person.

The need for devotion on the part of loved ones. Those
devoted relatives who keep visiting their loved one at a
mental hospital should read (on page 21) our author's statement about his loving wife. He says there was no conveyance
between his home and the asylum seven miles away but
"let the day be ever so stormy, there she was, true as the
sun to her time. To this, to her, I owe my preservation from
suicide or idiocy. These visits gave me something to think
upon; they were, as it were, a solid spot in a troubled ocean
whereon the spirit could occasionally rest."

When his wife saw that he was not getting any better,
she insisted on taking him home, and in this particular case,
she was wise, because, at home, with the affection of the
family about him, he got well. She knew there was a great
danger in having him at home, but she was willing to face
it and take the chance.

The patient's later experiences. After the author was well,
he thought that his mind "was clearer and stronger—my
conduct more rational, and my imagination, naturally very
strong, more under control."

Thirteen years later, "I went back to the hospital of my
own accord." Infirm health; anxiety about the family; the
death of a child, with other depressing circumstances,
brought it on. But this time he wasn't so bad; he went into
the mental hospital because he realized that his insane impulses might, at any moment, become uncontrollable. After
four nights without sleep, he knew he had better be shut
up, and after he got to the hospital, he felt much safer. This
time he knew that the hospital was a good place for him,
and so he didn't worry. He liked Dr. Mackintosh; he trusted
him, and soon his brain began to clear.

Some thoughts on insanity. Our author warns people
against religious fanaticism. He says, "Nothing assimilates
man more closely to the Fiend than religious fanaticism."
"Diseased veneration, or diseased religious feeling brings
on lunacy of a most acute, hopeless, and agonizing description." The Scotchman said that an insane man in the hospital
attacked his fellow patients "with the idea of provoking

them to kill him." This was his way of trying to commit suicide! Like the woman who wrote *The Maniac*, the Scotchman said it is unwise to *argue* with an insane man, but it can help briefly to divert the current of his thought "from the fiery channel in which it is flowing." This is why the Scotchman believed in setting up such workshops and art studios as are now to be found in most well-run mental hospitals.

A good point the author made is that all of us should always talk to a mental patient as if he "were rational and accountable." "Let kindness be ever mingled with firmness and decision." "So far as possible, allow the patient to have his own way." "Never, however, where it can be avoided, trust an insane person; and at the same time, never show your distrust. He may be trustworthy this minute, but the next minute, if you have given him an opportunity, he may destroy himself."

Our author states—as have other observers—that "female lunatics are much less susceptible of control than are males. They are more troublesome, more noisy, more abusive in their language; and much readier to use their teeth, their tongue, and their hands than males who have received the same degree of education and have moved in the same circle of society."

Altogether, this little book is so full of wisdom every student of psychiatry could learn much from it. It interests me greatly to see that just one hundred years ago, in Scotland, there was a beautifully run mental hospital. As yet, not many of our hospitals in this country would seem to be so good—judging from the report of a recent survey by the National Association for Mental Health. According to this survey, a large percentage of our mental hospitals have ancient buildings; they have too few psychiatrists, too few nurses, and too few attendants. In many of the state hospitals there can be very little psychiatric treatment—only custodial care.

The Mental Troubles of Arthur Symons

Arthur Symons's story of a lifetime of approaching insanity is one of the best ever written. He was a master of prose who could describe vividly what had happened to him. His is perhaps the best account available of the sort of temperament which can lead a person into insanity. His is the best description I know of the inability of the absolutely selfish psychotic person to feel or show affection.

When he was going insane, he described the beginnings of his experience in a chapter of his book—*Spiritual Adventures*. It is called "Christian Trevalga." In the first biographical chapter in this same book—a chapter called "A Prelude to Life," he said so wisely, "I am afraid I must begin a good way back if I am to explain myself at all satisfactorily. I can see how the queer child I was, laid the foundation of the man I became." How true! So often one can see in a child the beginnings of a psychosis which may not strike the victim down until he is in his fifties.

His childhood. Curiously, Symons, who probably was a very bright child, could not read until he was nine years old. He resolutely refused to learn. He liked to have his sister read to him; and one day, while she was reading the pathetic parts of *Uncle Tom's Cabin,* he felt sobs choking him, "and the passion of sorrow, mingled with the certainty that my emotion would betray itself, sent me into a paroxysm of rage, in which I tore the book from my sister's hands, and attacked her with my fists." Obviously, at that early day, he already was emotionally unstable.

When he went to school, he learned French and Latin easily, but German, he just couldn't stand. "When a thing did not interest me, nothing could make me learn it. I was not obstinate, I was helpless." At an examination in which he walked off with half the prizes, he couldn't answer a question in either geography or Euclid. "It was 'Don Quixote' which wakened in me the passion for reading. From that time I read incessantly, and I read everything." At school, like many schizoid lads, he made no friends. Curiously, when he was fifteen he wrote a monologue called "Mad."

He says, "I had always been delicate"; "I was uneasy about myself because I saw that others were uneasy about me; and my voracious appetite for life was partly a kind of haste to eat and drink my fill at a feast from which I might at any time be called away."

His heredity. Symons tells us that his parents were very religious. Some of his mental difficulties may have come from his father who, he says, was "a dryly intellectual, despondent person, whose whole view of life was coloured by the dyspepsia which he was never without, and the sick headaches which laid him up for a whole day, every week or every fortnight." "We had nothing akin; he never interested me." "My father bored me." And yet, "I respected him for his ability, his scholarship, and his character." Symons's mother was a much more likable person, but she was delicate in health. She had a queer brother who, for a while, was hospitalized, and the two of them had an odd old-maid sister. Arthur said that farther back in the family there was more insanity.

The extreme selfishness of the psychotic person. Remarkable is Symons's confession of his extreme selfishness and lack of any affection for anyone. He admitted he was "heartless, passionless, and indifferent." He said, "From as early a time as I can remember, I had no very clear consciousness of anything external to myself; I never realized that others had the right to expect from me any return for the kindness which they might show me or refuse to me, at their choice. I existed, others also existed; but between us there was an impassable gulf, and I had rarely any desire to cross it." He never had many friends but lived alone with his books and piano. He was fond of his mother but felt no affection toward anyone else nor any desire for the affection of others. All he asked was to be let alone, to live his own life. He raged because he could never escape entirely from contact with people who bored him. If people called, he went out of the room before they were shown in. "If I had not time to get away, I shook hands hurriedly, and slipped out as soon as I could." "People in general left me no more than indifferent; they could be quietly avoided. They meant no more to me than the chairs on which they sat; I was untouched by their fortunes; I was unconscious of my human relationship to them." Psychopathic criminals sometimes explain in this way their having murdered someone. A young man who put a bomb on a plane and sent his mother and forty innocent people hurtling to their death, said he felt no contrition. To him, people were no different from animals.

Even when Symons's mother came in to put some more coals on his fire, he says he would look up from his book furiously and ask why he could not be left alone!

Early difficulties. Early in life "I looked upon the relationship of man and woman as something essentially wicked"; "I was inexpressibly timid in the presence of a woman," which of course is typical of a shy, schizoid person. "I hardly ever met young people of my own age." And yet this man later wrote some of the most beautiful sensual poetry that has ever been written in the English language (*London Nights*). He would describe the ecstasies of a night of sex, but not of constant and unselfish and devoted love.

Early in life he began to walk in his sleep and to have nightmares. "Whenever I dreamed, it was infinite spirals, up which I had to climb, or of ladders, whose rungs dropped away from me as my feet left them, or of slimy stone stairways into cold pits of darkness, or of the tightening of a snake's coils around me, or of walking with bare feet across a floor curdling with snakes." He said that he had never known what it was to feel the earth solid under his feet.

His experiences with women. In London, he "lived—a queer, silent, sullen, not unattractive boy—among the students in whom he took so little interest." He wondered "why was it that he could not be as they were," "admire, like, love them back?" Later, when he reached maturity, he tried to find himself by falling in love, and he says women had not found it difficult to fall in love with him; his reticence, his enigmatical reluctance to speak out, the sympathetic sullenness of his face, a certain painful sensibility which shot like distressed nerves across his cheeks and forehead and tugged at the restless corners of his eyelids, seemed to attract them as to something which they could perhaps find out, and then soothe, and put to rest.

He says he had no morals and was too indifferent to refuse affection that was offered him. When it was no more than an adventure of the flesh, he accepted it simply; and eventually he "won the reputation of being both sensual and hardhearted, a sort of coldly passionate creature, that promised everything in the sincerity of one moment, and broke every promise in the sincerity of the next."

With all this, "he feared women." "To live with a woman, in the same house, the same room with her, is as if the keeper were condemned to live by day and sleep by night in the wild beast's cage. It is to be on one's guard at every minute, to apprehend always the claws behind the caressing softness of their padded coverings, to be continually ready to amuse one's dangerous slave, with one's life for the forfeit. The strain of it, the trial to the nerves, the temper! It was not to be thought of calmly. He looked around him, and saw all the other keepers of these ferocious, uncertain creatures, wearing out their lives in the exciting companionship; and a dread of women took the place of his luxurious indifference."

"It would be, he saw, a conflict of egoisms, and he could not afford to risk his own. Woman, as he saw her, is a beast of prey: rapacious of affection, time, money, all the flesh and all the soul, one's nerves, one's attention, pleasure, duty, art itself! . . . She requires the sacrifice of the whole man; nothing less will satisfy her; and, to love a woman, is, for an artist, to change one's religion."

Curiously, the one girl whom he almost loved, he would not accept. "The mere presence of any one he cared for, all the more if he cared for her a great deal, disturbed him, upset his life. And he must keep his life intact while he might." So he let his Rana "drift away from him, with an unavowed sense of failure, of having lost something which he could not bring himself to take, and which might yet have saved him. She parted from him, at the last, angrily, her pity worn out, her admiration stained with contempt; and with her went his last hold on the world."

The coming of hallucinations. Gradually he began to sense that possibly at times he was having hallucinations of hearing. He felt that as long as he could distinguish the true sounds from the false he was safe. Always, he had "felt that he was a piece of mechanism which was not absolutely to be trusted. There had been something wrong from the beginning; the works did not wear evenly."

Interestingly, when he was playing on his piano, the sound of the music appeared to him, as in Walt Disney's film *Fantasia*, as lines that he could see. One day these lines became abnormal, and he began to realize the more clearly that something was wrong with his brain. "He could not concentrate." "He seemed somehow to be slipping away from himself, dissolving into an uneasy vacancy. The people did not seem very real."

Gradually, more and more sounds came out of the air to him, and apparently he slowly slipped into insanity. When his friends came, "he awoke enough to realize that they thought him mad." "And it was with a very lucid fear that he waited now for the doctor who was to decide finally whether he might still keep his place in the world," or go into a mental hospital.

There is much more about Symons's insanity in his *Confessions*. This thin book of eighty-eight pages is unorganized and rambling, as one would expect it to be when written by a man who had been mentally ill. He said that when the thunderbolt fell on him which for a time destroyed his reason, he was unprepared for it. He admitted that he had always been eccentric, but he excused himself by saying that an artist—a man of genius—is fundamentally abnormal. The rules of society cannot be applied to him.

He tells of his youth, when, because of his awful dreams, he would wake with his hair damp with sweat, horrified with the feeling that in the night he had been given an impossible task and one that had to be finished in a second. In 1908, while he was in Venice, he became overexcitable, overstrained, irritable, and extravagant; he became hallucinated and obsessed. Often he couldn't stleep, and then he would get out of bed and write and write and write. At times rage would consume him.

He spoke of the Demon of Restlessness that had caused him to wander much, as if he "were driven onward by the intensity of a howling wind across a barren heath." He went to theater, but "the people who thronged the place disturbed me in the extreme; they irritated me." This feeling of irritation at everyone nearby is so typical of psychotic persons.

As his hallucinations developed, he wandered along the street, seeing the most horrible shapes and shadows. Like so many people going insane, he walked and walked. He wandered far out into the country, where some peasants fed him. Soon he was arrested and thrown into a dungeon. Fortunately, a friend found him and got him out; and a little later he was taken back to England to be hospitalized there. He says, "I became filled with fears and terrors, with delirious hallucinations." "I could neither read nor write."

Then he was taken to another mental hospital, which was like a prison. The people there treated him with the utmost mental cruelty. For instance, he who had never been able to sleep in the dark was made to do this. For a long time he hardly uttered a word or understood a word that was spoken to him.

He speaks of his loathing for the people about him. "This loathing, this disdain, this insolence, this haughtiness, this aloofness, this sense of pride, and of one's position in the world of letters, helped to keep me alive." Doubtless, it did not endear him to the people taking care of him!

Eventually, it appears that he got better and recovered so well that again he was able to write. One suspects that then he became slightly manic because he says he began to dash off in rapid order verses, satires, songs, translations, and plays. I have tried to find out what happened to him later but so far have failed, doubtless because he had no close friends who could write about him. The only source I have found is T. Earle Welby's *Arthur Symons, A Critical Study* (1925). Unfortunately for our purpose here, Welby's book is a commentary on Symons's writings. There is not even a brief mention of his period of mental alienation. According to Welby, Symons could be interested in a fellow human being *as an artist* but not as a man or a friend. W. G. Blaikie Murdoch's *The Work of Arthur Symons: an Appreciation* (1907) also deals only with the poet's writings.

A Man Who Was a Century Ahead of His Time

A hundred or more years ago, a certain Col. John A. Joyce was traveling about in the United States. In his book *A*

Checkered Life (1883), he tells how, in his youth, he studied so hard that he became mentally upset. In 1859, he got an idea of running the wheels of the world with power from a perpetual-motion machine. Although, of course, he got nowhere with this idea, he was strangely correct in some of his prophecies. He said, "I believe that the day is near at hand when the industrial machinery of the world will be run by electricity, and that we shall navigate the upper atmosphere with greater velocity and certainty than has ever been attained by man on land or sea."

He is committed because of an acute upset. One night he became so manic that they had to shut him up in a mental hospital. "My mind was so wild, and my muscles so strong, that it took half a dozen attendants to overpower me." "I tore off every garment from my body." One day "a big attendant felled me to the floor, and dragged me to a dark room, where I was chained to the wall, and strapped to a bare iron cot." "For weeks I was confined in a small basement room, with only an upper grated window to admit light and air." "Food was poked through an aperture." Like other prisoners in history, Joyce made friends of mice and spiders. "For a month I did not sleep an hour." But in two months he recovered and was discharged from the asylum.

His wise plea for better hospitals with open doors. When he got out, Joyce started pleading for better mental hospitals with better grounds for the patients. He felt sure the insane would get well faster if they had more freedom. He said, "Tear out the black bolts that bar the windows; paint in bright cheerful colors, let clambering vines, blooming flowers, running waters and the song of birds gain entrance to the weary mind, and let the soft sunshine into the black holes and damp dungeons that man has made for man."

What is sad is that these wise suggestions, made a hundred years ago by Joyce and by Dr. Mackintosh, the head of the Gartnavel Hospital (see Anonymous, *The Philosophy of Insanity*, 1860, earlier in this chapter) are only now being put into practice. Apparently, Joyce went on to live a most interesting life, without ever having another period of acute mania.

CHAPTER 13

Some People Who Were Only Mildly Disturbed

In this chapter I bring together the stories of a number of persons who were so little disturbed mentally that it is questionable if they ever needed to be locked up. I imagine they could have been taken care of, at least for most of the time, in the home of some kindly and sensible person— perhaps a retired nurse. Some could have been cared for in the new type of mental hospital in which the person stays only at night. By day he may go back to his job.

Some persons, when mildly manic, seem sane enough; all they need is to be kept from rambling about, wasting the family's funds, perhaps getting drunk, or getting into conflicts with the police and others. Some get to calling up their friends at 2 A.M., or they start throwing big expensive parties that they cannot afford. Many persons, like Jim Curran, need mainly board and lodging during the years in which their mind is so dulled they cannot work and earn a living. Miss Margaret Wilson could probably have been cared for in a home, if there had only been one open to her. William Moore seemed to have little need for confinement in a hospital. Henry C. Brown was a bit depressed, but he doubted if his thinking was ever much "muddled." Perhaps, in his case, as in that of many other depressed persons, he had to be in a mental hospital mainly to protect him from

taking his own life. People like Marian King, who was taking barbiturates in excessive doses, have to be locked up
for a few months until they can be taught to live again
without the help of a drug.

A Man Who, for Years, Was Just Unable to Work

The story told by Elsa Krauch (*A Mind Restored,* 1937)
is one of the best about the mental troubles of a man who
was only slightly disturbed. Even when he was at his worst,
I doubt if anyone meeting him at a luncheon would have
noticed anything wrong with him, but technically he was
insane because occasionally he had to be hospitalized.

Lack of ability to earn a living. The only reason for Curran's staying in a hospital as long as he did was that during
some of the years in which he was unable to earn his living,
when his family had gotten tired of taking care of him, he
needed board and lodging. Apparently he was always quiet
and inoffensive and well-behaved. His trouble was that he
had lost his drive, his business sense, and his ability to work.
He had a mild depression. He tells how for years he kept
slipping mentally. From being a prosperous businessman,
he "slid down hill," he lost his good judgment, and he became a less and less efficient salesman until finally he couldn't
get or hold any job.

The seeds of insanity can show up in childhood. Even as
a child, Jim had been a great worrier. "I worried at night
until every member of the household was home. I worried
because I was afraid that someone would drop into the
cistern under the house. I even worried about my dog. I
often cried myself to sleep." His mother had never been
well, and she, also, cried a good deal. She had a severe
diabetes. Jim's father also was a great worrier.

Curran had an idea that his mental troubles started when
his girl broke their engagement of several years' standing,
but I suspect this was only a trigger that upset a man who
was basically unstable and inadequate to stand up to the
strains of life.

The beginnings of the breakdown. "Five years passed,
and then I began to notice changes in my personality—

changes which did not seem so very important at the time, but which I have since come to believe indicated the beginnings of my mental breakdown." Significant of a desire to flee from life "was my purchase of a large piece of land on an island. What for? Not for investment; not for a happy home." At this time he was making a lot of money, but that did not make him happy. He married a girl, but that did not help him. Then came a definite urge to become a recluse, to creep away from society. "I had already retreated from life mentally, and I was preparing to do so physically too, as soon as possible." He planned to be a hermit. "I wanted to be alone to nurse my grief and disappointment."

As time passed, Curran became so restless he decided to do some of the traveling for his firm, and hence he started out "on the road." "But wherever I was I wanted to be somewhere else." "I couldn't stay at any one thing, whatever it was, for very long. So I had to keep going." "Like so many persons going insane, he soon began to suffer from recurring abdominal pains. And as so often used to happen when people suffered from a psychic pain in the abdomen, the doctor promptly diagnosed appendicitis and rushed Curran to a hospital for an operation. But, fortunately, the patient was so restless that that same night he took French leave. The doctor was furious at him, but the pain was gone, and so there was no operation!

Loss of business judgment. Later, as Curran said, "I began developing a new trait—obstinacy. I thought I knew better than others what ought to be done. I had slipped so much that I was no longer alert." So he sold his share in his prosperous company and bought into a business in which anyone could have told him he would lose his money. Worse yet, later, when things started to go downhill, and he saw the financial crash coming, he could not make a move to get out. He just watched in a numb terror. "Procrastination became my most predominant trait." He worried and worried and became more and more inefficient and tired. It was harder to think or to plan or to concentrate or to do anything for any length of time. The worst of it was that no one—not even he—guessed what was wrong. Then, stupidly, he began to borrow money on which to live and support his wife and children, and be began to get sorry for himself.

Apparent laziness. Like many people going insane, he began to think he was physically ill. His friends thought he was just lazy and stupid. He went back to selling but had no luck. Like many people going insane, he didn't want to see people, and he refused to see even old friends. He started spending his evenings in a hotel lobby, smoking one cigarette after another. About this time, his wife left him and took the children with her. "My restlessness increased from day to day. I walked and walked and walked." As we have seen, this is a common trick of psychotic persons. Another typical danger signal was his inability to read. This is definitely a sign of a disintegrating mind. Another bad sign was that he grew thinner and thinner. As so commonly happens in these cases, it did not occur to his physician— untrained in psychiatry—that there could be a mental basis for all of his patient's discomforts. Only after Curran had been going downhill *for five years* did the doctor send him to a hospital and call in a neurologist.

Relief on entering a general hospital. Curran liked being in the hospital, because there he didn't feel any distress over his not working. He dreaded leaving the place because that would bring back the problems of making a living. He got better, and for a while his wife came back to him.

He entered a mental hospital. Next, he was put into a mental hospital where he spent seven months. His friends kept telling him there was nothing the matter with him, but he only resented this.

For a while he was so negativistic that whenever anyone asked him to do something, he did just the reverse. He refused to bathe. He wouldn't play cards; all he did was to walk up and down. He dreaded seeing people. Then he left the hospital, unfortunately only a bit more bewildered.

What they said he needed was a change. "My relatives then had a new idea. They said I needed 'a change of scene.'" Relatives often say that; and usually they make a great mistake. His family sent him out West to do hard physical work in a grocery. They told him to "snap out of it." How he came to hate that phrase! Then he became terrified of new faces.

Again, he went into a hospital.

About this time he became much distressed because his family got disgusted with him. To them, he looked like a lazy failure—entirely to blame for all of the mess he had got into. Naturally, they became so hostile and bitter that he came to look on them as his worst enemies.

He had none of the usual symptoms of insanity. Still Curran had none of the usual symptoms of insanity, such as delusions and hallucinations; he just felt terribly tired, and uninterested in life. He gave up and decided he would never be well again. All he asked for was some let-up in his mental suffering. A year later, although he was no better, he was released from the hospital. He worked a while as a salesman, but still he would rarely speak to anyone outside of the store. He couldn't even play cards as he formerly had loved to do. He couldn't read a newspaper because he couldn't grasp the meaning of what he read. He much wanted sleep, but often that would not come.

Common stupidities in the care of the insane. Soon he had to quit work, and so he had to go back to a hospital so as to get bed and board. This time it was a state mental institution. In this hospital, everyone had to get up at 5:30 in the morning, no matter how badly he needed more sleep. This was one of those curious relics of medievalism—an utterly stupid regulation which no one had ever thought to change, even though it must have been just as much of a nuisance to the staff as to the patients.

As is the case with many derelicts in a state mental hospital, Curran could have been cared for just as well in the poorhouse. He had only a few queer sensations.

His family still thought him lazy, but as he says, he had the laziness of a man with a broken leg. Interesting, as showing how sane many legally insane persons can be, Curran tells about a brilliant attorney in the hospital who sometimes was borrowed by a lawyer in the nearby city to help him try a difficult court case!

One of the best things that happened to Curran came one day when it occurred to him that all his troubles hadn't been brought on him from the outside. "Maybe there was something inside of me that caused my illness." With this admission, Curran took a big step forward on the road to sanity.

The need for help in convalescence. Then came parole into the home of a nice attendant who had grown fond of his patient. As Curran said, "An interlude of this kind, between institutional life and the responsibilities of the outside world, can be of tremendous help. When Curran did go out into the world on his own, he was glad when a friend got him the job of running a freight elevator! This was lucky for him because, for the next two years, he wasn't ready for a job in which he would have to work with his brain.

Finally, he found he could do office work again, and then he improved rapidly. Instead of daydreaming or feeling bitter or sorry for himself, he began to "live almost wholly in the present, without worrying too much about yesterday or tomorrow." Eventually he again came to be interested in other people and their problems, and as he says, "That was a real triumph." The psychotic person is generally too completely self-centered. He thinks only of himself.

Curran recovers. Three years later Curran was pretty much himself again. He expressed the hope that as time passes we will have better facilities for the care of both the person who is going insane and the one who has just been discharged from a hospital. As he said, often it is a mistake for a patient to go *home* upon dismissal. Too often one of the causes for the person's attack of psychosis is to be found in his home. There, perhaps, is a nagging wife, or a domineering mother. Curran tells of some of his hospital buddies who went home to a mean wife and there did about the only thing they *could* do to escape her bitter tongue: they committed suicide. Curran tells of a psychiatrist who used to say that sometimes he wished, when he sent the patient home, that for a time he could *lock up the family!* If the relatives of the recently insane want their loved one to stay well, they had better not keep telling him what "an ornery and expensive bum" he has been.

A Bout of Mild Insanity after an Operation

Although Margaret Wilson (*Borderland Minds,* 1940) spent five years in a mental hospital, at no time was she much upset or confused or difficult to handle. She probably wouldn't have been hospitalized if she had had a family to take care of her. Unfortunately, when she became slightly depressed, after an operation for gallstones, she was rooming with a woman who couldn't very well take care of her. As a result, she had to go into a hospital. She writes that, on looking back over her early life, she could see how, unwittingly, she had forged the chains that later were to bind her, and how some mistakes and wrong decisions she had made had led her into an unhappy maze from which it was not easy to escape.

Emotional immaturity from childhood on. She tells how, as a child, she was a "troublesome brat" who tended to fly into passions. Later, she was a hoyden. In school, she was very bright, but her "behavior was unsatisfactory; she was emotionally immature.'" She was never very attractive to men. She was a bit neurotic and inclined to nervousness. She had indigestion and "colitis." Following her gallbladder operation, she lay in coma for two days and was hardly expected to live. She had either hysteria or a little stroke, due perhaps to a lack of sufficient oxygen with her anesthetic. She had to learn to talk all over again, and for a while she stuttered. She became irritable, dyspeptic, apprehensive, and unable to sleep. Then she grew despondent and thought of suicide. Later, when she became manic, she was very talkative, excitable, and unlike herself. She knew she was in the borderland of insanity.

Hospitalization. On Christmas Eve of 1931, she was deceived into going into an old-fashioned mental hospital where the discipline was overly strict and every patient had to take a dose of salts after supper! Cold packs were used as a punishment, or as a threat of punishment.

On one occasion, Miss Wilson almost succeeded in committing suicide by hanging. As she was contemplating suicide, she was interested to read in Revelations 9:6, "And in those days shall men seek death, and shall not find it, and shall desire to die, and death shall flee from them." This expresses the situation *very* well.

Some problems of a person in a mental hospital. Very interesting, and probably true, is Miss Wilson's statement that if, in one's home, one has a bit of a tantrum or, because of lack of appetite, fails to eat one's dinner, or fails to have a bowel movement, nothing is thought of it; but in a mental hospital, if one gets a bit miffed at someone, or has a tantrum, or fails to eat, or fails to go to the toilet, the attendants immediately chalk up a bad mark and assume that the patient's insanity has taken a turn for the worse.

Miss Wilson makes an interesting point that many an eminent person has gotten by for all his or her days with a marked eccentricity such as would have been looked on with alarm in a mental hospital. For instance, there was Emily Dickinson, for years a recluse; Elizabeth Barrett Browning, another recluse; "poor old Carlyle with his dyspepsia, his melancholy and his bad temper"; Amy Lowell with her cigar; Charles Lamb with his alcohol, his stuttering, and his spells of depression; and Edgar Allan Poe with his alcoholism. Miss Wilson suspects some of them might have been locked up if someone had only turned them in!

The Story of a Kindly Man with Just One Delusion

William L. Moore (*The Mind in Chains*, 1955), a college-educated ex-marine, after a year and a half in a mental hospital, has always doubted if he ever was really insane. In high school he became so strongly attached to a certain teacher of his, a Mr. Armstrong, that he almost worshiped him. Then, Armstrong died, and soon Moore got an idea in his head that his old friend would some day return from the grave, so that the whole world could appreciate his greatness.

Early psychic difficulties. As so often happens in these cases, when one goes back into the history of the patient, one finds that from early life, Moore had some problems of adjustment. Then, when he was seventeen, he had such an argument with his father over a small matter that his father said, "If you keep acting this way, I'll have to take you to a psychiatrist."

As Moore says, he always stood a bit apart from the crowd. Others often compromised with their beliefs in order to adjust to reality, but Moore couldn't. He says that often he was too forthright and stubborn.

In 1937, his teacher noted that he was nervous and was twitching and jerking a good deal. He became greatly interested in the Children's Crusade of the Middle Ages. After brooding over the tragic end of this crusade, Moore started out one day with $1.15 in his pocket on what he thought could be a bicycle trip to the eastern end of the Mediterranean. Fortunately, that night, he decided that he had better call off the trip and go home.

While at college Moore got the idea that his troubles had all been part of a gigantic scheme to make him face adversity. He felt that this had been planned for him by Mr. Armstrong, and hence "he must have only *pretended* to be dead. He must be directing everything from behind the scenes. There could be no other explanation!"

Moore is committed. Apparently, Moore did enough curious things so that his father had him placed in a state hospital for treatment. Moore was one of those persons who are practically normal except for one peculiar idea, which they cannot believe is a delusion. So long as Moore maintained that Mr. Armstrong was alive, the psychiatrists felt that he had better stay in the hospital and be treated. He had many insulin shock treatments, which he describes magnificently. Every psychiatrist ought to read at least this chapter of the book.

He says that after one has taken such treatments, one knows what it is to die. After a session, "Gradually, I returned to 'normal'; my being rejoined this world. I was once more what I used to be." "Going out under insulin is similar to going to sleep. If the dose is large enough, there [is] no recollection of the thought processes during the unconscious period." His first impression was that "the physical world had dissolved, and that I had left my body and was looking at life objectively. People were but phantoms or shadows, and the walls of the institution had disintegrated. It took me the longest time to come back to earth, to pin down just where in the universe I was." "Coming out of the coma is a crazy, out-of-this-world feeling."

Moore recovers and decides to devote his life to helping others. Finally, in 1954, Moore was discharged from the hospital. Ever since, he has been trying to help persons who have been dismissed from a mental hospital.

Like so many persons who leave a mental hospital, Moore immediately ran up against the terrible problem of where to find a job suitable for a man of his education. As I write this, Bill Moore, now my good friend, still hasn't the sort of job he should have, with his education and his possibilities for usefulness. To me, it is interesting to see that Bill, who as a boy so much wanted to do some great thing for the world, is still struggling to find some way in which he can help his fellow men.

An Excellent Description of a Period of Depression

In an excellent book (*A Mind Mislaid*, 1937) Henry Collins Brown tells of his breakdown. It seemed to be brought on by the great disappointment of failing to be elected director of a museum which he had spent years in building up. As so many ex-insane people say, "If only I or my family had known more about mental hygiene, and the early symptoms of a nervous crack-up, my break might have been avoided."

Brown wrote interestingly and well, and with a certain jauntiness which is pleasing. He showed how observant and clear-minded a man in a mental hospital can be. After he got well, he said, "Not only does a recovered patient dread to speak of his illness, but he looks upon himself as having brought disgrace on his family." "There are occasional exceptions, and I am one." On his return to the world, he made no secret of where he had been. Once, when he was to speak before a big audience, he was introduced as the only ex-crazy man who now brags about it! According to Brown, many of the patients in a mental hospital are "in there largely as the result of some damn-foolishness"; they did not live wisely.

He said, "I am powerless to describe the abject terror

which seized me when I realized I was within the walls of a mad-house." As is the custom, he had to sign a lot of legal papers which he could not understand. After a while, he got better; he began to look around, to pick out those few persons whom he thought he would care to talk to. Some were more sane and sociable than others. He realized that he would have to pull himself "out of the hole; the doctor could do but little."

A plea for eugenics. As Brown looked around him at many of the poor specimens of humanity, he got to thinking about the need for eugenics. One of the psychiatrists said that he hoped that some day when two people plan to marry and to raise children, they will look into the goodness or badness of their stock, much as a breeder of race horses does when he starts buying a stable. But, as the doctor said, none of us are likely to live long enough to see that day. People are not yet ready for this idea. For years to come, many a young woman, when choosing a father for her children, will look more at the size of the man's bank account than at the badness of his heredity.

An illness that came slowly and went slowly. Brown saw that, if only because his illness was a long time in coming, it was a long time in going. There were many little relapses. Brown did not recall ever having been muddled in his thoughts, but for a while he was so depressed as to be utterly indifferent. "In that state you seldom speak to anyone, and then only to snarl. A constant state of hostility would perhaps define the attitude." "Physical pain is bad enough, but mental pain is a thousand times worse."

Brown could not say that any one particular thing brought about his cure. As his spirits lightened, his body weight went up. It had gone down from 180 to 113 pounds!

Then, as Brown said, and as so many depressed persons say, "*the curtain began to go up.*" After many months, he got interested in things; and the idea of going out again into the world somewhat lost its terror for him. Again, he could talk with people.

His intelligent interest in the stock market. Brown maintained that even when he was in bad shape, he retained his interest in the stock market and what was happening there, and I see no reason to doubt this. As most people know, the mentally disturbed person can have a brilliant mind except for one quirk. Brown claims that about 1929 he saw that stocks were priced much too high and that a man would be very foolish to go on buying at such prices. So he wrote to several of his friends, begging them to sell quickly and get out; but they, thinking that he was only a "nut," disregarded his advice. As a result, when the big crash came, they lost hundreds of thousands of dollars. "One man who lost $65,000. still has the letter I sent in a vain effort to save him!"

Later, as he improved, Brown became very unhappy because he so missed his work. As he said, there is no blessing so precious as work. But actually, he still was in no shape to work. For a time, he didn't even want to get well. He preferred the idea of dying, and for a while he fought his returning health.

The desire for suicide. In a mental hospital the patient's "urge to commit suicide is something that constantly plagues the doctors." That is why each night all eyeglasses, neckties, suspenders, and bathrobe belts are collected and locked up. But even with all the watchfulness of the attendants and all the precautions that are taken, each year a number of the patients succeed in committing suicide. Brown reminds us that many a person occasionally will say, "I wish I were dead" without really meaning it. "The feeling that comes over you when mentally ill is altogether different; there is no comparison. The one is a passing emotion, the other represents an absence of any desire to live." "The natural fear of death, which we all have in normal moments, no longer exists." "A mental depression is something unspeakably horrible." The patient feels, "Why endure this cruel tumult of the mind when peace is within reach? Peace, blessed peace!" "The first law of Nature, self-preservation, has completely broken down."

His life in the hospital. The struggle to conquer fear was a bitter one. To return to the world seemed to be a terrible ordeal. For a time he couldn't face a return to the old life. For months he had been pacing the floor for 14 hours out of each 24. Then came a sign of recovery—the walking began to tire him. He had felt no fatigue for nearly three years, and so its return was a good sign. But still, he had a "what's the use" complex. Only gradually did he see that there might still be a place in the world for him. Soon the doctors got him into the occupational therapy shop, and that helped. He learned to make baskets. He noted that the patients who made the neatest baskets were the ones who got well first.

Curious is his statement that nothing was so annoying as his having to witness the moving pictures that were shown to the patients. This interests me because sometimes when I want to find out if the patient sitting before me in the office is sane, I just ask her, "Do you still enjoy the movies?" Sometimes then she, who I suspect is going insane, says, "I used to love the movies and went to see them every chance I got, but now I won't go. I am now so wrapped up in myself that I haven't the slightest interest in what those people are doing."

As Brown says, thoughtless people keep saying to mentally disturbed relatives, "Come now and snap out of it." For a while this phrase greatly angered Brown, because what he wanted most in the world was to "snap out of it."

Remarkable is Brown's description of a hypochondriac of an extreme degree whom he knew in the hospital. This man "spent most of his time examining a small swelling on his forehead which he was convinced was a cancer." He was constantly waylaying the doctors and asking them about the "lump." They all told him it was a harmless projection of his forehead, but such reassurance brought him no comfort.

Interesting and instructive is Brown's description of the griefs and terrors of Visitor's Day, when many a devoted mother or father or wife of a patient travels far to see the loved one—only to be snubbed or reviled in the most cruel way. "A peculiarity of mental illness is that it turns you against all those nearest and dearest to you." As Brown says, it is very necessary that the relatives realize that the cruel behavior of the patient is just a part of his illness and hence must be forgiven. It must not keep the relatives from returning.

Encouraging to many persons will be Brown's statement that, in spite of his having interviewed many of the patients, he never heard anyone say that he had been falsely locked up by a relative who wanted his money. He describes some of the alcoholics being "dried out" in the hospital. Some of them bragged to Brown that on the afternoon of the day of their release they would have a woman and a bottle and be stinking drunk again!

Brown tells us how, in a mental hospital, the attendants, whenever they have to take a number of patients from one place to another, are always counting them to make sure no one has slipped away and hidden somewhere. Brown says he got the habit of counting like this so ingrained in him that, for long after his release, when in an elevator he would count the passengers in the car!

Gradual improvement. Eventually, Brown sensed the "subsidence of something like a great storm at sea: the howling wind died down, the tumult of the waves seemed spent, and the tossing billows gradually sank to rest." Finally, there came brief spells with "a glorious feeling of tranquillity."

One of the signs of Brown's return to health came when he began again to read books and magazines and to write letters home. Eventually, he was dismissed, well. Cheering is his statement that on his return to New York City, all but a very few of his old friends welcomed him as if nothing had happened.

A Spoiled Young Woman for Whom Life Became Too Strenuous

A good description of the impressions gained by someone who enters a mental hospital with a mind fairly unclouded is that of Marian King (*The Recovery of Myself*, 1931). She was hospitalized because, for a while, she had been taking too much Veronal (to help her sleep). Then she had attempted suicide. Luckily, the doctors at the emergency hospital had quickly saved her.

She was a young woman of the smart set who drove herself to do too many things. She drove herself until she cracked up. Doubtless she had an inborn tendency to be selfish, because she said she was determined to get her own way in all things. Bad, also, was her inability to get close enough to her loved ones to talk over her problems with them.

On entering the hospital, she was shocked, as so many other patients are shocked, on seeing bars on the windows and on hearing the click of the lock as she was shut into her room. As so often happens, the girl's family had been unwise in not telling her what type of hospital she was headed for, and hence it upset her much when some fellow patients came in and said, "You are in the bug-house all right!"

As commonly happens in most hospitals, during the first few days, when the girl sadly needed rest and sleep, and should have had it, someone was constantly coming into her room, either to take a history or make an examination, or make some tests, or take some blood, or take her temperature. Even some of the other patients were allowed to come into her room to bother her. That she was slightly psychotic at the time is indicated by the fact that for several days she was negativistic and unwilling to eat. Also, when she refused to get out of bed, it took four attendants to get her up. She admits that at times she was so unsocial she would shut herself up in her room.

The factors that led to the breakdown. The girl tells us how, as often happens in these cases, she had been overdoing, and getting more and more tired and more and more unable to sleep, until finally, on her own, she started taking Veronal in large doses. She says that for months she had strained every nerve to keep up with the strenuous and exacting demands which her life had made on her. She would not complain to her parents or let them know that she was overtired. She feared to disgrace the family by not attaining high marks. Worse yet, she who was being forced along so hard in college, was going to art school; she was trying to learn to write stories; she was playing almost championship tennis; she had taken an active part in a field meet, and she had had to train for a charity benefit performance. Finally, in the evenings she had been doing some dating!

Then, she had to face problems of adjustment to life—problems of selfishness, problems of feigning illness to get out of work, problems of taking Veronal to drown her disappointments and help her with her problems of handling her parents so as always to get her own way. As she said, if she could not get what she wanted in one way, she would get it in another way. She admitted that her skill in getting herself more and more spoiled had led her into the mental illness.

The early symptoms of brain fatigue. Very important is Miss King's statement that there came a time when she could not concentrate. "Try as I would, I became restless and could not apply myself to a thing. . . . Sleep would not come. Do you know what it means to lie awake as the minutes drag into hours, fevered with the weight of the night, reaching for rest with your two hands?"

Her impressions in the hospital. Because Miss King was not much disturbed mentally, she was soon moved to an unlocked section of the hospital. Even in this unusually well-run place, she gained the impression that if some of the patients had been handled in a more gentle way they would not so greatly have resented their confinement.

Miss King admits she made many demands, and sometimes, when her requests were not immediately granted, she "became a picture of seething resentment."

As she wrote to her mother, when she was getting better, "I think that all my trouble lies in the fact that I never sought your confidence, no matter how much you asked for mine. I have learned now, Mother, what it is to confide in someone." She came to see that often she had made trouble for herself. This brought discontent upon her, and then she turned to the drug. When she entered the hospital, she told the doctor that her only fear was that she would not always get her own way. Later, suddenly, she saw herself as a spoiled child. But, as she said, "I have always been that way."

In the last weeks in the hospital, while Miss King was putting together picture puzzles, it suddenly occurred to her that when she came in, she herself was like a picture puzzle with the pieces all in a heap. The good psychiatrists had helped her to put the several parts into proper place so as to make a complete picture. As one of the doctors said, "We try to help a person to solve the puzzle of herself." Miss King felt that she had found her place in the puzzle, and she hoped that never again would she drop out of it. She felt that a happy consequence of her psychotic episode had been the development of a new and better relationship between her mother and herself. She lost many of her former fears of disappointment. She learned to take many a disappointment in her stride, just as she had learned to take defeats in her tennis contests.

CHAPTER **14**

People Who Could Not Believe
They Had Ever Been Insane

While many psychotic or definitely insane persons suffer
so terribly that they know full well that they are insane,
there are many others who are so little disturbed by their
few delusions and are so unable to believe that their odd
ideas are delusions that they never can believe that they
were once insane. Some of these persons for years will
spend all their energies trying to "clear their good name,"
and some of them will write a book to prove they never
should have been committed. The books described in this
chapter should all be studied well by those lawyers and
judges who often have to deal with insane persons who
maintain that they never were mentally upset.

As we shall soon see, most of these people prove to us
by their naïve confessions that at least for a time they were
much upset. The most remarkable of all these books was
written by a physician who later became a Member of
Parliament. Psychiatrists tell me that they marvel that a
physician, with all his training, could describe for us the
typical symptoms of an acute mental flare-up, while apparently not recognizing what they meant. Other men—
with legal training—when they went insane, spent years,
first, on habeas corpus proceedings to get themselves out
of a hospital, and later, on efforts to "clear their name."
280

The story by G. F. Adler could go here because the man was so sure he was sane, but his account of his experience is so typically that of a paranoiac that I have put it in Chapter 9.

A Member of Parliament Is Sure He Should Never Have Been Committed

A Member of Parliament, a physician, Dr. Donald McI. Johnson, has written two autobiographical books, one of them (*A Doctor Returns*, 1956) designed to prove that he never was insane and should never have been put in a mental hospital. Like practically all of the people who write such books, he was so honest as to supply his readers with a mass of facts likely to satisfy any psychiatrist or even layman that, for a time, he was mentally much disturbed and decidedly paranoid.

Dr. Johnson starts out by saying, so typically, "It is THEY who are drawing the circle round you to enclose you." For a while his brain was racing along to cope with the dangers that he thought were enveloping him. On every side he saw hostile gleaming eyes. He felt that the cunning of his enemy had a diabolic quality. He was being "framed," and there was no escape anywhere. His food was being poisoned. He was being watched and spied upon; his letters were being held by the post office, which was full of spies. Microphones were in his room, and everything that he said was being taken down.

For years, his energies were devoted toward escaping these devices. He ran to the police for protection, to his solicitor for legal aid, and to the editor of his local paper for help—but no one would come to his rescue. His story was not accepted anywhere. When he called an old friends, they said little and looked embarrassed. Some sent out word that they were too busy to see him.

The doctor tells that for a while he and his wife were afraid to talk because they felt sure that microphones had been installed in their rooms. In his book *The Doctor Regrets* he tells how when asked to conform to the rules of the new Health Act in England, he threw up his practice

and quit medicine, which suggests that he was always somewhat of an independent and unusual man.

In one place he speaks of the tendency of members of
his family to fight and to sue each other. This habit commonly means that there is a good deal of mild psychosis in
the clan. Apparently, from what he says, he had one uncle
who was erratic. In one place, Dr. Johnson speaks of having
"overestimated his own unpopularity." He speaks, also, of
troubles he got into because of his "unhappy facility for
doing things the wrong way round." He admits, also, that
with his first wife, he wasn't an ideal marriage companion.
He tells of what he suspected were hallucinations. He would
wake in the middle of the night, sweating and imagining
that he had heard the front door bell. He would run downstairs, but there would be no one there.

The day he became excited. Dr. Johnson then tells how,
on a certain evening, in his hotel rooms, he became so frantic that he soon had to be restrained. He told the hotel
manager that all the drinks in the hotel were poisoned and
all the rooms were contaminated and unfit to live in. He
demanded that a guard be posted outside his bedroom door.
He suddenly rushed from his room with a scream because
he thought he was being attacked. He ordered the manager
to discharge the whole staff because he was sure they were
implicated in the plot to poison him.

He thought he had been trapped by Continental gangsters; he was in the grip of Communists who were seizing
power in England. He was satisfied that many people all
over the country were also being poisoned. It was the visita-
tion of God on an irreligious community.

As the doctor says, after his wild episode in the hotel, his
doctor went before a magistrate, certified that his patient
was of unsound mind, and had him sent into a mental hospital.

His experience in the hospital. Like many mentally disturbed persons, after a couple of days, he "Entered a state
of revelation. Strange things were happening to me (so it
was revealed to me) for some undisclosed, but highly important purpose." Someone had gotten him in there "for
some special dedicated reason." We have heard exactly this

idea many times before from manic persons (see Anton Boisen, Chapter 6).

During the ensuing week, the doctor's imaginings continued to vary from day to day—they became, however, progressively more grandiose. "I was being selected as husband for Princess Margaret," and "I was head of the British Commonwealth." Then came an obsession that he could neutralize the poison in him by eating apples, and so he kept eating several a day. He was sure he was sane and everyone else was mad!

His years of search for the "poison" that had gotten him. Fortunately, Dr. Johnson soon came out of his excited state and in six weeks was dismissed from the hospital. He devotes 220 pages in his book to a discussion of how he could have been poisoned and what the poison could have been. For a year he spent much of his time in medical libraries, making a study of toxins and writing a book about them. Unfortunately, even with his early training in medicine, he failed to note that there is no poison known which, given in one dose, could have kept him upset mentally for six weeks, and then have kept him thinking in a paranoid way for the next several years. He thought this poison might have been hasheesh or hyoscine or belladonna, but actually, none of these old and well-known drugs will produce a prolonged paranoia.

There is only one feature that could suggest poisoning, and this is the fact that when Dr. Johnson went berserk, his wife Betty also became very nervous and excitable. But this could easily be explained by her having undergone the shock of seeing her husband become mentally deranged. Actually, in a few days his wife was all right, while for years he remained upset.

His great efforts to obtain vindication. He admits that ever since his mental disturbance he has been making plenty of trouble for many people. When he wrote his book, it was six years after his violent spell, and he was still fighting to prove that everyone but him was wrong! He demanded that his record of commitment be expunged by all official bodies in England. He appealed to his Member of Parliament, to the heads of the Public Health Service, and to the heads of the British Government. After he became a Member of Parliament, he appealed often for vindication by that body of men.

When first out of the hospital, he went to his lawyers to see if they would sue the Government, but they strongly advised against this. Next, he tried to show that no man should be deprived of his liberty by a judge. He seemed to forget that when a man becomes violent and begins to threaten the people about him, something has to be done to protect even himself from the results of his own illness.

One can easily see why, when Dr. Johnson got out of the hospital and began appealing for sympathy everywhere, he was first puzzled and then shocked to find that everyone tried to "brush him off." When his old friends, seeing him coming, "ducked down an alley," he said, "I no longer feel secure. If this can have happened to me, what else can happen? Anything can happen."

When Dr. Johnson got home from the hospital, he immediately demanded that all the doors of his apartment be locked. "It seemed to me that any time now THEY would take the opportunity to administer the *coup de grâce*—to finish me altogether." Then the doctor felt so afraid of what might happen to him in his summer home that he sold it. It took all the courage he had to spend even one night in the place. On occasions, he felt himself surrounded by people with glaring eyes. As he drove his car, he was continually looking back to see if he was being followed. He thought of fleeing to the highlands of Scotland and hiding there.

He felt he had discovered an important state secret. He felt that, through his misadventures, he had discovered something tremendously important to the British Government and the world, but no one would listen. He offered to give a great scoop to his newspaper friends, but they wouldn't use it. He said, "maybe I have found the secret of the Communist trials? Maybe I have the Russian 'truth drug'?" He even thought that if a Member of Parliament were to look into the matter of the poisoning, the Enemy would do something awful to the M.P. to get him out of the way.

Who was supposed to have done the poisoning? In only

one place in Dr. Johnson's book could I find him trying to answer the very important question: if he was poisoned, who *did* it? In order to have kept the doctor mentally disturbed for months and years, someone would have had to keep feeding him the supposed poison for a long time. Also, the villain would have had to gain access to the mental hospital to keep up the poisoning there. Who was he? Johnson said, "Yes, I have my villain, or at least my suspected villain, but I can give you no clue to him." "He has the protection of our stringent law of libel!"

When the doctor possibly became a bit manic. Once Johnson appears to have gone slightly manic because he says he became "on top of the world" and very talkative. He felt wonderfully well, as well as he had ever felt in his life before. The truth, as he saw it, kept "bubbling from [his] lips in a garrulous, never-ending stream."

Dr. Johnson says he will never give up his fight for justification. As Johnson said, most people in his position would have given up long before this, but he will never give in. So far as he can see, the rebuffs which he got from his friends could have only one explanation: the corrupting influence had infiltrated right into the established order of society. "The ring was closing tight," and his enemies had got him.

A Remarkable Book to Show the Bitterness of a Committed Man against His Family

A book by Fritz Peters about David Mitchell (*The World Next Door*, 1949) is invaluable because it gives such a remarkable word picture of the awful bitterness that can rage in the heart of an insane person—bitterness directed at some member of his family who at first had to arrange for a commitment and later had to refuse to let the patient be paroled home. David Mitchell tells us that when he was sent into a mental hospital, his mind was racing along in a disorganized way. From what he says, one gains the impression that for some time he had been a terrible problem in his home—because of his admitted irritability, his quick temper, his unreasonableness, and his inability to calm down and sleep.

The family stood all this, but when he went out on his front lawn in the nude, this was a bit too much, and something had to be done. As so commonly happens in these cases, the chief of police came, handcuffed the patient, and, without telling him why he was being arrested or where he was going, took him to a mental hospital. Eventually, David learned from the other patients that he hadn't committed any crime; he was just "crazy," and was, as he said, in a "nut-house."

The patient makes trouble in the hospital. He says that soon the rough attendants hammered into his head the idea that "if he made any trouble for them," or if he made a lot of noise, they would know how to take it out of his hide. Sometimes, they tied him down, sometimes (he says) they just knocked him out with a blow to his chin. One suspects that, at times, Mitchell was very trying.

Bitter problems that can arise when the patient is allowed to go home too soon. Mitchell was allowed to go home too soon, and the visit ended in a most distressing row with his mother. What happened was that he wanted his family to show enough faith in him to sign him out of the hospital and parole him into their care. But at the time he was so excitable and unreasonable and disturbed that they were not ready to do this. One could hardly blame them. But the patient suspected that his mother was intending to keep him locked up for life so that she could keep enjoying his compensation money. This so enraged him that he cursed her violently and promised her he'd surely come back some day and strangle her with his two hands. The family telephoned for the police, and again they came.

He said to his mother as he was being led away, "I want you to remember this moment as long as you live. I want you to remember when you wake up at night—that your son hates you and will always hate you. I want this moment to be burnt into your memory for ever. I want you to know that now they'll have to keep me in the hospital for ever, because if I *do* get out—and I will—the first thing I'll do is to kill you." "I'll kill all of you, unless . . . there is one person in this room who has the guts, the nerve, the honesty, the courage, the belief, the faith—that's it—the faith in another human being, to let me out *now*. If you have any faith at all, let me go. Let me go." Naturally, after listening to these threats, the family had even less desire to assume the care of the man.

Back in the hospital. Back in the hospital, Mitchell had some shock treatments, which quickly helped him. Soon he was much better, but still, when his mother came to see him, he only raged at her. As he watched her walk slowly away, crying, he felt glad. He had wanted to punish her and he had done it. "I had wanted to pay her back for that evening—to throw a knife into her insides and twist it around, stabbing the vital spot in her; and yet, now that I had done it, it was almost unbearably painful to me. I was gripped by alternating feelings of revenge and satisfaction; and by the horror of having caused real pain." "I felt a sensation of power, I could do this; I was not ineffective just because I was locked up. But I felt sick and empty inside. I wanted to vomit." In several of these books written by psychotic persons, one reads of this great tendency they have to hate with bitter hatreds. Apparently, a tendency to hate is one sign of a psychosis.

Mitchell was finally convinced that he had needed to be committed. Later, Mitchell kept arguing with the doctors and the administrators as to whether he should ever have been officially committed. The doctor one day helped him greatly by explaining that a big reason why his family had agreed to commit him was that if, when he was violent and murderous, he should kill someone, his being legally insane would save him from having to be tried for his life.

Later, one of the psychiatrists managed to get Mitchell to see that the great hate burning within him was doing him endless harm and was holding him back from recovery. Fortunately, the next time his mother came to visit him, he treated her fairly well. But again, they quarreled over her having permitted a judge to declare him insane. As a result, she left him in anger. But soon thereafter, he became so much better he was allowed to go home. Then, apparently, he and his mother were reconciled.

An Interesting Book on a Supposed
False Commitment

The next book (*The Monomaniac*) was written in 1864 by a certain William Gilbert. As usual, as one reads along, one becomes convinced that the man was insane, all right. Gilbert said, "I, a perfectly sane man, have been confined to an asylum for five long years." To his credit, he said, "I cannot in conscience accuse those of my family who placed me under restraint with any intentional unkindness or injustice." He went on to admit that many persons, knowing his story, might conclude that he had been locked up because he was not competent to handle his affairs.

He had quickly run through an inherited fortune. He admits that he had quickly run through three fourths of an inherited fortune and as a result had brought his family to the edge of ruin. He had spent large sums building a crazy "perpetual-motion" engine, which he was sure, in some miraculous way, would generate tremendous force and without any fuel would drive a ship through the waves. Actually, when he got his ship built, he found it would not move!

Typical of insanity is his statement that he became so convinced of the tremendous power that his invention had placed in his hands that it frightened him. Worse yet, he thought that with the enormous energy he would have at his disposal, God Himself would feel uneasy and inclined to accuse Gilbert of presumptuous blasphemy. This might bring down on Gilbert's head a terrible punishment, much like that which sent Satan hurtling down into hell! Finally, one night he escaped, and next day was back hard at work on his old invention.

He develops paranoid ideas. A day or two later, he read of some experiments in spiritualism performed by a Mr. Home, and the more he thought of Home's doings, the more convinced he became that Home had gotten even more power into his hands than he (Gilbert) had. He was convinced that Home must be looking for someone to help him with his plan to "war against the world, and who could that mortal be but myself?" Gilbert was afraid that "the power of Heaven itself must succumb to the combination of their two activities."

But somehow, with all this, he became convinced that Mr. Home was searching him out with some evil intentions. Accordingly, when Gilbert went on the street, he kept watching every face, prepared to flee if he saw anyone who looked like what he thought Home should look like. Then, one day, he saw a stranger who, he thought, might be Home, so he attacked him violently. The man disarmed him and turned him over to the police; and next day he was back in a mental hospital! Quite obviously, that is where he belonged.

The Troubles of Robert Fuller

Robert Fuller wrote a book (*Account of the Imprisonment and Sufferings of Robert Fuller,* 1833) to prove that he should never have been committed. After reading his claims, in which doubtless the essential parts of the story were left out, my hunch is that he had greatly worried his friends by getting a bit manic and trying to withdraw thousands of dollars from his bank so as to use the money in an unwise speculation. Apparently, the bank officer tried to save him from his folly. Obviously, something he did, which he does not tell us about, must have greatly worried his best friends, because, together with a physician, they called on him and suggested that he accept treatment in a mental hospital. Probably he answered them insultingly, because he says, "I soon found myself forsaken by all my friends, and at the mercy of these excited and almost infuriated men." His friends would hardly have acted in this way without some good reason. It is significant that apparently his wife did not come to his rescue.

Typical of an attack of violent mania is the fact that with all his excitement, within ten or twelve days he had worried off fifty pounds of weight. When committed, he apparently calmed right down, because he says that almost every day the doctors drove him around with them in the neighborhood of Boston, and within three months they set him free.

He admits that "all who took part in this melancholy tragedy did it under the guise of friendship." The book is a good example of those in which a man, trying to prove he was never insane, conceals the important parts of the story, but is so naïve as to leave enough to prove that he *was* insane.

A Lawyer's Story

Another beautiful example of the type of book which is published at his own expense by a man who is convinced that he was railroaded into a mental hospital and kept there unlawfully is that of John A. Chanler (*Four Years behind the Bars of Bloomingdale*, 1906). It is just a pile of legal documents which he filed in his attempt to get his freedom. In this case, the man came of a prominent family. He admits that his aunt was insane; and he admits, very significantly, that he was on bad terms with his brothers and all but one of his sisters. As I have said, this often happens in eccentric families. One of the surest signs of sanity in a family is that all the members like each other and get along beautifully.

Mr. Chanler admits that for long he had been a great student of weird forms of psychology; he says he could go into trances in which he would say and do things that could have caused an onlooker to have doubts as to his sanity. It is significant that, during some of the legal actions which he instituted, his own lawyers deserted him. Once when this happened, he appealed to William Randolph Hearst, a complete stranger to him, to supply him with funds.

Another Lawyer Fights the Charge of Insanity

Basil Hubbard Pollitt, when he wrote (*The Lawyer's Story*, 1958), was sure he had never been insane. He admitted, however, that he may at times have "lost control" and gotten a bit noisy. The story is typical of those written by a lawyer who, after becoming mentally disturbed, is committed, and then, because of his legal abilities, keeps getting himself back into the courts with writs of habeas corpus.

According to one hospital report which he introduces into the record, he tended to be "roving, amorous, and violent!" He is proud of the fact that his mother was a sister of Elbert Hubbard. He said he could not understand how anyone could doubt his sanity. Later, he escaped from the institution in which he was a patient—only to be arrested and sent back. Eventually, he was discharged.

A Nurse Doubts If She Was Insane

Another book (*Like a Lamb*, 1958) designed to clear the person's name was written by Ella Hales—a nurse, and apparently, in many ways, a likable one. Something evidently went wrong when she came up for her nursing certificate, because she was turned down, and the doctor said he doubted if she could ever nurse "in her state of health."

A fall on her lower back. Shortly afterwards, one morning as Miss Hales was hurrying down the attic stairs, she slipped and fell heavily on the bottom of her back. From then on, she kept suffering severe pain, mainly in her lower back. For weeks she could get no sleep. She was examined by several physicians, and was X-rayed, but nothing wrong was found. A doctor thought that her trouble was primarily mental and she must go into a mental hospital.

She admitted she had "fits of a sort, although I do not quiver." She soon fell out with her sisters, and particularly Jane, who had no sympathy for her. Ella remarked, "I must not give in to this demented feeling which the cold air seems to cause. God help me!" Later, she said, "I cannot see properly, and I feel frightened of everybody, I am terrified."

She is sent to a hospital. On the train to the hospital, she got so upset she jumped up and pulled the communication cord. A few days later, she was committed. Highly suggestive of mental trouble is the fact that for four weeks after hospitalization, she refused to eat. She said the food gave her pain somewhere, and it gave "the sort of fits—those terrible agonies in my spine and head." Because her doctor kept asking her if she still thought her sister was giving her poison, it would appear that, at home, she had a spell of paranoia. As in practically all of these books, while the writer is trying to prove she was never insane, she keeps constantly proving that she was mentally upset.

Typical of insanity was the fact that time and again she refused to speak to the doctors. She wouldn't answer their questions. As she said, "As soon as I see him, I think 'You old swine!'" She gives herself away when she says that after a while she was happy to find out that *again* she could read and concentrate. The superintendent of the hospital told her that when she came in, she was in a sort of fog, but this Miss Hales denied. After a while, she recovered and went home.

Another hospitalization. But soon she began to have indigestion and pain. Again, typical of paranoia is her statement that her thoughts were not her own. "All sorts of things come into my mind from other people's minds, and I have to throw them out." Soon, back she had to go to the mental hospital, but this time she complained not so much of the back pain as of severe indigestion and poor health, also, the "fits again, when I cannot open my eyes or call, and I have that searing pain in my spine and head. I struggle to open my eyes and to call, and to say I can't bear it. I can't bear it. It is such torture, so frightening." She could not keep her head still. She felt she had to roll it from side to side. One suspects either hysteria or a mild epilepsy.

Then she had her back manipulated under an anesthetic, but this didn't help. Later, a doctor thought he saw in her X-ray films a slight crack in a bone. But he remained much interested in her "dropped stomach." Later, Ella decided she was having a kidney colic. Whenever one finds a patient with many distressing complaints in many parts of her body, one must suspect that all of them have a nervous basis.

An attempt at suicide. Typical of a psychosis was Ella's determination to commit suicide. First she cut her wrist, and later she turned on the gas. So back into a mental hospital she went. There, this time, she talked about excruciating pain following eating, and also "kidney trouble." When she got home, she couldn't get along with her sisters and so had to leave.

The impression left on a psychiatrist would probably be that the doctors who repeatedly sent her into a mental hospital had good reason to do so. We know that mental patients commonly suffer severely from pains in several parts of their body. Some get "the habit of illness" and keep getting "one awful disease after another."

An Army Captain Tries to Clear His Good Name

A book (*Hell's Cauldron*, 1953) written by a Captain Thomas Wilkes is typical of those written by persons who keep maintaining to their dying day that they never were mentally upset. Some are sure they were railroaded into a mental hospital and held prisoner against all rules of decency and law.

Captain Wilkes tells us that he had just been retired from the Army—at his request—when he got into unpleasant arguments with the commanding officer of the post. Every day he got into more difficulties with his superiors until finally he was confined to quarters because of the suspicion that he had become manic and somewhat paranoid. The book is long and detailed and well-documented—a record of his efforts, first, to get out of the mental hospital; then to clear his name; then to divorce his wife, who, during the "storm," had turned against him. The book describes very well all the trials and tribulations that a man "trying to clear his record" can get into during the course of a few years.

A Schoolteacher Shoots a Gun Out of Her Window

Miss McGarr's small book (*And Lo, the Star*, 1953) is that of a schoolteacher who would seem at times to have been a bit eccentric. She got married twice, but each time something went wrong. Like so many persons put into a mental hospital, she was sure she was as sane as anyone—possibly "a little high-strung." She admits that once she thought she *was a star*, and at times she was too fanatically religious. Often she would spend the night rambling alone through the woods. Like many eccentric people, she loved living alone.

Apparently, her acute trouble had started with a small

stroke. She says, "Suddenly I felt a stinging feeling strike
through my scalp. I clapped my hand over the spot and ran
into the house." "I thought to myself in amazement, 'God
had laid his forefinger on my head.'" The "stinging thrust
I had felt became like some flaming sword; a giant red-hot
bolt or rivet torturing me, ever present in my head."

When people who are a bit eccentric get a little stroke it
can take away their self-control and their good sense. With
her, what happened was that she developed some paranoid
ideas: she felt she was being hypnotized by some evil person, and soon she was trying to elude the spies who, she
thought, were after her. She thought Nazi agents were
trying to get into her house to kill her; and so, one night,
she fired her revolver out the window. Naturally, this was
a bit too much for the neighbors, and so, next day, they had
her locked up.

For a while she had a hard time figuring out why she had
been committed, and she objected to being put in "with
crazy people." Fortunately, in the hospital she soon got better, and then some old friends were kind enough to take
her in with them. She also found a group of people called
"The Friends of the Mentally Ill," and they helped her.
Luckily, also, her school board was willing to take her back
as a teacher.

CHAPTER 15

The Distresses of a Man
with a Brain Tumor

As one might expect, the first symptoms of a man with a tumor growing in his brain are often those of a mental upset. Often there are puzzling changes in character and behavior, or there may be severe headaches, or sudden vomiting spells, or failure of vision, or weakness or numbness somewhere.

So far, I have found only one book written by a patient who suffered from a brain tumor. He was Frigyes Karinthy, a prominent Hungarian man-of-letters who, in his forties, began to suffer from symptoms typical of a brain tumor (*A Journey round My Skull,* 1939). The first thing he noticed was an occasional rumbling noise, like the roar of a passing train. Soon he realized it was an hallucination. For a few days he didn't pay any attention to the annoyance, but then he went to an ear specialist who told him that he had an inflammation of his Eustachian tube that runs from the throat to the ear. From time to time the doctor treated him for this.

Then came severe headaches. Karinthy went to a doctor who promptly said it was all psychic in origin. A few days later, the patient saw what looked like a mirror moving in front of him, and he knew it was an hallucination of sight. To some slight extent, he began to lose his grip on reality.

People sometimes did not seem to him to be real, and he wasn't sure that he was all there himself. One day he felt terrible and almost fainted. He thought he had had a little stroke. The experience was most distressing. The next doctor he saw also failed to examine him, but just said he had catarrh in his ears, and that he had been smoking too much. So Karinthy stopped smoking. But soon there came, each evening at six, a severe giddiness. Everything would whirl around. He still had the "train-noises." Karinthy's favorite waiter at the restaurant where he went for luncheon now had to stand behind him when he got up, because, for a moment, he would be so uncertain as to his position in space.

Then, two new symptoms were added to the "train-noise," the giddiness, and the fainting fits. He got violent pains at the back of his head. Fortunately, they were of brief duration. Then he began to have attacks of sudden retching. Again, his doctor wasn't much interested. Soon, Karinthy's son noticed that, as his father walked, he kept drifting to the left. His wife, when she received a letter from him, complained that his writing had become illegible.

About this time, Karinthy, who was unusually well educated in science and medicine, made the correct diagnosis. He said, "I have a tumor of the brain; I have the typical symptoms." The one important sign which hadn't yet been found was a swelling of the ends of the big optic nerves in the backs of his eyes. He went to an eye specialist, and, sure enough, there was the swelling—the so-called choked disk.

Then began the usual series of examinations by a number of neurologists in several of the hospitals of Budapest and Vienna. Later, Karinthy went to Stockholm to see Dr. Olivecrona, a brilliant pupil of Dr. Harvey Cushing. Operating under local anesthesia, Olivecrona found the tumor, and Karinthy describes the experience in detail. As a result of the removal of the mass, Karinthy soon became perfectly well again.

CHAPTER 16

A Few Descriptions of Psychoanalyses

Today, the practice of psychoanalysis is so widespread that I wonder why I have found so very few books written by ex-patients to describe what happened as they lay on the couch during the course of several years. Although these writers were never insane, I think it important in this volume to insert abstracts of their books. Their accounts will, I feel sure, be of much interest to many readers, just as they were of great interest and usefulness to me.

What would be very helpful in our judging of the value of psychoanalysis would be a pile of notes contributed by relatives and friends of analyzed persons, telling us what they thought had been accomplished for the patient by all of the many sessions.

A Fight against Fears

The best description I have found of years of psychoanalysis was written by Lucy Freeman, an able newspaperwoman (*Fight against Fears*, 1951). Her father was a famous lawyer. The book is so full of thought-provoking paragraphs that many a mentally troubled person and many a student of psychiatry would do well to read it. Not only are Mrs. Freeman's descriptions of her fears and hates instructive, but many of the comments of her able psychoanalyst are

worth remembering. He evidently was a philosopher and
a good student of the human mind.

Mrs. Freeman tells us that her neurotic troubles came
early in life. Always she was afraid of madness. When asked
why she worked so hard, she would say, "To keep from going crazy." She said that in college she needed more a psychiatrist than a set of professors! She says that anxieties
took a terrific toll of her, and had much to do with her
sleeplessness, her abdominal distress, and her vomiting.

A somewhat unorthodox psychoanalysis. Some old-time
or new-time psychiatrists may not agree with all of the explanations the analyst gave for his patient's troubles. Also,
the analyst was a bit unorthodox in that, all along the way,
he kept advising his patient what to do. He kept constantly
giving suggestions, many of them of the sensible type that
any old general practitioner might have given. In some
places in her book, Mrs. Freeman says she absorbed and
appropriated much of his philosophy; in other places, she
says she was unable to do it.

There is another feature of this psychoanalysis which may
surprise some persons. They may have read that as soon as
a patient had been brought to see whence came his childhood sexual traumas and psychic injuries, he should lose
his neurosis. Mrs. Freeman thought this had happened
when, at the beginning of her analysis, she lost a stuffiness
of her nose. But, later on, she admitted that the stuffiness
had come back. In one place in her book she says that understanding what is wrong does not cure.

*Some of Mrs. Freeman's acquaintances doubted if the
analysis had accomplished much.* Mrs. Freeman admits that
some of her friends who knew her well found it hard to
see wherein the five years of analysis had changed her.
They felt that she was still much the same eccentric and
hard-driving person she originally was. We can only take
her word for it that, in some ways, she was better. In one
place in the book she said that, for years, she had grown
steadily worse emotionally. She admits that after John (her
analyst) had been telling her the same thing again and
again for five years, she still hadn't learned much of it well
enough and hence could not always control her inner vio-

lence. One gains the impression that at the end of her five years she would go to someone else for another period of analysis.

The patient's inborn difficulty. Many readers will suspect that the patient's difficulties were due not just to her failure to get enough love from her mother, but more to her having been born with a difficult personality. She summed up her problem when, at the beginning, she said to her analyst, "For months I have felt like a caged animal, snarling at the world." Like many people who hate bitterly, she says she also *feared* greatly, and she always felt insecure. As we have seen, all these complaints are typical of neurotic people.

The lady kept making tremendous efforts to succeed in life, hoping, she said, that this would impress people favorably. Like all persons with difficulties of adjustment, she tended to stay wrapped up in herself, and this made it hard for her to love anyone. Like a schizoid person, she had a fear of touching people. She hated to kiss even her sisters. Naturally, she felt terribly lonely. Like some children who seem greatly to crave the love of their parents, she at times took delight in infuriating them. As she said of her mother, "Something drove me to see how furious I could make her." In one place Mrs. Freeman says her parents sometimes wondered if she was crazy. They spoke of her as "that crazy kid." So often, when a girl feels rejected, it would seem that she must have acted in such a way that it would be an unusually kind and forgiving parent who could love her at all.

If Mrs. Freeman could easily have changed, she might have changed in a month. Toward the end of her book, Mrs. Freeman said something that is very true and very thought-provoking. Commenting on the fact that after five years of analysis, she still was pretty much her old self, she said, "If [hearing] words were enough, I would have needed only a few weeks of analysis, for the words could all have been spoken by then." Actually, also, for years she had read widely in the literature of psychoanalysis. "If words were enough, I could have followed the advice of well-meaning souls who kept urging, 'slow up, relax, take it easy.' Instead, these suggestions only infuriated me. *I knew what I should do, but I stood powerless to change.*" The words did not "soak in."

To Mrs. Freeman, her experience described in this book seems to prove the value of psychoanalysis, but to an untutored bystander, it seems to prove also how little one can get out of spending several hours a week for five years trying to change a personality that either cannot be changed or refuses to be changed. To a few readers, this book will suggest that most persons are born to be what they are. Certainly, many cannot change themselves to any great extent.

Mrs. Freeman's story tends to disprove the idea, now so popular, that environment is everything. Why? Because in many ways, this woman had a splendid environment, going about as she did, studying humanity every day as a reporter, and having a chance to meet many interesting people. And yet, in middle life, she appeared to be just about as rebellious, anger-driven, fearful, and emotionally disturbed as she had been when she was a little girl.

As Mrs. Freeman said, what she needed more than advice was a new feeling about herself. She needed, also, to do what she knew she ought to do. As she said so well, "Some of the sickest people understand all the words, yet writhe in unhappiness." "Words never cured anyone of emotional illness." She says so truly that even some of the things that are written ten times in her book are not yet written once in her heart! She still hadn't the courage to accept these truths and let them penetrate any deeper than her intellect.

One of the many things she thinks analysis did for her was to give her a secure feeling while she was on the couch and for a little while afterward. She felt she had to trust someone and lean on someone, at least for a while.

Eventually came a time when she thought she ought to bring her analysis to an end. But when the analyst agreed with her, she became very angry with him and went into some melodramatic performances which suggested that she still was a spoiled child. Amusingly, Mrs. Freeman tells that, in the end, a friend, who had never had any faith in what analysis had done for her, grudgingly admitted it had worked two changes: she no longer whispered when she talked and she no longer had her sinus trouble! Mrs. Freeman says she had lost her old tendency to vomit, and she had lost much of her fear of illness. She had lost some of her fear of constipation, and she had lost her menstrual cramps. She had thrown away her eyeglasses, and she had fewer nightmares. Obviously, no sensible physician would think of claiming that all these changes which had come in the course of five years were due to any one particular cause, such as the analysis.

Why was Mrs. Freeman so eccentric? As Mrs. Freeman kept asking herself all through the years, Why was she so different from most other girls of her age? Why didn't she quickly get married, as they did, and live and love in a chintz-filled cottage? Why did she one day fear and hate sex and the next day crave a sexual life? Why was she so uncertain about her sexual nature? Several times she says she was not sure whether she was a boy or a girl. Why was she originally a tomboy?

Some psychiatrists might have accused her of being somewhat homosexual, but this seems highly improbable when she says she was revolted at the mere thought of kissing or touching another woman, or even of touching a woman accidentally. She could not even touch her sisters. She rarely dared hug her sisters (or her brother), although sometimes she felt so inclined.

She went on to say that she "did not like boys either." In one place in her book she said that, in her sight, all men were enemies. And yet, she adds that she usually got along well with them. Significant is the fact that usually she quit a man the day he showed signs of getting interested.

Such a woman can be *asexual.* Hundreds of thousands of persons do not care to be loved by either a man or a woman, and this trait can be inherited. I have known families of six or seven brothers and sisters in which perhaps five never "dated," and never showed any interest in either a man or a woman. In my experience, this inability to love anyone is found most often in families in which there is much eccentricity or psychosis or epilepsy (see my book *Practical Leads to Puzzling Diagnoses*).

The fear of sex. A sign of a mental warping, perhaps from birth, was Mrs. Freeman's feeling that she was wicked and deserving of death because she possessed sexual feelings. Once she said, "I am scared to death of sex. Even saying the word makes me feel funny." Sex seemed so sordid. And yet, "Part of me envied women who worked in houses where sex was their business." One great trouble probably was that "our family was not too affectionate. We never kissed each other on the mouth." "Mother, I felt, found it difficult to accept affection." "She always drew away from me when I would try to get close." (Perhaps this lack of affection later brought about the mother's divorce.)

Perhaps typical of Mrs. Freeman's relations with men was her statement about her analyst; part of her liked him, but another part would not trust him, even though he had proved himself to be the most gentle person she had ever met. He had always acted toward her as a good friend. Why, then, couldn't she trust him?

Mrs. Freeman adored her brilliant and able father, although they often clashed. He was famous for a quick temper. Naturally, Mrs. Freeman's analyst felt that the affection for her father was wrong and dangerous.

Many questions. Why did Mrs. Freeman think that her mother hated her? Why was she so constantly filled with furies against people who hadn't harmed her? Why did she so dislike herself? Why, when success and acclaim came to her, was she still so desperately unhappy? Why did she go to a psychiatrist for help, and then be so hostile and evasive that she tried to keep from telling him the things he needed to know?

As her analyst said one day, "People who do not like themselves cannot like anyone else." And she retorted, "I doubt if I ever have liked anyone." For the most part, the pronouncements of the analyst were sensible and helpful. Occasionally, he said things that only an analyst could say, such as that "many murderers are unconsciously carrying out the wishes and fears of their parents!" Or, "the unhappy person wages a continuous battle against the unconscious fear of death." "He wishes to murder; he fears being killed by someone else, and he fears he will kill himself." Nonanalysts will wonder how much good this sort of teaching can do to a person whose thinking is already muddled. No normal young woman should be obsessed by the fear of death. Mrs. Freeman kept asking why she was so unhappy, and the analyst answered, "because she didn't like herself."

She tried marriage. A time during her analysis came when Lucy had a chance to get married, and suddenly she took it. But the alliance did not last. As she said, "In getting married, she was not fair to either the young man or herself." In order to show her readers how childish she still was, she tells about a tremendous row she had with her husband when he refused to buy her an ice-cream soda! As she said, if looks could kill, she would have wound up in the electric chair. She was enraged to think that her husband could have done such a thing to her. He knew he was infuriating her, but he also was so childish he would not give in.

So often when a physician watches a couple heading for the divorce court, he is so impressed with the fact that they —both of them—are acting like little children, and spoiled brats at that. Their sense of values is so terribly deficient. No sane adult would have quarreled violently over an ice-cream soda. Lucy admitted she had married to fill unconscious needs; she had felt she *had* to get married. She said, if there had been a choice, she would have waited!

As any wise physician could have told her, for a woman of her type, just living with someone else in an apartment would probably prove painful. She says that, like many neurotic women, when she woke in the morning she hated herself and was so irritable that she would feel like committing murder. She admits that she vented on her unfortunate husband many childish feelings of anger; also, that, unconsciously, she used him as a target for the rage that really she would like to have let loose on her parents.

She said she could not make a success of her marriage because she lacked the capacity to give love to anyone. It is true that after leaving the man, she hated to go back each night to a lonely room, but that was "preferable to living in a coma of suppressed rage." Tragic is Mrs. Freeman's confession that she used people to satisfy her emotional yearnings and was more interested in what they could give her than what she might offer them. Such selfishness is typical of neurotic persons. When she married, she picked up one or two strikes against her when she kept her job and did not settle down to make a home.

In some places in her book she claims that she much desired a home and children; she says even that she was frantic for children, but the reader finds it hard to believe this.

The tendency to hate. The important point that Mrs. Freeman seems to have forgotten is that ordinary persons with a good nervous inheritance are not filled with such inner fury all their days. Eventually, she came to see that she was tending to destroy herself by her anger.

As I have read many books and abstracted them for the making of this book, I have been impressed by the fact that never in my life have I heard of so many persons who were full of hate and fury.

Some honest confessions. Eventually, she saw that in the production of her troubles the influences that came from others in the outer world were less important than were those that came from inside her. There was nothing wrong with her *mind*, but there was something decidedly wrong with *her*. She admitted that she had lived a lie; she had had to deceive herself in order to make life bearable. There was a great emptiness in her life, and this she tried to hide by seeking excitement and work. She presented a smiling face to everyone. If she felt someone was getting to know her too well and "glimpsing the horror underneath," she fled.

She felt that, emotionally, she was still an unhappy child. She had to keep living through her rebellion against being a girl; she had to live feeling jealousy of her brother and sisters. *She had "never changed inside."* This is a most important statement. Many of her demands on life were still those of an unhappy four-year-old. She admitted to her analyst that she could not change, and he said, "Perhaps you *won't.*" But she kept maintaining that she just couldn't.

At the end of the book, very wisely, Mrs. Freeman says, "No one experience caused my emotional illness. No single event or series of events, painful or humiliating though they might have been, sparked my unhappiness." She thought it arose from the quality of the atmosphere in which she lived. But she might have added that it arose also because she was born with a strange, perverse, angry, unloving, perhaps asexual, and unhappy temperament.

In concluding, Mrs. Freeman admitted that sometimes she forgot the many generous things that her mother had done for her through the years, and how much her mother had done in an effort to cheer her up. Actually, she saw that her mother had meant more to her than anyone else in the world. The qualities which she disliked most in her parents were those which she had in herself—anger, impatience, self-hatred, fear of sex, and a complaining manner. Later, she came to look on her parents as her best friends. At times she could see them as warm lovable persons with troubles of their own, some of them every bit as important as hers.

Another Interesting Story of an Analysis

A very interesting and thought-producing book (*The Spectacle of a Man,* 1939) was written by Dr. Alvan Barach, an able internist of New York City, who, for a while, did much psychotherapy. He wrote under the pen name of John Coignard. He told me recently that Arnold Harvesting and Mary were real persons who had the experiences which he describes so well. This book should certainly be read by anyone who is interested in psychoanalysis, because it is so full of knowledge of the workings of the human mind in odd persons, people who cannot always make up their mind that they really want the love that is offered them. The material here presented was obtained largely by analysis, and partly through letters.

An odd, poorly adjusted man. The book is the story of the search for love by an odd, highly intelligent, studious,

and well-read man of the sort who tends to live alone because he finds it difficult to get close emotionally to anyone.
At times, as is the case with many insecure persons, he
stammered. He admitted that when he met a woman his
desire to feel superior was often more intense than his
desire to find love. While he was always ready to condemn
pride, vanity, and selfishness in the woman, he usually failed
to recognize these defects in himself.

He was troubled by an extreme fear of ridicule. Thus, one
evening when a merry girl he had met evidently liked him,
and had kissed him several times, he was suddenly seized
with the suspicion that she was laughing at him. With this,
he got panicky and fled without saying good-bye to her.
The next day he felt terrible. Then he felt he could not
bear to stay in town any longer, fearing that he would be
an object of ridicule. This desire of a man to flee after he
thinks he has made a *faux pas* is typical of many of these
odd, shy, self-conscious people. After his psychoanalysis
had gotten under way, he began to feel more cheerful than
he had been in years, and he was able to see that most of
his troubles were of his own invention.

He meets a divorcée who likes him. Then he met a
divorcée named Mary who obviously was much attracted to
him and was on her way to falling in love with him. But
he and she were both such poorly adjusted people that they
had great difficulty in getting together. Then, one night, as
if by mutual consent, they kept on drinking until his shyness was removed. Then, he kissed her again and again,
and she took him into her room and her bed. This was his
first sexual experience. Soon he was much in love with her.

But then a terrible jealousy and a dreadful doubt of
Mary's love took possession of him. "He felt an agonizing
pain over his heart which he said he could not bear without
screaming, or making a terrible exhibition of himself."
When invited to a party by Mary, he disgraced himself
by drinking too much and becoming silent and dull.

Marriage was not for them. When Arnold suggested to
Mary that they get married, she said very wisely that they
weren't ready for marriage. She might have added that
at the time he was not sane and mature enough for mar-

riage with anyone. Then he went on making trouble for himself and Mary by his insane jealousy. Mary did not help the situation by telling him of other lovers she had had, and of one with whom she still was deeply involved. She upset Arnold badly by confessing that, for a while, she had continued to sleep with this man while she had been sleeping with Arnold. She maintained that this did not mean anything because she was only *fond* of the other man, while she was really *in love* with Arnold. She said that sex with the other man was "meaningless."

The differences between Mary's two men. She insisted on going out twice a week, dancing with her playboy, because he was fun; he made her laugh, and she liked that. He made her feel desired and superior and proud of herself. "It is a nice feeling for a woman to have." And yet, she said she couldn't marry him, for she had had very little emotional contact with him. She had never felt intimate with him in the way in which she felt with Arnold. The playboy didn't seem to put his heart into his love-making, and this she sensed and resented. He was most fun in a crowd, "but in an intimate relation he lacked the erotic preoccupation with her femaleness which she wanted."

"You see, Arnold, Jim gave me all the superficial pleasures, whereas you gave me almost none of them." But Arnold gave her a "feeling that seemed more necessary than happiness." And still she knew that if she had to live with him, she would have to suffer much from his mental remoteness and his lack of real concern about her. She accused him of continuing to withhold something from her. She said she was giving him all her secrets, and he was withholding his. Also, with his primness, he kept making her feel often as if she were doing something wrong. She sensed that if they were to marry, he would "still inspect her pleasures with his microscopic eye" and would ferret out something that would make her uncomfortable. This would spoil her fun. As she said, "I must be the way I am. Why must you put this pressure on me to be different? Why don't you love me as I am?"

The love affair starts breaking up. Because of all this, Arnold sometimes got to feeling so wretched that he doubted if he could ever learn to endure it. He got so depressed he thought of suicide. It bothered him that Mary's love for him did not interfere with her having other pleasures on the side, and soon he was feeling unsure of his love for her. She said, "Sometimes when we are out I can see you watching me with that jealous look of yours. I feel as if you were holding a handkerchief over my mouth; I can't breathe. I hate jealousy. It destroys me."

Finally, they got so irritated with one another that it looked as if they'd never get together again. But then, one night, Mary said, "Let's get tight." She wanted sex but knew that in the mood in which she then was she could not have it unless she were well anesthetized with alcohol. She and Arnold could not get together happily because they were both struggling to attain mastery—one over the other. They then had a sexual experience, but it left a bad taste in his mouth—so bad he wanted to leave Mary. But then he realized that if he were to go, there would be for him an "abyss of loneliness." Later, Arnold suspected that Mary "was employing him simply as a male," and naturally, he deeply resented this.

He finds another girl. Eventually, he met a girl named Margot who intrigued him sufficiently that Mary's hold on him quickly began to be relaxed. When he admitted to Mary that he wasn't as jealous of her as he had been, she said, "If you're not jealous of me, you're not in love with me. I know you well enough to know that." Then Mary tried to get him to promise to marry her, but he wouldn't do it. He told her what was true, that they were not likely to "make a go of it."

When people spar at each other. Typical of the way in which some people—instead of being just natural and friendly—spar at each other, was the way in which he and Mary chatted when they met after having somewhat drifted apart. He asked her, "How do you feel?"

"Why do you ask?" she answered.

"Because I'm interested," he said.

"Not very much," she answered.

"Why do you say that?" he asked, feeling a little resentful and guilty at the same time.

"If you really cared how I was you would have phoned me to find out."

And so it went. There could be no happiness for people who talked in that querulous way. As Mary said, "You loved me in your way, I know that, but it was a selfish, safe little way." "I was simply part of your inner development."

He and Mary were too different. Each one of them had tried to make the other one over, and that was a poor start for a marriage. As Arnold said, "You offered me the valley of life to live in, but alluring as it was, I could not live there." "You have a rare capacity to spend an afternoon with others, sitting on a lawn, doing nothing but talking leisurely, pleased with the moments as they pass. You know how necessary it is for me to be more definitely occupied with something, either intellectually or emotionally." Mary could just enjoy life, but Arnold had to study it and reason about it, and worry about it. Eventually, Mary agreed with him that they should not marry.

Before they parted, Mary got him to go to bed with her again, but later "he thought how the memory of desire had urged his body on to satisfy itself, while his soul stood off and surveyed the scene, a reluctant participant." They agreed that their attempts to get back to their original basis of love didn't make sense. Later, Arnold married Margot.

A Scientist Gets Psychoanalyzed

Much of *The Story of My Psychoanalysis* (1950) by John Knight is taken up with a discussion of his struggles as a victim of anti-Semitism which for long had distressed him. Knight says that he had three hundred analytic sessions over the course of five years. He started when he was thirty, hoping to get relief from a duodenal ulcer.

Here and there in the book one finds some of the strange pronouncements of some psychoanalysts, such as "the common phantasy of returning into the womb is a substitute for the desire for coitus." For a while Knight fought against the idea of undergoing an analysis, but later concluded that it was helping him. He tells us how, at his first interview with Dr. Maxwell, he had to discuss the big item of expense. At $15 a session, the cost of his treatment would have to average $75 a week, or more than $3,000 a year for at least two years.

Some problems of a psychoanalysis. Knight tells how at times he felt kindly toward Dr. Maxwell, but at other times he felt such intense hostility toward him that he even felt an urge to kill him! How often in this book we have had to marvel at the violence of the hatreds that fill the minds of many mildly psychotic persons. Interestingly, the doctor discouraged Knight from talking about his *current* mental problems. His argument was that with such talk the patient could avoid going far back over the old buried memories which the doctor wanted most to hear about.

In some cases an analyst refuses to help the patient with his everyday problems, such as an impending divorce, or an unhappy job; he is so deeply concerned in unearthing the mental traumas that he feels sure were suffered in infancy. For instance, Dr. Maxwell wanted to find out how much psychic injury had been done to Knight on the eighth day of his life when he was circumcised!

More logical probably was Maxwell's concern over Knight's conflicts with his decidedly unpleasant father. This father had always been a distressing person to have around the house. He resented his son's going into a life of learning, and kept sneering at him for it. Each time the son came home from college, his father used to torment him by refusing until the last minute to give him the money he needed for the next semester.

As Knight said, he imagined that the greatest objection he had to entering into a psychoanalysis was to be found in his deep-seated resistance to putting the most intimate details of his life completely into the hands of a man who, at first, would be a stranger. It must take a while before the patient can decide how far he will go along these lines.

The analysis helped but did not cure. After the analysis had been under way for eight months, Knight had achieved some relief from tensions and anxiety. The thought then occurred to him that he was cured, and he began to resent the hours he had to spend with the doctor. But Maxwell decided that the analysis must go on; so it did.

In the next several months, the doctor went into the problems of Knight's sexual life and eventually got him to see that, for him, sex had been more of an aggressive physical attack than a loving act.

Next, in many sessions, Knight was made to confess to his fears of appearing to be a sissy, and hence his efforts to become a hunter, a fisherman, and a mountain climber.

Dr. Maxwell pointed out to Knight that many people enter analysis with the rosy idea that it will change them completely. Naturally, it won't change a man's intellectual capacities or his psychic make-up, but it can help him to become a more effective person. Dr. Maxwell helped Knight to deal more adequately with the snubs that had formerly upset him so terribly.

Emotional storms that came when the analysis was about to be terminated. Then, Dr. Maxwell said the time for ending the analysis was in sight, and for a while Knight felt proud and happy. But then, like Lucy Freeman, he hated the doctor for planning to give him up. Obviously, Knight was still not an entirely adult person. There was a part of him that resented any withdrawal from the pleasant, childlike, protected atmosphere that the analysis had been providing. Then, as the time of termination approached, Knight had moments of fear and panic . . . and he had one severe anxiety attack which was very disconcerting.

From this, it would appear that even after a long period of psychoanalysis, a man can be anything but mature in his reactions; he can still be unable to stand comfortably on his own feet. One day, Knight got a very disturbing phobia that he might have to jump off a bridge.

Dr. Maxwell thought that his plan to terminate the sessions was stirring up in Knight painful memories of the two most important terminations and separations of his life—first, his birth, with the cutting of the umbilical cord, and second, the removal of his foreskin!

A physiologist, of course, would be unable to believe that the decidedly unfinished brain of a newborn infant, who sleeps almost all day, could be sufficiently well developed to be concerned over either his birth or the loss of his foreskin.

After three years had passed, Knight felt that he was better, but the treatment had not cured his ulcer. He still had many days when he was much troubled by new anxieties, tensions, and fears; and then he wished that he had never had an analysis. On other days he was glad he had had it.

He who had been discriminated against became intolerant. It is interesting to read Knight's frank confession that after having suffered terribly all his life from anti-Semitism, he had the utmost contempt for certain minority groups, and even for the less well-educated people in his own religious group. He marveled at this trait in his character. Actually, of course, many philosophers have reminded us that consistency, as a human trait, is rarely seen.

The Analysis of a Delinquent Lad

Dr. Robert M. Lindner has called his analysis of Harold, a psychopathic youth, *Rebel without a Cause* (1944). It is the report of a lad who loafed about, often getting into malicious mischief. Like a child, he did what he liked to do, when he felt like doing it. As is the case with most psychopathic delinquents, he had no desire to work toward some success in life—his idea was to steal whatever he needed. When he got some money, he was likely to spend much of it for whiskey. He had no thought for the rights of others. Already, as a boy, he loved to shoot out street lights and windows. In some ways he was like a movie bad man in the Wild and Woolly West who enjoyed being bad and never thought of being sorry. When this study was made, Harold had already seen the inside of several courtrooms.

His family apparently was full of mental abnormality. Harold speaks often of alcoholism in an uncle and a vile temper in an aunt. An uncle had the psychotic's tendency to take long solitary walks in the woods. "An uncle" had a daughter who was sexually loose. There was a cousin Joe and an uncle, both of whom did time in prison. Harold's sister Marie was quick-tempered and loved to argue and get into fights. When angry she "threw things." A younger sister was tough and also wanted to fight with everyone. A brother, Perry, appears to have had a tendency to depressions. When in "one of his moods," he would not talk and would be downhearted and miserable. "He would be 'like in a daze.'" Aunt Vanya was quick-tempered and a fighter, while Aunt Louise was more calm, like Harold's mother. "My uncle sometimes gets in the same kind of moods that I do; he doesn't want to speak to anyone." One uncle would sometimes quit work for a few months and just drink, and another uncle also drank a lot. One uncle "just didn't give a damn about a thing; when he wanted to quit, he just quit." One uncle, at the age of eighteen, killed a man.

Time and time again, when I have heard that a certain psychopathic delinquent had "a perfectly normal family," and hence "his trouble could not be hereditary," the psychiatrist evidently meant that no member had been insane or psychotic enough to be treated. But when I questioned the members of the family, I found few who had been what one could call desirable citizens. As was the case in this family, there were several vile-tempered, scrappy, irresponsible, and alcoholic people.

Dr. G. N. Thompson tells us in his book on psychopathic delinquents that nearly all of them have physical as well as mental signs of a defective nervous system. Harold had a bad squint which got him into a good deal of trouble because, when boys jeered at him and called him "Squinty," he would proceed to beat them up. His eyes also had a nystagmus in which they would keep jerking from side to side; also, the muscles that held his upper lids were weak—and so the lids drooped. He was sullen-looking and fidgety. He lacked insight and judgment, and was resentful against the world.

He was always a "wild kid" who played hookey from school, and sometimes would disappear for two or three days. One reason these boys later have to be criminals is that, without schooling, they are almost illiterate. Harold went with a tough gang. Often he gambled and drank, and often he would hitchhike somewhere; like a psychotic person he would ramble about aimlessly. Early in life he was stealing bicycles, or burglarizing stores, or committing acts of vandalism. He drank three pints of coffee a day.

It is possible that he was a carrier of epilepsy. This could have explained his sullen, wicked temper and the violence of temper of others in the family. He may have had one seizure because he tells of a time when, while he was sitting on the front porch, his bowels suddenly emptied out.

As Harold said, "I don't talk to many people; they irritate me. I like to get off by myself and just think about nothing, and talk to myself." Typical were his statements that he didn't care much about anything. He didn't care what happened to him or to the world. He didn't care what people thought of him. His nerves were on edge. He felt like hitting people. He was in a nasty mood almost every day. Certainly, he should have had electroencephalograms made. They might have shown much more about him than did the "analysis."

Harold says he took delight in carrying a gun. A hundred times he was much tempted to use it on someone. He admitted that he never expected to get married. "I don't know what love means." Only the physical act of sex interested him.

According to Harold's statements, in his set, boys of nine or ten were frequently having sexual intercourse with girls of eight or older. When he was ten, he often had intercourse with his sister or with other little girls. In his set, if a boy found a girl who would permit intercourse, he was supposed to share her right away with his gang of perhaps ten or fifteen boys.

That Harold had some paranoid tendencies was shown by the fact that when in a crowd he thought everyone was looking at him.

At the close of the analysis, Dr. Lindner apparently thought that he had greatly helped Harold, but this is hard to determine. Some able psychiatrists who have spent years trying to help lads like Harold have few illusions about their ability to work a cure. Youths of this type are born with a peculiar brain, and no one can expect to make it over into a normal one, any more than they can hope, by talking to them, to straighten their squinting eyes.

Another Analysis of a Mentally Troubled Lad

Dr. Harold K. Fink, in *Long Journey* (1954), told of the analysis of Pedro, a lad who started out in life suffering from shyness and diffidence. He liked to daydream, imagining himself a Tarzan or a Superman. Perhaps, unfortunately for the cause of scientific accuracy, in school he had taken courses in psychology, and hence knew the jargon of the analysts. Apparently he knew that he should fear castration; he knew he should have been disturbed in infancy by seeing his parents having intercourse; and he knew that he should have resented his father's love for his mother.

There was nothing remarkable about the lad. This boy was not particularly interesting or different from hundreds of other boys in his low social stratum. He does not seem to have been very psychotic. He said he was too sensitive. At times he would stutter, and it distressed him when he blushed violently. He was always thinking of sex, but then, as he says, practically all the lads in his set had the same propensity, perhaps in even a worse form.

Interesting is his statement, on one page, that his earliest recollection of his father occurred at the age of five, and on another page, that when he was less than one year old, looking over the top of his crib he saw his father having sexual intercourse with his mother!

He hoped that he would not have to exist always in the dull uninteresting type of home his parents had, a home in which there never was a book or a magazine! Partly because he saw his parents unhappy, he had a fear of marriage. He suspected that for him the sexual side of marriage would soon degenerate into a bore, and then he'd have to start looking around elsewhere for his fun. Sometimes he thought of suicide. Once he said he resented Christ. Like many a psychotic person, he "wanted to be God's right hand man." But he did not have any real interest in religion. One of his troubles was that he resented his (I suspect Mexican) origin.

Dissatisfactions with sex. In his boyhood he was a voyeur who walked around late at night looking through windows at women who started to disrobe before turning out the light. To him, a source of mental conflict was the tendency of his widowed mother and his sister to walk around up-stairs in bra and panties. When this would stimulate him sexually, he would feel guilty and disgusted with himself.

He thought his *fantasies* about sex with a girl were usu-ally more satisfying than actual intercourse with her. As he said, "I build her up so high in my mind that in comparison the reality stinks." Also, "when a girl no longer resists my love-making I lose interest in her." "If she is too ready to undress I lose interest." Although he seemed to have great interest in pictures of nude women, when with a prostitute he hated to see her undressed, and he was relieved when she put her clothes back on. As one might have expected, he wanted girls only for physical gratification. He knew he was too self-centered ever to love anyone. He did not love even his mother or sister or brother. He had scruples about seducing a virgin; "the idea of sex with a virgin revolts me." "With me, going with a girl is a *job* rather than a pleasure!"

He never cared to please anyone. Significant was his state-ment that he had never tried to please anyone. "If a girl's attractive I won't admit it to her. Why should I praise a girl when it might go to her head? She might then think herself better than me and stop dating me. She'd think me weak, and that I was falling for her. I want to be harder to get than other guys." Sometimes he was deliberately rude to a girl, to show her who was boss. If there was to be any shoving around to do, he was going to do it. At a dance he shunned attractive girls, because if he chose a homely girl it was easier later to get rid of her!

Apparently, toward the end of the analysis, Pedro decided that genuineness of character could bring him more atten-tion and reward than he had ever gotten from his old hostil-ity. He said the analysis had helped him to be less serious about himself. Fink says that eventually he became a teacher, as he had wanted to. One can hardly imagine him as ever becoming a kind, loving husband for any woman.

Summary. It would be interesting if we could draw con-clusions here as to the value of these psychoanalyses just described, but we can hardly do this. What we would like to know is whether the relatives and friends of these people thought they had been much helped or changed or made over. We do not know if some of these people went back later for more years of analysis. This paucity of what physicians call "follow up study" has made it difficult for psychiatrists to judge the value of psychoanalysis. As psychiatrists point out, it is impossible to be sure that some improvement in a person's psychic status, noted at the end of a five-year period of analysis, can all be ascribed to the work of the analyst. We physicians see many poorly adjusted persons who, without any treatment at all, will go into a long period during which they are normal enough.

CHAPTER 17

The Modern Treatment of the Neuroses and Psychoses

Because many who have read the preceding chapters may now be wondering what is being done today to help mentally disturbed persons, and what improvements are being made in the care of troubled persons who have to be hospitalized for a while, I am adding here a few notes on the subject.

A careful examination. As an internist who, for fifty years, has spent perhaps a third of each day trying to help nervously troubled persons to remake their lives and to find their way back to health, I would say that the first and often the most important part of the treatment consists of a thorough and careful examination, followed by a frank discussion of the results obtained. This explanation, if it is to be convincing, must be made in ordinary English terms—so simple that any layman can understand them.

Often, then, a patient who, let us say, greatly feared that the symptoms produced in his nervous colon were those of a cancer goes away saying, "Well, if there is nothing wrong with me but nerves, I won't worry any more; I can handle the situation; I am just about cured."

The diagnosis of a neurosis or psychosis should be made positively from the symptoms and not just by exclusion. I feel I must stop for a moment to protest against a common habit many of us physicians have of diagnosing a neurosis "by exclusion." I think all able psychiatrists would agree with me that this is a bad type of practice, and one that often has a bad effect on the patient.

The physician should not diagnose a neurosis or psychosis as a last resort, simply because he cannot find anything else. He should usually make his diagnosis because, as an able psychiatrist would do, he has recognized a neurotic or psychotic or poorly adjusted or unstable or alcoholic person either the minute he walked into the consulting room or as the history was being given.

The able physician or psychiatrist recognizes the syndrome (group of symptoms) of a neurosis or psychosis the minute he hears it described—it is like the face of an old friend he has seen so many times over the years that he knows it well.

There are decided advantages to this type of practice. When a physician knows that "whatever else the patient has," what is really bothering him is a nervous trouble arising in his brain, he will not be likely to accept as a diagnosis a silent and harmless and symptomless gallstone that happens to turn up in an X-ray film. He will say to the patient, "Your symptoms cannot possibly be explained by that gallstone."

Another great advantage of diagnosing a neurosis or psychosis positively from the symptoms is that the patient is then much more likely to stop his long search for an "organic" (visible or tangible and local) cause for his or her symptoms. If a patient thinks the doctor made the diagnosis of a nervous trouble simply because he couldn't find anything wrong, what will he do? In hundreds of cases he will promptly go in search of another doctor who, he hopes, will give him many more tests and thereby find an ulcer or a cancer or something that can be cut out. I have seen this done hundreds of times.

But when the patient sees that his doctor recognized his depression, or eccentricity, or schizoid state the minute he saw him, and then examined him only to rule out some possible accidental finding, he may settle down, because he feels the doctor "knows his case." In many such cases, if then I ask the patient to let me refer him to a psychiatrist for expert help, he is likely to take my advice and go to the man.

The need for finding out if the patient wants much to get well or has the intelligence needed for cooperation with the psychotherapist. As even some of the ancient Greek physicians knew, the first essential to the cure of a nervous trouble is that the patient really wants so much to get well that he will make an effort to mend his ways. Fortunately, early in my medical life I learned that there is no use trying to cure a person against his will; it is hard enough to cure him when he is anxious to cooperate with his physician and to do what he is told.

Early in my career I learned, also, how much it helps in treating a nervous person if he has the intelligence to understand what is being said to him, and to see the importance of it. We physicians often say of a certain patient who is doing poorly under psychotherapy that he has no *insight* into the psychic nature of his troubles. After all that has been said to him, he still cannot see that his dissipation or his tantrums of temper or his worries have most to do with producing his symptoms. Without cooperating at all, he wants to be cured with a few pills out of a bottle.

It is very hard for a physician to cure a man who, whenever life gets difficult or a disappointment comes, takes to the bottle. It is hard, also, to cure the person who was born sickly. He or she can, however, be taught to hoard energies, and to live within his or her means of strength.

Psychotherapy. Psychotherapy can be quickly curative in thousands of cases in which the person's trouble is a neurosis; but it is not so helpful in cases of psychosis, in which, for a while, the brain acts badly, as if it were poisoned by some drug.

In cases of neurosis, the physician can often help his patient to triumph over anxiety and worry and fear; he can help him to face up to sorrow or disappointment, or feelings of insecurity, and he may be able to show him how to let up on overwork and then get some rest and sleep. In many a case he helps the patient to do something constructive about a bad situation in his home or office. In other cases he will help a woman by getting her to see that, with her husband's moderate income and their three small children, they just cannot finance the separation or divorce they are constantly talking about. Under the circumstances, she will be much healthier if she will settle down to try to make her home a happier place.

Often, also, the doctor must try to get the patient to live more hygienically, going to bed earlier at night, and perhaps using less alcohol. In many cases, the patient will be much helped if only he can talk out his troubles before the physician, and get a good look at them.

I should add here that not all physicians are helpful to nervous patients. Some positively dislike treating nervous troubles and naturally are not good at it. They do well to refer their nervous persons to physicians who are skillful in taking care of them. By saying the wrong thing a physician can make many a nervous person much worse.

Some few men have a God-given skill in handling nervous or psychotic persons—in getting them to tell their secret and sometimes shameful story, and in helping them to get well.

The wise psychotherapist lets the patient do most of the talking: he lets him get things "off his chest."

Naturally, some persons will go away happy and pretty well straightened out with one good talk. They will say, "I see now what is wrong; I see what I must do; and I will go home and try to do it." Other patients may have to keep coming back at intervals for weeks or months or years—to get help and reassurance and counsel.

Psychotherapy is often needed when "organic" disease is present. We must not forget that in thousands of cases in which serious organic disease has been found during the examination, the patient much needs good psychotherapy. Often I have to say to a man who, months after recovery from a mild heart attack, is still afraid to go back to work, "You are not suffering from heart disease; your disease is *fear* of heart disease." Similarly, a woman who has had her breast removed for cancer or has had a hysterectomy may be much in need of good "supportive" psychotherapy.

Any person who is facing death may much need help from a kindly philosophic physician.

I think most physicians would gladly turn this work over to psychiatrists, but as yet there just aren't enough of such well-trained men in the country. Because of this, the family doctor and thousands of physicians in every specialty, must take care of the many persons they see with nervous troubles.

Able psychiatrists with years of experience agree with me that there isn't much chance of anyone's remaking the character of a man or woman who has a poor nervous inheritance and from childhood has always been maladjusted, hard to live with, strongly opinionated, undisciplined, or violent-tempered. Some of these persons are inclined to be alcoholic, and this adds greatly to their difficulties in living and working and earning a living. Many maladjusted people can be helped for a while, and then they tend again to get into difficulties; but fortunately some stay reformed.

As I said in previous chapters, a high percentage of manic-depressive persons are able and successful people, and many schizophrenic, schizoid, and paranoid persons live useful lives. What is unfortunate is that so many of these mildly psychotic persons never know what is basically wrong with them. As a result, they are likely to spend a fortune going from one doctor to another. Some get operated on many times, and to little purpose.

Rest and vacations and sedatives. In many a case the doctor must try to figure out some way in which for a while a very tired person can get a little more rest and sleep, and perhaps a vacation. Often the doctor must prescribe a barbiturate to relieve a severe insomnia; also perhaps a tranquilizer to relieve great tension during the day. When the patient's trouble is a psychosis, a vacation, even with a good rest, is not likely to do any good; and this is diagnostic of a serious trouble.

A few persons cannot be helped because their illness is so very useful to them that they won't give it up. They may need it to explain and excuse their incompetence or laziness or failure in life, or to protect them from the wrath of a spouse, or to punish or hold in subjection someone. Rarely, one can cure a woman like that by convincing her that her illness is becoming more of a nuisance to her than it is worth, and hence she had better get rid of it quickly before it completely enslaves her.

In my medical youth, I learned that I must never try to cure someone against his will; it may be hard enough to cure him when he is frantic to get well. As the men in Alcoholics Anonymous well know, it is a waste of time to try to straighten out an alcoholic until he comes to them admitting that he is licked and saying that he is frightened and anxious to get help.

Other persons who are hard to help. Many able psychiatrists say what I feel sure is true, that there is little sense in trying to talk a *depressed person* into "snapping out" of his spell. He would so gladly terminate his terrible mental suffering that it seems foolish to spend time exhorting him to hurry up and do it. As one such person put it, the doctor might just as well urge an epileptic to stop having his seizures.

There seems to be little sense also in trying psychotherapy on a man who is utterly miserable with a lifelong *schizophrenia*. Commonly, this disease is so closely built into the man's body—as well as his mind—that one cannot hope to eradicate it completely. While trying to talk the man into being more friendly and sociable, one might as well try to talk him out of some of the physical discomforts that go with his disease.

As I said in a previous chapter, there is little use in trying to convince a *paranoiac* that his many suspicious are groundless. When he feels that his brain is being controlled by radar, naturally he feels sure that someone in the neighborhood must be sending out the rays. The psychiatrist must never say that the man does not feel radar; all he can say is that he doubts if the patient's interpretation of his feelings is correct.

Long ago I learned that it is useless to try to talk a pronounced *hypochondriac* out of his long-lasting delusion that he has heart disease or a cancer of the stomach. I can show him his normal electrocardiograms and his normal

X-ray films, but I do not expect this demonstration to influence him.

I will never forget how, when I was an intern, my chum
and I thought we could easily cure a psychotic man who
said he had a frog in his stomach. We said we would get
it out for him. We gave him an emetic, and while he was
vomiting, we slipped a palmed frog into the basin. The man
was thrilled; he felt so justified, and he was so grateful. The
only trouble was that he returned next day to tell us we had
been a bit too late—a dozen baby frogs had hatched out
and were hopping about in his stomach!

*A little-needed surgical operation is seldom a good form
of psychotherapy.* In the old days many a surgeon thought
that he could cure a neurotic patient by operating, and
saying later that he had found and removed a badly diseased
organ. This idea seemed reasonable, but years ago, by
talking to some 250 patients who had had such an operation,
I showed that in almost every case the patient was like the
man with the frog—on finding his old distress unchanged,
he knew he had not been cured.

Phobias. Phobias are very hard to cure, as we learned
while reading the abstracts of *The Locomotive God* and
Autobiography of a Suicide. It does no good to tell the
patient that his fears are groundless and that nothing will
happen to him if he goes out for a walk—he knows this
already. About the only thing one can do is to encourage
him to keep struggling to overcome his fear. He must not
give in to it, but must keep forcing himself to go out for
a walk, or to eat in a restaurant, or get on a bus.

A simple way of curing some anxious persons. In scores
of those many cases in which, for years, a highly neurotic
man has been suffering from "tizzies" due to his great fear
of going insane, as did perhaps his mother, an aunt, or a
grandmother, I have almost cured the fellow by pointing
out what was true, namely, that the working out of the
inheritance that he dreaded was no longer to be feared,
because *he had it already;* it accounted for his eccentricity,
or his jittery spells, or his other nervous symptoms. Obviously, then, he could see what his share of the family

tendency was, and he could see that it was bearable. Naturally, he left my office feeling enormously relieved.

Why psychotherapy is often difficult with the psychotic person. Very interesting is the statement of the woman who wrote *The Maniac.* She said that after she recovered, she was told that twice a day during her weeks of great mental confusion, her doctor had reasoned and argued with her for an hour. He had accomplished nothing. Why? She said he failed because she neither saw him nor heard his reasonings. . . . "I was then in actual, literal reality, *out of my mind.*" And yet, at the time when she was so full of delusions, she could talk to the doctor so clearly that he thought her sane enough for psychotherapy.

Similarly, Mrs. Kruger said she was too nervous to listen to her doctor when he reasoned with her; besides, at the time, she "could not think straight." Often persons who had been badly disturbed wrote that when their doctor tried to argue them out of their false ideas, he could not get anywhere because they thought they were sane and he was the "crazy" one! Several of the writers explained also that when they were having delusions these seemed more real to them than did the real happenings of the day!

Psychoanalysis. A form of usually long-continued psychotherapeutic treatment is called psychoanalysis. With this, the patient is seen perhaps four times a week for several years. During the sessions, he is encouraged to keep talking of whatever enters his mind, preferably, about distressing things and sexual experiences that happened to him when he was a child. During the process, the analyst may say little, feeling satisfied that as time passes the patient will come to see how and why he became ill, and hence what he must do to get well.

Obviously, not every patient can afford so long and so expensive a treatment. Unfortunately, in many cases, even a few years of any form of treatment will not make much change in the essential character of a mildly psychotic person. Probably most psychiatrists would agree that different types of patients need different types of treatment.

Psychoanalysts have shown wisdom in not trying to cure the insane in hospitals. They have concentrated their efforts on neurotic and mildly psychotic persons of the type who are sane enough to remain out in the world and carry on their usual activities.

Group psychotherapy. If only because of the shortage of psychiatrists in the land and the shortage of funds in our state treasuries and in many mental hospitals and clinics, a number of patients are now being treated at one time in a group. The psychiatrist talks to them about their problems—about the reasons for their fears and perplexities, and about how they can work their way back to health. After the lecture, individual patients may get much help from discussing their problems with other patients or with the class. Often a man is much cheered and helped on finding that he is not alone in his misery; others are suffering as he has suffered. Better yet is the encouragement that comes when a man who is still suffering can chat with a number of persons who once were similarly afflicted, but who now are evidently well on the road to recovery. After a class session a patient can get great help from chatting with someone who has the same type of psychosis, and from learning how he got better.

Hypnosis. Right now the practice of hypnosis is going through a stage of popularity. It is a method by which the psychiatrist can suggest strongly to the patient that he do certain things and that he believe certain things. Psychiatrists tell me that they will use the technic in handling certain patients, but they insist that it will be only one of the methods they will use in the treatment of the patient. Unfortunately, the effects of the suggestion are often only temporary. Unfortunately, also, it is not always easy, even in a big city, to find a competent and ethical and medically trained hypnotist.

Tranquilizers. As is now well known, during the last few years a number of drugs called tranquilizers have been found helpful, not only by nervous persons who must keep at work, but by restless or unruly persons, such as are to be found in mental hospitals. With these new drugs, many hospital patients can be so calmed down that they will listen to what the psychiatrists want to say to them; also, in some hospitals three out of four of the inmates are so quieted by the new drugs that they can go home and be cared for there. The drugs are not "cures" for psychosis, but they make it possible for the patient to obtain help in other ways.

Several years ago at a meeting of the American Medical Association there was a very striking demonstration of how the action of a tranquilizer differs from that of a sedative. On a table, a man had three monkeys of the usual vicious and untamable type. The one on the man's left, which had been given no medicine, attacked the demonstrator every time he had a chance and tried to bite through his big thick glove. The monkey on the man's extreme right, which had been given a *sedative* (barbiturate), lay down and drowsed or slept. The monkey in the middle had been so tamed by a tranquilizer that he let the man handle him without the slightest protest. He sat the whole day much interested in watching the crowd in front of him. The important difference then between the actions of a barbiturate and a tranquilizer was that the tranquilizer quieted the monkey without making him sleepy.

Unfortunately, some persons get unpleasant side effects from the use of some of the tranquilizers, and hence persons who are taking them would do well to remain under the care of a physician.

The use in a mental hospital of a long-continued warm bath. Sometimes a highly excited and agitated and very restless patient, on entering a mental hospital, can be calmed down by being left for hours in a bath of water which is kept at a certain warm temperature with the help of a thermostat. The person usually lies on a canvas sling. In addition, tranquilizers will probably be given.

Insulin shock treatments. Some of the schizophrenics who cannot be helped in any other way can be straightened out mentally with the help of a course of insulin shocks. To produce this type of shock, the patient is given such an overdose of insulin that he becomes for a while unconscious. For an excellent description of these shocks from the patient's point of view, see William Moore's story in Chapter 13. Sometimes schizophrenics are given some electroshocks, but usually I think they do better on insulin shocks.

Electroshocks. Persons who are in a bad depression can often be shaken out of it and into perfect health again with a few electroshock treatments. In one of the books I here abstracted, Lenore McCall tells of the great joy that came to her one morning when, after a series of electroshock treatments, she woke with her mind clear again. In the old days, before shock treatments became available, many depressed persons had to remain in a miserable state for several years.

It is true that some patients, after having been brought out of a spell with electroshocks, will slip back in again. But then a few more electroshocks may bring the person right back to sanity. A psychiatrist friend of mine tells me of an able woman with a tendency to melancholia whom he keeps well with the help of an electroshock given once a month.

Fortunately, in recent years, electroshocks have been made so brief and mild, and so without any marked convulsion, that they seldom do any harm. Because the person becomes unconscious the moment the doctor touches the button (switch), there is no pain to be feared; but because most patients dread the procedure, many psychiatrists give, first, a small dose of an anesthetic. The only disadvantage—which usually follows only a long course of treatments—is the temporary loss of some memory.

Prefrontal lobotomy. In years past, in some mental hospitals, a number of the patients who were hard to control and who no longer showed any tendency toward recovery were helped with an operation called a prefrontal lobotomy (leucotomy). In this operation, in a moment, the surgeon makes a cut between the front part of the brain and the middle part. As a result, the patient usually quiets down and loses much of his old drive and initiative and tendency to make a nuisance of himself. The only trouble is that he may become somewhat of an automaton, of no use to anyone; and he may develop some highly undesirable symptoms. In some cases he will quiet down to such an extent that he can be taken home.

Because of the occasional unpleasant side results of the operation, most psychiatrists dislike using it, and of late there has been a tendency to resort to it as seldom as possible. In many cases, one of the new drugs can quiet the patient sufficiently so that he does not have to have the operation. When relatives of a patient in a mental hospital are much puzzled as to whether or not they should consent to a prefrontal lobotomy, they had better get a consultation with another psychiatrist.

The Now-emergent New Psychiatry

Very hopeful for the future of psychiatry is the fact that in the last few years, in the hands of a number of teachers of this subject, psychiatry has been changing markedly. A few clinicians are now working hand in hand with those laboratory researchers and brain surgeons who are finding out much about how the brain works in health and disease.

The chemistry of the brain. Chemists are now finding more and more drugs which, in a few minutes, will change a normal man into what looks and feels and acts like a psychotic patient; and they are finding drugs which will either stimulate a depressed person or will calm down a manic one. Obviously, if the clinical picture of a psychosis can be produced in a normal man in a few minutes, and if a profound depression can be cleared up in a few days with the help of a drug or a few electroshocks, a number of the old theories about the production of psychoses must be reconsidered.

Already, it has been found that in a few cases the mental retardation of a child is due to an inherited inability of his or her body to detoxify chemically and thus excrete through the kidneys a certain poisonous chemical; and already some of these children are being greatly helped with a special diet, which is lacking in the offending substance.

The great value of the electroencephalograph. Scientists using the electroencephalograph (an instrument that greatly amplifies and then records on a moving sheet of paper the tiny electric currents constantly being formed in the brain) are now showing us that some sixty per cent of "difficult" or delinquent children, or children who have great trouble learning to read or write, have abnormal graphs. Some of the children who are mildly psychotic or delinquent or mentally retarded are now being found to be suffering from a type of mental epilepsy in which there are no seizures. Many of these children have inherited the tendency, while others have had a part of their brain injured by an unrecognized attack of encephalitis (inflammation of the brain) that followed measles or mumps or polio, or some other acute illness. These children, then, are not just *bad*; they are sick children with demonstrable disease of the brain.

Fortunately, today, with the help of new "anticonvulsive" drugs and dextro-amphetamine, many problem children are being helped. Often then their schoolwork greatly improves. More and more often in the future, the new type of neuropsychiatrist, who carefully examines his patients, and who gets a set of electroencephalograms made before he starts treatment, will find that a man who had been thought by someone to have been nervously upset by some bad parental influence, or bad environment, or early sexual experience has definite demonstrable disease in his brain.

More and more often, also, the modern psychiatrist will be interested in the genetics of psychoses and hence inclined to take a detailed history of the mental status of every one of his patient's near relatives.

The fear that "inherited" means "incurable." Most psychiatrists hate to mention the factor of heredity in producing mental disturbances because, as they say, so many of their patients and the patients' relatives hate to face the fact that a tendency to mental disease runs through their family and is perhaps built into the very warp and woof of the person affected. One can easily see why this idea is very discouraging, not only to the patient, but to his doctor. As I have said in this book, there can be no question that it is much easier to help the essentially normal person who, through strain, grief, overwork, or much insomnia, has developed a neurosis—than it is to help a man who, from childhood onward, has always been difficult, undisciplined, irresponsible, ill-tempered, eccentric, and perhaps a "screwball."

But with all this, no one must assume that just because a disease is hereditary in nature it must be regarded as untreatable and hopeless. Everyone today should know that some definitely inherited diseases, such as diabetes and pernicious anemia, can now be kept under control for a lifetime.

Another important point that must be emphasized is that, commonly, it is not a disease that is inherited but a *tendency* to it. For instance, hundreds of thousands of people inherit a tendency to diabetes. If for fifty years a susceptible person overeats and gets fat and puts great strain on his insulin-forming cells, he is likely to get diabetes, while if he eats moderately and stays thin, he may never get the disease. Similarly, many a person who, in his college days, comes to see that he has inherited a family tendency to psychosis, may live out his days well enough if he will only live sanely and practice good mental hygiene, with no dissipations, plenty of sleep, and constant self-control. In living such a good life he may be able to get much help from his family physician and a good, kindly psychiatrist.

The avoidance of hereditary disease. From now on, more and more intelligent persons, when they are thinking of marriage, and when they know that in several generations of their family there are a number of cases of insanity or epilepsy or mental underdevelopment, will go to a heredity counselor to ask him if it would be wise for them to have several children. If they should have children, what would be the chances that one or two would be abnormal? The counselor will not tell them not to have children; he will only say to one of the contracting parties, "With this disease showing up again and again in your stock, if you should have several children, according to the laws of genetics, one quarter (or one half) of them could have the defect. As you can easily see, the chances of trouble should be still greater if your spouse should also happen to be a carrier of the same defect." Today, with new tests, many lucky persons will be told by the counselor that he thinks they did not inherit the defect and hence cannot pass it on.

Already, with the necessary information in their hands, many intelligent and well-informed young people are deciding not to marry or not to have children. Almost every week now I get letters from fine women who say, "I have epilepsy, apparently of the hereditary type, and I have suffered so terribly that I just won't run the chance of bringing a child into the world to suffer as I have done."

New and Better Forms of Hospitalization for Mentally Disturbed Persons

First, I should emphasize here that readers of this book should not be too appalled at the criticisms of mental hospitals made by some of the ex-patients. In many of these cases, the hospital was an old one—of a type that is now being superseded. Every year now efforts are being made to build better mental hospitals and to run them with good sense and kindness. Unfortunately, in many places there is still need for improvement. In spite of the fact that approximately one quarter of the funds appropriated by a state for health purposes go for the care of the mentally disturbed, the state hospitals are usually understaffed. They are short of doctors and nurses and orderlies.

What is hopeful is that in the last few years great improvements in the mental hospitals have been proposed, and some changes are now being made. More and more now, the thought is to get away from the big old prisonlike state hospitals and to build smaller units. Also, in many hospitals, some of the divisions have open doors, and as many as possible of the patients are allowed to go out into the grounds and even out through the town.

The need for several types of mental hospital. There would seem to be much need for several types of hospital, designed to care for patients with different forms and degrees of mental trouble. To be sure, in a big state hospital there are a number of wards designed for the care of different types of patients, but there would be advantages in putting the different patients under different roofs.

One of the biggest reasons for doing this is to avoid the great objection that the relatives of a mildly disturbed patient always have to putting their loved one in with a lot of patients who are decidedly insane. In a well-run hospital, this is avoided, but people on the outside are not sure enough that their son will be put with people with his same good intelligence and education, and his same degree of sanity.

Evidently, then, the type of hospital most needed in every state is a comfortable and attractive one designed to care for those persons who, perhaps for a few months, will need just enough restraint to keep them from traveling about, running up big bills, perhaps drinking too much, and then getting into clashes with people. When kept in a sanatorium, away from alcohol, most of these people are almost normal.

A good type of place for such mildly disturbed persons is a closed wing in a general hospital. A tremendous advantage of having such a place in which the local psychiatrists can take care of their nonviolent patients is that these persons can later go back into the world without the serious stigma of having been in an "insane asylum." Because few nurses and attendants and resident physicians are needed for the care of nonviolent patients, the daily charge for such hospitalization does not have to be excessive.

In a number of places, an attempt is being made to care for mildly disturbed patients for only part of a day. They stay in for either the daytime or the nighttime. In this way, perhaps a housewife can keep contact with her husband and children. During her hours in the hospital she will receive treatment.

Recently, I visited in a newly built closed wing of a memorial hospital, and later in the open (unlocked) wing of a big private mental hospital, and in each place I found a pleasant clublike atmosphere with a big lobby where the patients sat about reading, chatting, playing cards, looking at television, or just resting. If I hadn't known where I was, I might have thought I was in a college dormitory.

A second type of hospital might be one for patients all of whom, for some time after they come in, are so disturbed that they need expert care. They need treatment with drugs and perhaps electroshocks and insulin shocks. In such a place there is need for many nurses and attendants and physicians.

A third type of hospital might be one designed for the care of those few patients who, after two or three years, show no sign of improvement. In such a hospital might be placed also the type of childish or confused old man or woman with a senescent psychosis.

A fourth type of hospital might be like a boardinghouse built around a shop where mildly disturbed or only occasionally disturbed patients would work. Perhaps they could earn their keep and even save some money against the day when they would be discharged.

A fifth type of hospital should be a strongly built place for the care of dangerous patients such as the criminally insane.

A sixth type of hospital, now much needed in most states, would be for the care of mentally disturbed children.

A seventh type of hospital might be one just for alcoholics who have fallen into such a state of undernourishment and near-DT's that in order to save their lives it is necessary to hospitalize them for some months. The Federal government maintains two big hospitals—in Lexington, Kentucky, and Fort Worth, Texas—where addicts can get used to going without the morphine or Heroin they have been taking.

An eighth type of institution, when some day it is built, can save this country a few billion dollars a year. It will be built, preferably, on an island. There thousands of persons will be cared for and treated as kindly as possible. Most will work and earn their keep. To this island will be sent all of those thousands of persons who are too weak-minded or childish or psychotic to resist the many temptations of the world. Many such persons will be good and able and useful citizens as soon as they are kept away from alcohol and opiates. Many more will be all right if there is nothing around that they can steal and sell to a "fence." Without a "fence" there will be no sense in stealing. When protected from temptations, a high percentage of these weak-willed persons will work, and many will make a good living. Many will have their families with them. Anyone who persists in making a nuisance of himself will be sent to a prison.

The use of private rather than state hospitals. Many persons of average means, when confronted with the need for committing a relative, so hate to send him into a state hospital (even when perhaps the family can pay part of the expense) that they send him into a private institution.

There, with expenses running perhaps over $1,500 a month, the family soon goes broke, and then they just have to send the patient to a state institution. As one of my psychiatrist friends says to the families of his patients, "If you will soon have to send your loved one to a state hospital, why not do it at the start? Why wait until you are broke and perhaps deeply in debt?"

The need for "transition homes" and "protected" or "sheltered" shops. Today there is great need for transition places in which a patient just discharged from a mental hospital can be helped and watched over and given work. For six months or more he may find himself unable to go back into the competitive world. This, of course, is especially true of the person who hasn't a good home to go back to. Sometimes when he has a home to go to, it is a bad or impossible place for him because in it there are one or two relatives who will keep scolding him for "his foolishness— that got them all into such trouble and expense and disgrace."

Part-pay clinics for the mentally disturbed. Much needed today are part-pay psychiatric clinics to which persons with moderate means can go for help. Such clinics could help the patient to solve an acute nervous or mental problem that has come up in his life. In some cases the problem can be solved best by pooling the trainings and skills and wisdoms of a social worker, a psychiatric nurse, a psychologist, perhaps a legal aid worker, an internist, and a psychiatrist.

To illustrate what one of these clinics can do: a cabdriver just let out of the Army was in an awful fix because, with a "psychoneurosis discharge," the state licensing bureau would not give him a permit to drive a car. As a result, he and his family were on relief. In the clinic, the psychiatrist and the psychologist quickly decided the man was perfectly sane; a social worker questioned the license bureau to find out just what sort of a certificate would satisfy them; the necessary certificate was then written; the man got his license; and with this, he went back to work.

The "Recovery Incorporated" type of group. In more and more cities there doubtless will be formed groups of ex-patients such as that called "Recovery Incorporated," which for years has been doing good work in Chicago. In this club-like organization, troubled persons meet with men and women who once were mentally ill. Because of this experience of the "cured" persons, they can often help disturbed persons even better than a psychiatrist can. The person who is struggling with fears and perhaps mild delusions greatly respects the advice of a man who "has been through the mill" and hence knows what he is talking about. This, of course, is one of the secrets of the great success of Alcoholics Anonymous in keeping people "on the wagon."

A much-needed new type of psychiatric department in a medical school. Today there is a great need for the setting up in medical schools of a new type of psychiatric department in which the pupils will start out with a good practical course in the diagnosis and treatment of nervous and "functional" troubles—those for which no disease can be found in the patient's body. Most of this training could best be given by wise elderly internists who have learned to recognize and help those *many nervous or neurotic or mildly psychotic patients who, by the million, are seen and treated by nonpsychiatric physicians.* Unfortunately, until recently, most of these patients got a poor deal from many of us physicians. Because, years ago, in medical schools the students had almost no training in psychiatry, when they got out into practice few of them could recognize a psychotic person when they saw him. As a result, the man was given many needless tests, often many useless "shots" of this and that, and sometimes a useless operation or two.

Today, deans of medical schools are doing much to improve this situation, but still, many of the students hate to attend the course that is offered them in psychiatry. They doubt if they will ever need the training in this field, and they hope no psychotic patients will ever come into their offices. Actually, of course, hundreds of mildly psychotic persons who don't realize what is wrong with them, or who have refused to accept the diagnosis of a neurosis made by several men, will come in, hoping they will be told that all their discomforts are due to some disease below their neck. I have spent much of my life trying to get young doctors to see that many of the patients in their reception rooms are troubled only by a neurosis or a minor psychosis.

What is still much needed today in many medical schools is a fine course on the everyday *handling* and helping of nervous and poorly adjusted persons. We physicians need more often to sit down with a patient and take a long and careful history—one good enough to reveal the existence of great strains or unhappinesses or frustrations in his home or office. Often the person feels better when he talks over his problem in living—and comes to see that it is the cause of his distresses. Often, then, he decides to settle down and accept the unpleasant features of life that he cannot change.

The difficulties in finding the type of psychiatrist an individual wants or needs. One of the great difficulties often encountered by a disturbed patient is that when he needs and wants a psychiatrist he has a hard time finding the right man. Often, all he wants is one good chat with a fine, sensible, and kindly man. Perhaps his wife has just become mentally disturbed, and he wants advice as to where in the state he can find a hospital that will take care of her for a monthly fee that he can pay. Or perhaps a man's family physician will say, "I think all your wife will need for her depression will be a few electroshock treatments." Or perhaps the man has gone into a nervous state and needs mainly reassurance from someone who will chat with him for half an hour and then assure him that he has none of the symptoms of a beginning nervous breakdown.

What often happens is that the patient finds that one psychiatrist's appointment book is full for a month ahead; another man appealed to turns out to be a psychoanalyst who takes patients for only a three-year course of almost daily sessions; and another doctor is so interested in dynamic theory—in searching back in the patient's childhood for the cause of his nervous symptoms—that he hates to bother with a man who has a problem only of this day and week.

Hence, when a man starts looking for a psychiatrist of a certain type, blessed is he if he has an old medical friend who can perhaps tell him where to go to find the sort of man he wants and needs.

A needed new type of brain institute. What is much

needed today are "brain institutes" in which, built around a small, well-endowed hospital, there will be specially equipped laboratories for the study of the several functions of the brains of men and animals—in health and disease— also, for the study of the new drugs which have such profound effects on the brain. The institutes should be staffed with able students of several disorders, such as psychoses, epilepsy, brain tumors, and nervous injury such as is produced by big and little strokes, encephalitis, polio, multiple sclerosis, spastic paralysis, and other diseases.

The several specialists would do well to work together, using modern physiologic and physical equipment, such as the electroencephalograph. All of them would then be able to consult frequently, not only among themselves, but also with neurologists, pediatricians, and experimentally minded brain surgeons. Next door to the specially equipped operating rooms there should be laboratories in which physiologists would be studying the workings of the brain in monkeys and other animals.

A good example of the magnificent work such an institute can do is to be found in the reports of Dr. Wilder Penfield's Neurological Institute, which is connected with McGill University in Montreal. Fortunately, as I write this, a number of men are working hard to find the money needed to set up in the United States at least one ideal institute and hospital of the type now so much needed.

Take hope. To all persons who are mentally troubled or who have a loved one who is so troubled, I would say, "Take hope; in the last twenty-five years, greater advances have been made in psychiatry than ever before; and in the last five years many of these advances have been spectacular. Every year new and more powerful drugs that affect the brain are being found, and every year chemists are becoming more skillfull in synthesizing drugs for some special purpose, such as cheering up a depressed brain, or quieting the seizures of an epileptic child."

I hope this book will now bring hope to thousands of people, showing, as it does, that many persons who were once mentally disturbed recovered, and went back to everyday life and work.

ANNOTATED BIBLIOGRAPHY OF WORKS BY PEOPLE WHO WERE ILL AND WROTE UP THEIR EXPERIENCES. THESE BOOKS ARE IN THE LIBRARY OF DR. WALTER C. ALVAREZ

PSYCHOTICS

ARISTIDES, AELIUS
Aelii Aristidis Smyrnari (vol. 2, edited by Bruno Keil)
Weidmann, Publ., Berlin, 1958
A Greek philosopher of ancient times tells of his psychosis, his hypochondriasis, and his long search for a cure.

B. C. A. (with an introduction by Morton Prince, M.D.)
My Life as a Dissociated Personality
Badger, Boston, 1909. Paper

BOISEN, ANTON T.
The Exploration of the Inner World: A Study of Mental Disorder and Religious Experience
Harper, New York, 1936 and 1952
A classic. A minister of the Gospel who had several acute spells of insanity became the second chaplain to a mental hospital. He made a study of many insane men. He struggled with the problem of the similarity between the experiences of the saints and the insane.

BOISEN, ANTON T.
Out of the Depths
Harper, New York, 1960
A detailed account of Boisen's life, his inability to win the girl he loved, and his mental upsets.

BROWN, HENRY COLLINS
A Mind Mislaid
Dutton, New York, 1937
An excellent description of a depression that followed a period of overwork and then a great disappointment.

CAMMELL, CHARLES RICHARD
Aleister Crowley: The Man, the Mage, the Poet
Richards, London, 1951
Crowley was a gifted crackpot. *See also* Symonds.

CAMP, REV. JOSEPH
An Insight into an Insane Asylum
Munford, Alabama; published for the author, 1882
A poorly written book by a poorly educated psychotic minister.

CHAMBERS, JULIUS
A Mad World and Its Inhabitants
Sampson Low, Marston, Searle, and Rivington, London, 1876
A man says he faked his way into a mental hospital.

CHANLER, JOHN ARMSTRONG
Four Years behind the Bars of 'Bloomingdale,' or, The Bankruptcy of Law in New York
Roanoke Rapids, N.C., 1906
A lawyer maintains he should never have been committed.

DAILEY, ABRAM H.
Mollie Fancher: The Brooklyn

339

Enigma. An Authentic Statement of Facts in the Life of Mary J. Fancher. The Psychological Marvel of the Nineteenth Century
Brooklyn, N.Y., 1894

A remarkable study of a woman who probably suffered from hysteria, and went from one trance to another.

DAVIDSON, D.
Remembrances of a Religio-Maniac
Shakespeare Press, Stratford-on-Avon, 1912

The story of a lad who first had hallucinations of hearing and later became overly religious and insane.

DERBY, JOHN B.
Scenes in a Mad House
Samuel N. Dickinson, Boston, 1838
Paper-bound

Brief and of little value. He describes a few people he met in the mental hospital.

FELDMAN, HARRY
In a Forest Dark
Thomas Nelson and Sons, New York, 1960

The story of a most unhappy childhood which resulted in a psychosis.

FULLER, ROBERT
Account of the Imprisonment and Sufferings of Robert Fuller
Printed for the author, Boston, 1833

A man who probably went into a brief manic spell and wanted to spend all his savings on an insane speculation was committed by his friends. He maintained he was never insane.

GILBERT, WILLIAM
The Monomaniac, or Shirley Hall Asylum
Jas. G. Gregory, New York, 1864

The story of an insane man who had to be committed after he had almost ruined himself, making a perpetual-motion machine.

GORKI, MAXIM
My Childhood
Century Co., New York, 1916

At times mildly psychotic, he tried to commit suicide.

GORKI, MAXIM
Reminiscences of My Youth
(transl. by Veronica Dewey)
Wm. Heinemann, London, 1924

He was at times mildly psychotic, and he tried to commit suicide.

GRIFFIN, RICHARD
Bug House Poetry, the Complete Works of R. Griffin
No publisher, no city mentioned, 1913(?)

Jingles written by a man who realizes he is "a bit off."

HARVIN, EMILY (pseudonym)
The Stubborn Wood
Ziff-Davis, Chicago, 1948

Said to be based on an actual case in which a philandering husband wanted to have his wife kept in a mental hospital.

HILLYER, JANE
Reluctantly Told
Macmillan, New York, 1926

A young woman gives an excellent description of her spell of insanity and slow recovery.

JAYSON, LAWRENCE M.
Mania

Funk and Wagnalls, New York, 1937

The interesting story of a man who "cracked up" when, in 1929, he lost all his money.

JOYCE, COL. JOHN A.
A Checkered Life
S. P. Rounds, Jr., Chicago, 1883

The story of a brief episode of mania.

Joyce had a remarkable vision, in 1883, of what a modern mental hospital should be.

KERKHOFF, JACK
How Thin the Veil
Greenberg, New York, 1952

The story of a newspaperman who was insane for 45 days after a drinking spree. He gives an interesting picture of life in a mental hospital.

KING, MARIAN
The Recovery of Myself: A Patient's Experience in a Hospital for Mental Illness
Yale University Press, New Haven, 1931

A young woman, probably a bit odd from birth, after much overdoing, started taking Veronal in large amounts and had to be committed. She gives a good picture of the workings of an expensive private sanatorium.

KRAUCH, ELSA (writing for Jim Curran)
A Mind Restored
Putnam, New York, 1937

The story of a successful businessman who became just psychotic enough so that he failed in his work, lost all his money, and, largely for lack of money for room and board, had to live in a mental hospital.

LATE INMATE OF THE GLASGOW ROYAL ASYLUM FOR LUNATICS AT GARTNAVEL
The Philosophy of Insanity
Greenberg, New York, 1947

A splendid story by a fine Scotchman who twice went insane. It should be read by all psychiatrists.

LEONARD, WILLIAM ELLERY
A Man against Time: An Heroic Dream
Appleton-Century, New York, 1945

The author of *The Locomotive God* writes of his last marriage and writes in a hurry—against time.

MACLANE, MARY
The Story of Mary MacLane by Herself
Henry S. Stone, Chicago, 1902

A vividly written, very frank diary of a strange, very lonely girl who suspected she was slightly homosexual.

MACLANE, MARY
I, Mary MacLane, A Diary of Human Days, by Mary MacLane
Stokes, New York, 1917

A second installment, telling in brilliant sentences more of the girl's psychotic loneliness with her concentration on herself. She admits she was half insane and half Lesbian.

DE MAUPASSANT, GUY
The Horla (transl. into English)
Classic Publishing Co., London and New York (printed in U.S.A., 1928)

The story of the writer's hallucinations that came as he was going insane.

MAYOS, DR. CHARLES E. (compiler)
Poetry of the Insane
Privately printed, 1933

Dr. Mayos, a psychiatrist, for years collected hundreds of poems written by the insane.

McGARR, MARGARET ATKINS
And Lo, the Star
Pageant Press, New York, 1953

An eccentric schoolteacher who became confused and fired a revolver from her window was committed. She doubts that she needed hospitalization.

DE NERVAL, GERARD
Le Rêve et la vie
René Hilsum, Paris, 1931

This was written when he was insane; yet it seems logical. *See also* Rhodes.

NIETZSCHE, FRAU FÖRSTER
The Lonely Nietzsche (transl. by Paul V. Cohn)
Heinemann, London, 1915

A life of the great philosopher, with two chapters about the insanity that was ushered in by strokes.

NIETZSCHE, FRIEDRICH
My Sister and I (transl. by Dr. Oscar Levy)
Boar's Head Books, New York, 1953

The remarkable story of Nietzsche and his incestuous relations with his sister, written during his incarceration in a mental hospital.

PIERSALL, JAMES, and ALBERT HIRSHBERG
Fear Strikes Out: The Jim Piersall Story
Little, Brown, Boston, 1955

A major league baseball player has a strange spell of insanity.

PETERS, FRITZ (writing for David Mitchell)
The World Next Door
Farrar, Strauss, New York, 1949

One of the best books to show how bitter a psychotic man can become against his own mother when she has to have him committed and later does not dare to parole him out.

POLLITT, BASIL H.
Justice and the Justices
College Publishing Co., Daytona Beach, Fla., 1954

A lawyer trying to prove he was never upset mentally.

POLLITT, BASIL HUBBARD
The Lawyer's Story
Published by the author, Miami, 1958

The typical story of a lawyer who claims he was never insane.

PRINCE, MORTON, M.D.
The Dissociation of a Personality: A Biographical Study in Abnormal Psychology
Longmans, New York, 1910

PRINCE, WALTER FRANKLIN, Ph.D.
"The Doris Case of Multiple Personality," part 1
In *Proc. Amer. Soc. for Psychical Research*, Sec. 13. Amer. Inst. for Scientific Research, vol. 9, Aug., 1915

A woman who had five personalities.

RHODES, S. A.
Gérard de Nerval, 1808–1855: Poet, Traveler, Dreamer
Philosophical Library, New York, 1951

One of France's able writers was, from youth onward, eccentric. He may well have been epileptic as well as psychotic.

SASSOON, SIEGFRIED
Sherston's Progress
Faber and Faber, London, 1944
A British writer tells of crack-ing nervously during World War II. Of little value.

SIMPSON, JANE
The Lost Days of My Life
Allen and Unwin, Ltd., London, 1958
The poignant story of a girl who, when compelled to live with a mean, psychotic mother, took refuge in mental hospitals where, for twenty years, she was cruelly treated. Eventually, a kindly psy-chiatrist cured her.

SOUTHCOTT, JOANNA
The Second Book of Wonders
Printed by Marchant and Galu-bin, London, 1813
A pathologically religious in-sane woman who nearly founded a new religion.

SYMONDS, JOHN
The Great Beast: the Life of Aleister Crowley
Rider, London, 1951
A psychotic poseur tried to be the most wicked man in England.

SYMONS, ARTHUR
Confessions, A Study in Pathol-ogy
Jonathan Cape and Harrison Smyth, London and New York, 1930
The story of the insanity of an able writer who, from birth, had been self-centered and prob-ably schizoid.

SYMONS, ARTHUR
Spiritual Adventures (contains "Prelude to Life," and "Christian Trevalga")
Constable, London, 1905

Parts of the story told by a great English poet and essayist of his descent into insanity.

THELMAR, E.
The Maniac (a realistic study of madness from the maniac's point of view)
London, 1909; 2d ed., The Amer-ican Psychical Institute, New York, 1932
A remarkable story of auditory hallucinations and acute insanity.

THIGPEN, CORBETT, M.D., and HERVEY M. CLECKLEY, M.D.
The Three Faces of Eve
McGraw-Hill, New York, 1957
The story of a woman with three personalities. See her own autobiography.

THOMPSON, FLORENCE S., and GEORGE W. GALVIN
A Thousand Faces
The Four Seas Co., Boston, 1920
This is in novel form, but Dr. Galvin says the facts are correct. The book was written to improve matters in mental hospitals.

VICTOR, SARAH M.
The Life Story of, for Sixty Years. Convicted of Murdering Her Brother, Sentenced To Be Hung, Had Sentence Commuted, Passed Nineteen Years in Prison, Yet Is Innocent. Told by Herself
Williams Publ., Cleveland, 1887
The dull story of a woman with insane relatives who, when her brother committed suicide, was accused of a crime and railroaded into prison. For a while she was insane.

VINCENT, JOHN
Inside the Asylum
Allen and Unwin, London, 1948

An overly religious manic-depressive paranoiac with a bad heredity became a prominent evangelist. He spent a while in a mental hospital.

WARD, MARY JANE
The Snake Pit
Random House, New York, 1946
The story of a woman who was in a mental hospital.

WILKES, THOMAS G. E.
Hell's Cauldron
Stratton-Wilcox, Atlanta, 1953
An Army captain got to arguing so violently and constantly with his superior that he was treated as a psychotic. He spent years, first getting himself out of the mental hospital, then divorcing his wife, and then "clearing his name."

WILSON, MARGARET
Borderland Minds
Meador, Boston, 1940
An ex-patient from Blackmoor. She was a business woman, always a bit odd, who after an operation became mildly upset.

WINGFIELD, ALYSIA
The Inside of the Cup
Angus and Robertson, London, 1958
A terrible indictment of stupidly and sadistically run mental hospitals.

SCHIZOPHRENICS

ANONYMOUS
I Question
Nashville, Tenn., 1945
The story of an insane man who writes like a schizophrenic.

MARTENS, DAVID
The Abrupt Self
Harper, New York, 1946

The diary of a schizoid and solitary professor who couldn't make up his mind what he wanted to do with his life.

NIJINSKY, ROMOLA
The Last Years of Nijinsky
Simon and Schuster, New York, 1952
More on the dancer's last illness.

NIJINSKY, ROMOLA
Nijinsky
Simon and Schuster, New York, 1936
Much on Nijinsky's life.

NIJINSKY, VASLAV
The Diary of Vaslav Nijinsky (ed. by Romola Nijinsky)
Simon and Schuster, New York, 1936
The diary of an eminent ballet dancer—a schizophrenic.

OGDON, J. A. HOWARD
The Kingdom of the Lost
Bodley Head, London, 1947
A schizophrenic escaped from a mental hospital. Although for the next two years he was mentally disturbed, he worked in a factory and hung onto his sanity.

SCHREBER, DANIEL
Memoirs of My Nervous Illness (transl. by Ida Macalpine and Richard A. Hunter)
Wm. Dawson and Sons, London, 1955
The classic story of a schizophrenic judge.

SÈCHEHAYE, MARGUERITE
Autobiography of a Schizophrenic Girl (transl. by Grace Rubin-Rabson)
Grune and Stratton, New York, 1951

The remarkable visions of a schizophrenic child.

MANIC-DEPRESSIVES

ABRAMS, ALBERT
Diary of a Physician
Modern Press, New York, 1923
A quack who once wrote on the blues and was apparently a manic-depressive. His writings were dull, with weak attempts at humor.

ABRAMS, ALBERT
Progressive Spondylotherapy
Philopolis Press, San Francisco, 1913
A quack, probably manic-depressive. This is a description of one of his supposed medical discoveries.

ABRAMS, ALBERT
Transactions of the Antiseptic Club
E. B. Treat, New York, 1895
The rather stupid writing of a manic-depressive who wrote a book on the blues.

AGNEW, ANNA
From under the Cloud, or Personal Reminiscences of Insanity
Robert Clarke, Cincinnati, 1886
A woman who suddenly went insane wanted to do away with her children.

ANTHONY, KATHERINE
The Lambs
Knopf, New York, 1945
Much interesting material of the occasional spells of insanity of Charles and Mary Lamb.

BALDWIN, MERCY
Gray Songs
Harold Vinal, New York, 1927

A physician's wife went into a menopausal depression and found she could write poetry.

BEERS, CLIFFORD W.
A Mind That Found Itself
Longmans, New York, 1908
The classic and perhaps best-known story of a man who went insane.

BENSON, A. C.
The House of Quiet
Dutton, New York, 1906
A charmingly written story, largely autobiographical, of a lonely bachelor subject to spells of depression which he describes superbly. All psychiatrists should read the book.

BOSWELL, JAMES
London Journal, 1762–1763 (prepared for the press by Frederick A. Pottle)
McGraw-Hill, New York, 1950
Boswell tells of his spells of familial depression.

CECIL, LORD DAVID
The Stricken Deer, or the Life of Cowper
Constable, London, 1929
A biography of the famous poet who was many times badly depressed and for years overly religious.

COWPER, WILLIAM
Memoir of the Early Life of William Cowper (2d American ed., from the 2d London ed.)
Philo B. Pratt, Newburgh, 1817
A remarkable story of repeated long spells of depression, with years of pathologic piety, plus an interesting story of a prolonged attempt at suicide. See also Quinlan.

CUSTANCE, JOHN
Wisdom, Madness, and Folly: The Philosophy of a Lunatic
Pellegrini and Cudahy, New York, 1952
A thought-producing story of manic-depressive insanity by a well-educated man.

CUSTANCE, JOHN
Adventure into the Unconscious
Christopher Johnson, London, 1954
Custance tells much more about his life with many spells of insanity.

DAHL, ROBERT
Breakdown
Bobbs-Merrill, Indianapolis, 1959
A good story of a manic-depressive which shows how hard it is to handle a friend and relative who is going insane.

FOX, GEORGE
George Fox: An Autobiography
Friends' Book Store, Philadelphia, 1919
A great religious leader who all his life thought only of religion tells of his early depression and his later hallucinations.

GRAVES, ALONZO
The Eclipse of a Mind
Medical Journal Press, New York, 1942
A newspaper correspondent tells at great length of five spells of depression. He gives a splendid story of an abnormal family.

JEFFERSON, LARA
These Are My Sisters
Vickers Publishing Co., Inc., Tulsa, 1947
The remarkable and vivid story of a woman, written as she went raving mad.

KRUGER, JUDITH
My Fight for Sanity
Chilton Co., Book Division, Philadelphia, 1959
The best story of a *post partum* depression.

LAMB, CHARLES
Literary Sketches and Letters— Final Memorials of C. Lamb.
Appleton, New York, 1848
Lamb was occasionally depressed and occasionally alcoholic.

McCALL, LENORE
Between Us and the Dark
Lippincott, Philadelphia, 1947
A very revealing and well-written description of a slowly developing depression.

MOORE, WILLIAM L.
The Mind in Chains: The Autobiography of a Schizophrenic
Exposition Press, New York, 1955
A slightly manic lad with a few delusions and a great desire to do good in this world.

PIERCE, S. W., and J. T. PIERCE
A Layman Looks at Doctors
Harcourt, Brace, New York, 1929
An excellent story, showing several types of treatment for a long depression.

QUINLAN, MAURICE J.
William Cowper: A Critical Life
University of Minnesota Press, Minneapolis, 1953
Cowper was depressed and overly religious for much of his life.

VIDAL, LOIS
Magpie: The Autobiography of a Nymph Errant
Little, Brown, Boston, 1934
A manic-depressive young woman who, in her manic stage, rambled about the country.

PARANOIACS

ADLER, G. F.
Letters of a Lunatic: A Brief Exposition of My University Life during the Years 1853-1854
Printed for the author, 1854
A remarkable story told by a paranoiac professor who thought everyone was trying to annoy him.

HACKETT, MARIE
The Cliff's Edge
McGraw-Hill, New York, 1954
The story told by a paranoiac's wife of her life with him and his inability to find a job when he came home from the mental hospital.

HACKETT, PAUL
The Cardboard Giants
Putnam, New York, 1952
The story of a paranoiac who may have been a carrier of epilepsy. He spent time in a mental hospital.

HAZLITT, WILLIAM
Liber Amoris: Or the New Pygmalion with Additional Matter Now Printed for the First Time from the Original Manuscripts
Great Britain, privately printed, 1894
Only a man out of his mind could first have conceived such a violent love for a stupid, unresponsive girl and then have insisted on having the disgraceful correspondence published. He was paranoid and violent and at times depressed.

JOHNSON, DONALD McI., M.P.
A Doctor Regrets
Christopher Johnson, London, 1949
A British doctor who later had a number of distressing mental symptoms tells of his early life and practice.

JOHNSON, DONALD McI., M.P.
A Doctor Returns
Christopher Johnson, London, 1956
A British physician who, years ago, was held for a short while in a mental hospital thinks he was poisoned. He has filled this book with the description of symtoms which psychiatrists would probably regard as typically those of paranoia. The doctor hopes he is "clearing his good name."

JOHNSON, DR. DONALD McI., and NORMAN DODDS (eds.)
(Introduction by them to eight stories)
The Plea for the Silent
Christopher Johnson, London, 1957
Eight interesting autobiographic stories of persons, some of whom may, as they said, have been committed without much justification.

STRINDBERG, AUGUST
The Confession of a Fool (transl. by Ellie Scheussner)
Viking Press, New York, 1925
A paranoiac's story of his wrecked marriage.

STRINDBERG, AUGUST
The Inferno (transl. by Claud Field)
Wm. Rider, London, 1912
Autobiographical book by a famous paranoiac.

STRINDBERG, AUGUST
Legends, Autobiographical Sketches
Melrose, London, 1912
The best story of the life of a paranoiac.

STRINDBERG, AUGUST
The Son of a Servant (transl. by Claud Field)
Putnam, New York, 1913
   A remarkable story by a paranoiac.

STRINDBERG, FREDA
Marriage with Genius
J. Cape, London, 1937
   The story of Strindberg's second marriage, wrecked by his paranoia.

WOOLSON, ARTHUR
Good-by, My Son
Harper, New York, 1960
   The remarkable story of a father's efforts to help his paranoiac son.

PSYCHOANALYSIS

BARACH, DR. ALVAN
The Spectacle of a Man (written about John Coignard)
Jefferson House, New York, 1939
   The very interesting story of the psychoanalysis and sexual attractions and repulsions of a man and woman, both too immature for a successful marriage.

BIEZIN, J., M.D.
The Torments of a Frigid Woman: A Case History of a Sexual Difficulty (transl. from the French by J. Beaumond)
Cadillac Publishing Co., New York, 1953
   A poorly adjusted young woman tells of her search for love and her revulsion from it when it came. Her analyst explained everything.

FINK, DR. HAROLD KENNETH
Long Journey
Julian Press, New York, 1954

   A rather dull story about the analyzing of an uninteresting Mexican (?) lad who was dissatisfied with many phases of his life.

FREEMAN, LUCY
Fight against Fears
Crown Publishers, New York, 1951
   An able newspaper reporter, who says she was always mixed-up about sex and other things, tells of five years of psychoanalysis, and her marriage, which soon went sour. It is not clear how much good her analysis did her. The book is well written and deserves study.

KNIGHT, JOHN (pseudonym)
The Story of My Psychoanalysis
McGraw-Hill, New York, 1950
   The story of a scientist who was much upset by the anti-Semitism he had encountered. It is not clear that the psychoanalysis made him over into a mature person.

LINDNER, ROBERT M.
Rebel without a Cause: The Hypnoanalysis of a Criminal Psychopath
Grune and Stratton, New York, 1944
   The analyst seems to think this delinquent was made over into a good citizen.

REIK, THEODOR
The Search Within: The Inner Experiences of a Psychoanalyst
Farrar, Straus and Cudahy, New York, 1956
   His psychoanalytic story of his own fears and sexual conflicts; see his Part 2.

PHOBIAS

ANONYMOUS
The Autobiography of a Suicide
Golden Galleon Press, Lawrence, New York, 1934

The story of an able man who got so phobic he could not go more than a few yards from his house.

DAVID —
The Autobiography of David —
(ed. by Ernest Raymond)
Victor Gollancz, Ltd., London, 1946

A good description of a severe agoraphobia and a compulsion to expose himself, written by an able newspaperman who spent some time in mental hospitals.

LEONARD, WILLIAM ELLERY
The Locomotive God
Century Co., New York, 1927

An eminent professor of English for much of his life could not go more than a few yards from his house.

LEONARD, WILLIAM ELLERY
Two Lives
Viking Press, New York, 1933

An eccentric, mildly psychotic, and highly phobic professor of English tells in magnificent poetry the story of his marriage to an insane young woman who committed suicide.

EPILEPTICS

CLARE, JOHN
Sketches in the Life of John Clare
(written by himself, now first published with an introduction, notes and additions, by Edmund Blunden)
Cobden-Sanderson, London, 1931

The story of a poorly educated, epileptic, and insane farm worker who wrote beautiful pastoral poetry.

DOSTOEVSKY, FYODOR
White Nights and Other Stories
(transl. by Constance Garnett)
Macmillan, New York, 1918

Writings of an epileptic with some autobiographical touches. See also Slonim.

EVANS, MARGIAD
Autobiography
Basil Blackwell, Oxford, 1943

Another part of the life story of an epileptic. Not nearly as good as her other book.

EVANS, MARGIAD
A Ray of Darkness
Roy, New York, no date

A classic. The story of 40 years of distress with an epileptic type of erratic nervous system.

GRIMES, G.
A Treatise on Insanity, the Only Work of the Kind in the United States or Perhaps in the Known World: Founded on General Observation and Truth (3d ed.)
Graham, New York, 1847

Written by an inmate of the Lunatic Asylum of Tennessee, an epileptic who spent 18 years in a mental hospital. The book is of little value.

HALES, ELLA
Like a Lamb
Christopher Johnson, London, 1958

A nurse who mentions paranoid ideas and fits that caused her to be committed several times maintains that she never was insane. The book is poorly written.

SLONIM, MARC
The Three Loves of Dostoevsky
Rinehart, New York, 1955
Much autobiographic material by an excitable and difficult epileptic.

TIBBLE, J. W., and ANNE TIBBLE
John Clare: A Life
Oxford University Press, New York, 1932
Contains many poems by a gentle insane man who was also epileptic.

VAN GOGH, VINCENT
Dear Theo: The Autobiography of Vincent Van Gogh (ed. by Irving Stone)
Riverside Press, Cambridge, Mass., 1937
A remarkable series of letters by a strange, difficult man who was probably schizophrenic and certainly epileptic.

ALCOHOLICS

ANDERSON, DWIGHT, with PAGE COOPER
The Other Side of the Bottle
A. A. Wyn, New York, 1950
Excellent story of coming out of a memoryless stage in a hospital. This man has studied alcoholism, and hence his book, like Free's, can be very helpful.

ASTOR, MARY
My Story: An Autobiography
Doubleday, New York, 1959
A fine actress and able woman who, for years, drank heavily but did not let it keep her from work. Her love life was unsatisfactory.

BARRYMORE, DIANA, and GEROLD FRANK
Too Much, Too Soon
Holt, New York, 1957

The sad story of a girl who inherited great abilities as an actress, also a great thirst that ruined her. She could not get close to either her beautiful and gifted mother or her brilliant father.

BENSON, LUTHER
Fifteen Years in Hell
Carlon and Hollenbeck, Indianapolis, 1885
A man who inherited a terrible thirst; he said he was mentally abnormal from birth. He got "cured" but still had to wage a battle.

BISHOP, JIM
The Glass Crutch
Doubleday, Doran, Garden City, N. Y., 1945
The story of William Wynne Wister. The man used alcohol as a crutch to make him popular. The day after his marriage he telephoned his pals to come and have a wild party with him. He well described the downward path. He gives much on the psychology of the alcoholic.

BLYTHE, SAMUEL G.
The Old Game
Doran, New York, 1914
An alcoholic who points out how much more time for real living a drinker has when he quits.

BOYINGTON, COL. GREGORY USMC, RET.
Baa Baa Black Sheep
Putnam, New York, 1958
A vivid story of a very likable alcoholic daredevil Army ace who admits he was emotionally immature and a screwball. Eventually he was helped by AA.

BROKENSHIRE, NORMAN
This Is Norman Brokenshire: An Unvarnished Self-portrait
David McKay, New York, 1954
A prominent radio announcer drank himself out of his job and down to the depths. He managed to climb out again.

BROWN, CARLTON
Brainstorm
Farrar and Rinehart, New York, 1944
The story of Mike, a close friend. He was a New York editor and an alcoholic who led a most unhygienic life until he broke mentally and was committed. An excellent picture of a certain type of Greenwich Village life.

BURNS, ELIZABETH
The Late Liz
Appleton, New York, 1958
The well-written story of an undisciplined and wealthy and often alcoholic woman who had many troubles in her love life. Eventually she won out.

DAY, BETH
No Hiding Place (The Story of Vincent Tracy)
Permabooks, New York, 1958
Well written, and perhaps the best of the books written to show why a man drinks and how he can be cured.

DONER, THOMAS
Eleven Years a Drunkard: Or the Life of T. Doner
Arnold Brothers, Sycamore, Ill., 1878
An alcoholic who lost both arms trying to jump on a moving train.

DOUTNEY, THOMAS N.
The Life Struggle, Fall and Reformation of Thomas N. Doutney
Boston, 1876; paper cover
An ex-alcoholic and a temperance lecturer tells of the terrible years when at times he wasn't sane.

DRAKE, JOHN H.
Thirty-two Years of the Life of an Adventurer
Printed for the author, by Wm. H. Colyer, New York, 1847
A small old book by an alcoholic, possibly epileptic, often depressed, at times manic, and at times so violent he had to be locked up. He made a mess of his life.

DUTCHER, GEORGE M.
Disinthralled: A Story of My Life
Columbian Book Co., Hartford, Conn., 1873
An old-fashioned story of a reformed alcoholic who became a temperance lecturer. In Poughkeepsie he found a group like AA today.

ELLIS, JAMES H.
To Hell and Back: The Story of an Alcoholic
Vantage Press, New York, 1953
A shy, mildly psychotic, highly religious man became an alcoholic. He joined the Army and still drank heavily. He went insane. Later, he was helped by AA.

FRANCIS, JOSEPH H.
My Last Drink
Empire Book Co., Chicago, 1915
A Chicago alderman and successful businessman with a happy and devoted family drank himself into Skid Row and remained there for a long time. He admits that an alcoholic is insane. He

describes unusually well the life on Skid Row. He describes DT's.

FREE, JAMES L.
Just One More: Concerning the Problem Drinker
Coward-McCann, New York, 1955

Perhaps the best book written by an alcoholic for alcoholics who want to know where to turn for help. He tells of all the several ways in which an alcoholic can get on the wagon.

GARRISON, JAMES HOLLEY
Behold Me Once More (ed. by W. McI. Merrill)
Houghton Mifflin, Boston, 1954

A mildly psychotic, highly alcoholic black-sheep brother of William Lloyd Garrison. The best description of the awful troubles an alcoholic sailor can get into.

GRAY, JERRY
The Third Strike
Abingdon-Cokesbury Press, New York, 1949

A small book brilliantly written by an alcoholic who apparently came of a line of alcoholics. He had terrible DT's in a hospital. He tried to figure out why he drank, and he discussed well the problems of the alcoholic. Eventually, he committed suicide.

HEWLETT, SAMUEL MUDWAY
The Cup and Its Conquerer: Or the Triumphs of Temperance, as Exhibited in the Life, Travels and Adventures of S. M. Hewlett
Redding, Boston, 1862

A small book by a gifted actor and storyteller and alcoholic who spent years wandering around. Then he signed the pledge and became a prominent and hardworking temperance lecturer.

HOUGH, HENRY BEETLE (as told to)
An Alcoholic to His Sons
Simon and Schuster, New York, 1954

An excellent description of an alcoholic advertising man who didn't think he was alcoholic. He describes the downward course.

HOY, J. F.
Confession of a Drunkard (includes poem, "The Drunkard's Dream")
Albany, about 1860
A paper-covered pamphlet

A lawyer who ruined himself with alcohol. Of little value.

"INMATE WARD 8"
Behind the Door of Delusion
Macmillan, New York, 1932

An able editor, unable to stop drinking, committed himself. In a few days sober, he wrote one of the best available descriptions of life in a mental hospital.

JACKSON, CHARLES
The Lost Weekend
Farrar and Rinehart, New York, 1944

The famous story of an alcoholic spree: a novel, written with great knowledge of the subject.

KARPMAN, BENJAMIN
The Alcoholic Woman
Linacre Press, Washington, D.C., 1948

An excellent book based on autobiographical material about three alcoholic women. One tells of her bad heredity. The second quickly went into a psychosis; she also had a terrible heredity. The third was very promiscuous with men; she was homosexual and possibly epileptic.

LONDON, JACK
Jack Barleycorn
Century Co., New York, 1913
Perhaps the best description of the way in which heavy drinking in youth eventually turned into enslaving alcoholism. In the end, London committed suicide.

LONG, MASON
The Life of Mason Long, the Converted Gambler, Written by Himself
Donnelly Loyd, Chicago, 1878
A remarkable story of a professional gambler who bucked other gamblers' games and lost everything.

MAINE, HAROLD (pseudonym)
If a Man Be Mad
Doubleday, New York, 1947
A highly informative book by an alcoholic, to show his feelings of inadequacy and insecurity and inability to live long in any place.

MIDDLE-AGED MAN
Passages from the History of a Wasted Life
Benj. B. Mussey, Boston, 1853
A well-written story of a physician and writer too alcoholic to get a practice. He tells of DT's and a week of madness.

MOLONY, WILLIAM O'SULLIVAN
New Armor for Old
Holt, New York, 1935
An alcoholic, for a while in a mental hospital. Suffered from agoraphobia and claustrophobia. He could not eat in public. He attempted suicide.

OWEN, EMERSON D. (pseudonym "North 3-1")
Pick up the Pieces
Doubleday, Doran, New York, 1929

An alcoholic who was committed after smashing up his marriage and losing everything in life. In a previous incarceration a strait jacket was tied so tight he lost the use of both his arms. He eventually sobered up.

PFAU, FATHER RALPH
Prodigal Shepherd
Lippincott, Philadelphia, 1958
A wonderful story of a fine priest who inherited a terrible thirst. After years of alcoholism, he found success in helping other alcoholics. He lectured widely for AA.

POLE, J. L.
When—A Record of Transition
Chapman and Hall, London, 1929
The well-written story of a British writer who drank until he had to be committed. He always did what he wanted, recking not of the harm he'd do to himself and his loved ones. He may have been epileptic.

RAND, FESTUS G.
Autobiography
M. F. Wilson, Printers, St. Albans, Vt., 1878
A reformed alcoholic. One bitterly cold night, while drunk, he fell off his horse and lay in the snow until he lost hands and feet. He became a temperance lecturer.

RICHMOND, A. B., ESQ.
Leaves from the Diary of an Old Lawyer
American Book Exchange, New York, 1880
Intemperance; the great source of crime.

ROBINSON, EDWARD G. JR., and others
My Father, My Son
Frederick Fell, New York, 1958
An alcoholic, spoiled, and emotionally neglected son of one of the country's leading actors tells his story.

ROMAN, CHARLES
A Man Remade: Or Out of Delirium's Wonderland
Reilly and Britton, Chicago, 1909
A well-written book by a newspaperman who gives the best and longest description of delirium tremens.

ROOT, J.
Horrors of Delirium Tremens
Josiah Adams, New York, 1844
In 1844 a man described well, and at length, his DT's. Much of his book is on religion.

ROSENFIELD, JOE JR.
The Happiest Man in the World
Doubleday, Garden City, N.Y., 1955
A very successful radio announcer who went down to Skid Row and then came back again.

ROTH, LILLIAN
I'll Cry Tomorrow
Frederick Fell, New York, 1954
An actress started to become an alcoholic with her first drink because it gave her the feelings of sociability that she wanted. She went to the depths, and then came back.

RUNYON, DAMON, JR.
Father's Footsteps
Random House, New York, 1953
An ex-alcoholic newspaper man whose father was a cured alcoholic.

SEABROOK, WILLIAM
Asylum
Harcourt, Brace, New York, 1935
An able writer who when he saw he was drinking himself to death had himself committed, and wrote a good book on alcoholics.

SEABROOK, WILLIAM
No Hiding Place, an Autobiography
Lippincott, Philadelphia, 1942
One of the best books ever written on alcoholism and the dissatisfactions, restlessness, feelings of failure, and desire to keep running away that keep a mildly psychotic man drinking.

STEELE, ROBERT
One Man
Mitchell Kennerley, New York, 1915
He writes in the form of a novel but it is evidently an autobiography of a delinquent boy who, for a while, drank heavily. He was in prison two years.

STONE, IRVING
Jack London, A Sailor on Horseback
Doubleday, New York, 1956
This life of Jack London will help the reader to understand "John Barleycorn." Jack apparently was mildly manic-depressive. In spite of a world full of admirers, Jack felt terribly alone. He feared he was going insane.

WHITE, JOHN
Ward N–1
A. A. Wyn, New York, 1955
One of the best studies of alcoholism. A writer of TV scripts gives a description of the lives and conversations of a lot of Skid Row characters he met in Bellevue Hospital. He describes well

the "drying-out" feelings in the hospital.

DRUG ADDICTS

COBBE, WILLIAM ROSSER
Dr. Judas: A Portrayal of the Opium Habit
Griggs, Chicago, 1895
A remarkable scientific type of study of the opium habit.

COCTEAU, JEAN
Opium, the Diary of a Cure
(transl. by Margaret Crosland and Sinclair Road)
Grove, New York, 1958
A disjointedly written book on smoking opium.

COLE, H. G.
Confessions of an American Opium Eater; From Bondage to Freedom
Woodbery, Boston, 1905
A gambler and user of morphine tells of his adventures in the late 1800's.

CROWLEY, ALEISTER
The Diary of a Drug Fiend
Collins, London, 1922
The story of a man and woman on a drug debauch, written as a novel by a man habituated to Heroin.

DE LENOIR, CECIL
The Hundredth Man: Confessions of a Drug Addict
Kendall, New York, 1934
He was told that only 1 dope fiend in 100 gets well and stays well.

DE QUINCEY, THOMAS
Confessions of an Opium-eater
Roycrofters, East Aurora, N.Y., 1898
A classic.

AN HABITUATE
Opium-eating: An Autobiographical Sketch
Claxton, Remsen and Haffelfinger, Philadelphia, 1876
Interesting as a picture of opium eating in the eighteen hundreds.

HOLLIDAY, BILLIE, with WILLIAM DUFTY
Lady Sings the Blues
Doubleday, New York, 1956
A famous singer tells of her fifteen year fight with Heroin.

HULBURD, DAVID
H Is for Heroin
Doubleday, Garden City, N.Y., 1952
The sad story of a teen-age girl who got hooked first on marihuana and then on Heroin.

KING, ALEXANDER
Mine Enemy Grows Older
Simon and Schuster, New York, 1958
An able man had a hard time getting off morphine.

LIEPMANN, HEINZ
Case History
Shakespeare Head, London, 1952
A story of a morphine addict.

LOFLAND, DR. JOHN
The Poetical and Prose Writings of Dr. John Lofland, the Milford Bard
Murphy, Baltimore, 1853
A collection of his writings with the story of his experiences with opium.

LUDLOW, FITZHUGH
The Hasheesh Eater. Being Passages from the Life of a Pythagorean
Rains, New York, 1903
Well written.

MARKS, JAN, M.D.
Doctor Purgatory
Citadel, New York, 1959
   A physician who became addicted to Demerol tells of the hell he went through for years trying to get off it.

MEZZROW, MILTON ("MEZZ"), and BERNARD WOLFE
Really the Blues
Random House, New York, 1946
   The frank story of a jazz musician who loved marihuana.

NESBIT, EVELYN
Prodigal Days: The Untold Story
Messner, New York, 1934
   The story of her disaster with Harry Thaw. She wound up a drug taker.

PAUL, BRENDA DEAN
My First Life: A Biography
Long, London, no date
   An English girl, undisciplined and at times depressed, who burned the candle at both ends in the smart set and took to morphine.

ROBINSON, G. P.
Testament: The Confessions of a Drug-taker
Duckworth, London, 1922
   A drug addict describes his life vividly.

ROBINSON, CAPT. H. R.
A Modern de Quincey: An Autobiography
Harrap, London, 1942
   A British captain, working in the Orient, got to smoking opium and could not quit. To commit suicide, he shot but only blinded himself.

SPILLARD, WILLIAM J.
Needle in a Haystack (as told to Pence James): *The Exciting Adventures of a Federal Narcotics Agent*
McGraw-Hill, New York, 1945
   The interesting story of a narcotics agent.

STERN, BILL, with OSCAR FRALEY
The Taste of Ashes
Holt, New York, 1959
   A moving story of one of the best sportscasters, who got to using drugs, and finally was cured and went back to work again.

STREET, LEROY, with DAVID LOTH
I Was a Drug Addict
Random House, New York, 1953
   A Heroin addict tells of 13 years of degradation.

THORP, RAYMOND
Viper: The Confessions of a Drug Addict
Hale, London, 1956
   An addict and drug "pusher" tells of his life.

ECCENTRICS

ANONYMOUS
The Story of a Lover
Boni and Liveright, New York, 1919
   According to Mabel Dodge Luhan, this is the true love story of her close friend Hutchins Hapgood. The man was so "shattered nervously" and made such demands of his wife that their love almost foundered.

BARONTE, GERVÉE
Life and Loves of a Prodigal Daughter, Being the Intimate Memoirs of Gervée Baronte
Baronte Press, London, 1935
   A gifted eccentric and rambler

on the face of the earth tells of several love affairs.

BASHKIRTSEFF, MARIE
The Journal of a Young Artist, 1860–1884 (transl. by Mary J. Serrano)
Cassell, New York, 1889
A diary which, by its frankness, startled the world. *See also* CRESTON.

BASHKIRTSEFF, MARIE
The Last Confessions of Marie Bashkirtseff and Her Correspondence with Guy de Maupassant
Stokes, New York, 1901
Letters written by the famous Marie.

BAUDELAIRE, CHARLES
The Letters of Baudelaire (trans. by Arthur Symons)
Albert and Charles Boni, New York, 1927
The man—a genius—was close to madness all of his strange life.

BERNARD, THEOS
Hatha Yoga: The Report of a Personal Experience
Rider, London, 1950
The story of an eccentric who went to Tibet to learn the odd practices of Yoga.

BERNHARDT, SARAH
Memories of My Life: Being My Personal, Professional and Social Recollections as Woman and Artist
Appleton, New York, 1907
The remarkable story of a brilliant, gifted, and often violent-tempered and eccentric woman.

BODLEY, R. V. C.
In Search of Serenity
Little, Brown, Boston, 1955
A most thought-provoking and valuable book by an eccentric British officer who went to the Sahara Desert to live for years with the Arabs.

BOTCHKAREVA, MARIA
Yashka: My Life as Peasant Officer and Exile
Stokes, New York, 1918
A woman who, in Russia, insisted on fighting as a soldier in a man's regiment.

BOWEN, CROSWELL, and SHANE O'NEILL
The Curse of the Misbegotten: A Tale of the House of O'Neill
McGraw-Hill, New York, 1959
The story of the great playwright and his son Shane who suffered from a poor nervous heredity.

CORVO, BARON FREDERICK
Hadrian the Seventh
Knopf, New York, 1953
A remarkable, vividly written book by a paranoid, highly eccentric homosexual—a would-be priest who imagines that he became a Pope.

CRESTON, DORMER
Fountains of Youth: The Life of Marie Bashkirtseff
Dutton, New York, 1937
A life of the famous diarist.

DALI, SALVADOR
The Secret Life of Salvador Dali
(transl. by Haakon M. Chevalier)
Dial, New York, 1942
A gifted artist who, as he said, is "destined to a truculent eccentricity, whether I wish it or no."

DELL, FLOYD
Homecoming: An Autobiography
Farrar and Rinehart, New York, 1933
An eccentric, an ardent socialist, an able poet.

DUNCAN, ISADORA
My Life
Garden City Publishing Co., Garden City, N.Y., 1927
The story of an eccentric dancer.

EDSTROM, DAVID
The Testament of Caliban
Funk and Wagnalls, New York, 1937
A gifted sculptor whom Ellen Key called "the most primitive and uncivilized creature she had ever known." His violent temper suggests a basic epilepsy; his inability to be friendly suggests schizophrenia.

FORT, CHARLES
The Book of the Damned
Boni and Liveright, New York, 1919
A strange, rambling, poorly planned book by a man who spent his life trying to prove that science was foolishness.

FORT, CHARLES
The Books of Charles Fort
Holt, New York, 1941
Reprintings of Fort's books. He was an eccentric who had neither acquaintances nor friends. Having some private income, he spent twenty-six years in libraries making thousands of notes about odd circumstances, or about statements which he felt made scientists look foolish.

FORT, CHARLES
Lo!
Kendall, New York, 1931
A weird collection of clippings from newspapers.

FORT, CHARLES
New Lands (Introduction by Booth Tarkington)
Boni and Liveright, New York, 1923
A book that would delight students of flying saucers.

FORT, CHARLES
Wild Talents
Kendall, New York, 1932
A collection of weird and unexplained stories of disaster found in newspapers.

GARRETT, MRS. EILEEN J.
Adventures in the Supernormal: A Personal Memoir
Creative Age Press, New York, 1949
A woman who went into trances and served as a medium.

GUGGENHEIM, PEGGY
Out of This Century
Dial, New York, 1946
The remarkably frank story of the amours of an eccentric woman.

HAMNETT, NINA
Laughing Torso
Long and Smith, New York, 1932
The interesting story of an eccentric woman who knew most of the artists and eccentrics in Paris.

HUTCHINS, MRS. MAUDE
A Diary of Love
New Directions, New York, 1950
A book so frank it was banned in some cities.

KARLIN, ALMA M.
The Odyssey of a Lonely Woman
(transl. by Emile Burns)
Gollancz, London, 1933
A strange little German woman with a great fear of being raped goes all around the world on a shoestring.

Loisy, Alfred
Choses passées
Noury, Paris, 1913
The story of a very learned priest, born in 1857, whose studies came into conflict with his religion and wrecked his life.

Luhan, Mabel Dodge
Intimate Memories, vol. 1, *Background*
Harcourt, Brace, New York, 1933
The years from 1879 to 1900. She describes two Lesbian experiences. In another volume she speaks of a male component in her character. She tells of her depressions.

Luhan, Mabel Dodge
European Experiences (vol. 2 of *Intimate Memories*)
Harcourt, Brace, New York, 1935
A frank story of her experiences in Europe.

Luhan, Mabel Dodge
Movers and Shakers (vol. 3 of *Intimate Memories*)
Harcourt, Brace, New York, 1936
A very frank story of friendships and love affairs with many distinguished persons, also of mildly psychotic difficulties, and of some psychoanalysis.

Luhan, Mabel Dodge
Edge of Taos Desert: An Escape to Reality (vol. 4 of *Intimate Memories*)
Harcourt, Brace, New York, 1937
Mabel Dodge suggests that she was manic-depressive—that she had no "roots, continuity or conviction." She married an American Indian.

Luhan, Mabel Dodge
Lorenzo in Taos
Knopf, New York, 1932

A remarkable woman writes of her friendship with D. H. Lawrence.

MacMillan, William J.
The Reluctant Healer: A Remarkable Autobiography
Crowell, New York, 1952
The story of an eccentric man who discovers that he is a healer.

Mannin, Ethel
Confessions and Impressions
Hutchinson, London, 1936
A valuable, thoughtful, and honest book by an able writer who described several prominent persons.

Paul, Eden and Cedar Paul (transls.)
A Young Girl's Diary
Seltzer, New York, 1921
Freud thought this very frank diary to be a valuable human document. It tells of the girl's great interest in sex.

Scott, Cyril
My Years of Indiscretion
Mills and Boon, London, 1924
An egocentric, migrainous musical composer who loved to go to quacks of all kinds.

Seroff, Victor I.
Rachmaninoff
Simon and Schuster, New York, 1950
Not autobiography, but some letters from a sad, unhappy, at times depressed man who could not realize that he was a success.

Simpson, Doris G.
The Plague of Psychiatry: A Diagnosis, a Warning, and a Call to Christian Action
Greenwich Book Pubs., New York, 1957

An angry woman writes violently about psychiatrists and electroshock treatments.

SPENDER, STEPHEN
World within World
H. Hamilton, London, 1951
A philosophical and thought-producing autobiography by an eccentric, possibly bisexual man.

SYMONS, A. J. A.
The Quest for Corvo
Michigan State University Press, East Lansing, Mich., 1955
The life of a remarkable character, a psychotic homosexual who wrote a number of books.

SEXUAL DEVIATES

ANONYMOUS (with preface by Jean Cocteau)
The White Paper
Macaulay, New York, 1958
An excellent book by a man who was bisexual.

BANNON, ANN
I Am a Woman in Love with a Woman; Must Society Reject Me?
Fawcett, Greenwich, Conn., 1959
A novel which appears to be autobiographical.

CASAL, MARY
The Stone Wall:
An Autobiography
Eyncourt Press, Chicago, 1933
A moving story of a homosexual woman.

CORY, DONALD W. (pseudonym)
The Homosexual in America: A Subjective Approach
Greenberg, New York, 1951
One of the best available discussions of homosexuality, written by a well-educated and thoughtful homosexual.

COWELL, ROBERTA
Roberta Cowell's Story
British Book Centre, New York, 1954
A remarkable story of a British fighter pilot, married and with children, who was changed surgically into an attractive woman.

DOUGLAS, LORD ALFRED
The Autobiography of Lord Alfred Douglas
Secker, London, 1929
The life story of Oscar Wilde's closest friend.

FREDERICS, DIANA
Diana: A Strange Autobiography
Dial, New York, 1939
An excellent story of a homosexual woman.

GENÊT, JEAN
Our Lady of the Flowers (transl. by B. Frechtman)
Morihien, Paris, 1949
A famous but crazily written cryptic book from the pen of a homosexual in prison.

GENÊT, JEAN
The Gutter in the Sky (transl. from the French)
André Levy, Philadelphia, 1955
A famous autobiographic book.

GIDE, ANDRÉ
Corydon
Farrar, Straus, New York, 1950
Gide explained his homosexuality in what he thought was his most important book.

GIDE, ANDRÉ
The Journals, vol. 2, *1914–1927* (trans. by Justin O'Brien)
Knopf, New York, 1948
Written by the famous homosexual.

GIDE, ANDRÉ
If It Die (transl. by Dorothy Bussy)
Secker & Warburg, London, 1951
An uninhibited autobiography of a well-known homosexual.

GIDE, ANDRÉ
Madeleine (Et Nunc Manet in Te) (transl. by Justin O'Brien)
Knopf, New York, 1952
An excellent description of a physically sexless marriage.

HALL, RADCLYFFE
The Well of Loneliness
Covici-Friede, New York, 1929
The famous story of a homosexual woman.

HALL, RADCLYFFE
The Unlit Lamp
J. Cape and H. Smith, New York, 1929
A novel by the homosexual author of *The Well of Loneliness*.

LIND, EARL ("Ralph Werther"—"Jennie June")
Autobiography of an Androgyne
Medico-Legal Jour., New York, 1918
Perhaps the world's strangest autobiography of a "man" with large breasts who behaved with other men like a nymphomaniac. *See also* WERTHER.

LITTLE, JAY
Maybe—Tomorrow
Pageant, New York, 1952
A homosexual story.

MOUNTCAIRN, MONSIEUR
The Strange Confession of Monsieur Mountcairn
Privately printed, copyright, J. A. Nocross, 1928
The most remarkable document showing how hard it is for a refined homosexual man to follow the demands his body makes of him.

PORTAL, GEORGES
The Tunic of Nessus: Being the Confessions of an Invert (transl. by Eric Wensleydale)
Astra, Paris, no date
The rare story of a very aggressive homosexual who was proud of himself.

PROUST, MARCEL
Letters to a Friend (transl. by Alexander and Elizabeth Henderson)
Falcon, London, 1949
According to D. W. Cory, there is no question that Proust was homosexual.

REESE, TAMARA
Reborn: A Factual Life Story of a Transition from Male to Female
No publisher listed, 1955
A fraily-built man was operated on and changed to a woman who has since married several times.

SCULLY, ROBERT
The Scarlet Pansy
Royal, New York, no date
A discussion of homosexuality.

TCHAIKOVSKY, PETER ILYICH
The Diaries of Tchaikovsky
(transl. from the Russian by Wladimir Lakond)
Norton, New York, 1945
The great composer was often sad because of his homosexuality. Once, after a debauch he wrote, "Oh what a monster of a person I am." He became at times depressed and painfully lonely.

WEGENER, EINAR
(ANDREAS SPARRE)
*Man into Woman: an authentic
record of a change of sex. The
True Story of the Miraculous
Transformation of the Danish
Painter Einar Wegener* (ed. by
Niels Hoyer) (transl. by H. J.
Stenning)
Dutton, New York, 1933
    A "man" became Lili Elbe.

WEIRAUCH, ANNA ELISABET
The Scorpion (transl. by Whit-
taker Chambers)
Greenberg, New York, 1932
    A homosexual novel, apparent-
ly autobiographical.

WERTHER, RALPH–JENNIE JUNE
(EARL LIND)
The Female-Impersonators
The Medico-Legal Jour., New
York, 1922
    A sequel to *Autobiography of
an Androgyne*. Part of the re-
markable story of a transsexual
with large breasts.

WILDE, OSCAR
De Profundis
Putnam, New York, 1909
    One of the last writings of
Oscar Wilde.

WILDEBLOOD, PETER
Against the Law
Weidenfeld and Nicolson, London, 1955
    A moving story of the vicious
and unjustified attack of the
police on a fine man who was not
harming anyone.

HOBOES

BOX-CAR BERTHA, as told to DR.
BEN L. REITMAN
*Sister of the Road: The Auto-
biography of Box-car Bertha*
Macaulay, New York, 1937
    The story of an intelligent
woman hobo.

CRAWFORD, J. H.
The Autobiography of a Tramp
Longmans, London, 1900
    The story of an English tramp
and his family.

DAVIES, WILLIAM H.
*The Autobiography of a Super-
Tramp*
Preface by Bernard Shaw
Knopf, New York, 1917
    The story of an English tramp
who wrote good poetry.

FRIEDMAN, I. K.
The Autobiography of a Beggar
(prefaced by some of the humor-
ous adventures and incidents related in The Beggars' Club)
Small, Maynard, Boston, 1903
    Written in dialect.

KEMP, HARRY
*Tramping on Life: An Autobio-
graphical Narrative*
Boni and Liveright, New York,
1922
    A Jack London type of man, in
his early days a hobo and a wan-
derer, learned to write well.

ORWELL, GEORGE
*Down and Out in Paris and
London*
Harcourt, Brace, New York, 1933
    Apparently the true story of a
man who lived always close to
starvation.

STARKE, BARBARA
*Touch and Go: The Story of a
Girl's Escape*
J. Cape, London, 1931
    The frank, well-written story
of a girl hobo.

TULLY, JIM
Beggars of Life
Boni, New York, 1924
The story of hoboing by a man who became a fine writer and playwright.

WORBY, JOHN
The Other Half: The Autobiography of a Tramp
Furman, New York, 1937
An intelligent hobo gives us some idea of why some men must always be on the move.

PROSTITUTES

ADLER, POLLY
A House Is Not a Home
Rinehart, New York, 1953
A classic story of New York's leading madam and her adventures with gangsters and others.

BÖHME, MARGARETE (ed.)
The Diary of a Lost One
Sisley's, London, 1907; also, Hudson, New York, 1908
The diary of a prostitute.

COUSINS, SHEILA
To Beg I Am Ashamed
Vanguard, New York, 1938
A remarkable story, showing the psychology of a London prostitute.

HARRIS, SARA
They Sell Sex: The Call Girl and Big Business
Fawcett, Greenwich, Conn., 1960
Several call girls tell of their being hired by big business firms to entertain buyers.

"NELL"
I Had No Choice: The Diary of an Unfortunate
Chapman and Hall, London, 1940
Apparently taken from a real diary, written by an intelligent London prostitute.

O. W.
No Bed of Roses: The Diary of a Lost Soul
Macaulay, Gold Label Books, New York, 1930
The story of a prostitute, compiled from diaries.

SLADE, CAROLINE
Sterile Sun
Vanguard, New York, 1936
The story of a prostitute—it rings true in every word.

WILSON, HARRIETTE
Memoirs
Peter Davies, London, 1929
A high-class kept woman.

TOZER, BASIL
The Story of a Terrible Life: The Amazing Career of a Notorious Procuress
Stratford, Boston, 1929
An amazing story told by this famous French madam. Her description of the typical prostitute is excellent.

YOUNG, GEORGIE
A Magdalen's Life
No publ., no date
A frank well-written book, which gives a remarkable picture of a child neglected by society.

CRIMINALS AND PRISONERS

BERKMAN, ALEXANDER
Prison Memoirs of an Anarchist
Mother Earth Publ., New York, 1912
A famous anarchist tells of his life.

CHESSMAN, CARYL
Cell 2455, Death Row
Prentice-Hall, New York, 1954
   The story of a man who staved off death for many years.

MARTIN, JOHN BARTLOW (as reported by)
My Life in Crime: The Autobiography of a Professional Criminal
Harper, New York, 1952
   One learns much about the underworld of crime.

A PROFESSIONAL THIEF
The Professional Thief (annotated and interpreted by Edwin H. Sutherland)
University of Chicago Press, Chicago, 1937
   A sociologist helped a thief to write a remarkable study of the close working relationship between thieves and law-enforcement officers.

RUNYON, TOM
In for Life: A Convict's Story
Norton, New York, 1953
   A "lifer" tells of his lonely life in prison.

SHARPE, MAY CHURCHILL
Chicago May, Her Story
Macaulay, New York, 1928
   An able woman, a criminal, who spent 15 years in jail.

SHAW, CLIFFORD R.
The Jack-Roller: A Delinquent Boy's Own Story
University of Chicago Press, Chicago, 1930
   A criminal lad tells much about his life.

SHELLY, GORDON
I Take the Rap
Fell, New York, 1957

A man who has spent much of his life in jail writes well.

ZYWULSKA, KRYSTYNA
I Came Back
Roy, New York, 1951
   The story of a woman who, in World War II, was imprisoned for years in a notorious extermination camp.

CRIPPLED IN MANY WAYS

ALEXANDER, LARRY
The Iron Cradle (as told to Adam Barnett)
Crowell, New York, 1954
   A man with four limbs paralyzed by polio—in need of an iron lung.

BAKER, LOUISE
Out on a Limb
McGraw-Hill, New York, 1946
   An able woman who lost a limb in a childhood accident.

BARBELLION, W. N. P. (with an introduction by H. G. Wells)
The Journal of a Disappointed Man
Doran, New York, 1919
   A remarkable picture of a gifted young man who deeply resented having to die with multiple sclerosis.

BARBELLION, W. N. P. (Bruce Frederick Cummings)
A Last Diary
Chatto and Windus, London, 1920
   Barbellion wrote *The Journal of a Disappointed Man,* dying with multiple sclerosis.

BARBELLION, W. N. P.
Enjoying Life and Other Literary

Remains of W. N. P. Barbellion
Doran, New York, no date
By the man who wrote *The Journal of a Disappointed Man.*

BARTON, BETSEY
And Now To Live Again
Appleton-Century, New York, 1944
A lovely girl of sixteen had her back broken and became paralyzed from the waist down.

BARTON, BETSEY
The Long Walk
Duell, Sloane, and Pearce, New York, 1948
A story of a man whose body was wrecked; written by a woman who knows from personal experience what it is to be maimed.

BROWN, CHRISTY
My Left Foot
Simon and Schuster, New York, 1955
A very moving story of an Irish boy who triumphs over a severe cerebral palsy.

CARLSON, EARL R., M.D.
Born That Way
Day, New York, 1941
A boy with a severe spastic paralysis somehow got through colleges and became a physician.

DEAN, MRS. VERA
Three Steps Forward
Faber and Faber, London, 1957
A woman struggled with a severe cerebral palsy.

GOLDMAN, RAYMOND LESLIE
Even the Night
Macmillan, New York, 1947
This man at the age of four was stricken with severe polio; later came deafness. He triumphed and became a successful writer.

HATHAWAY, KATHARINE BUTLER
The Little Locksmith
Coward-McCann, New York, 1942
A beautifully written, thought-producing story of a girl who became a little hunchback.

HATHAWAY, KATHARINE BUTLER
The Journals and Letters of the Little Locksmith
Coward-McCann, New York, 1946
A vivid picture of the thoughts and sufferings of a little hunchback woman.

HOOPES, G. GERTRUDE
Out of the Running
Thomas, Springfield, Ill., 1939
An able woman was badly handicapped physically by a birth injury.

HUNT, AGNES
This Is My Life
Putnam, New York, 1942
An able nurse who started the first orthopedic hospital. She was a cripple herself.

JONEZ, HINTON D., M.D.
My Fight To Conquer Multiple Sclerosis (as told to Miriam Zeller Gross)
Messner, New York, 1952
For some time the doctor treated hundreds of people with multiple sclerosis.

LE COMTE, EDWARD
The Long Road Back: The Story of My Encounter with Polio
Beacon Press, Boston, 1957
A professor of English suddenly found himself paralyzed by polio.

McADAM, TERRY
Very Much Alive: The Story of a Paraplegic
Houghton, Mifflin, Boston, 1955

In an auto accident, Terry had his back broken and was paralyzed from that point down. He tells of the emotions of a ward full of men like himself.

MCKEE, JOHN DE WITT
Two Legs To Stand On
Appleton-Century-Crofts, New York, 1955
A man with a bad cerebral palsy triumphed over it.

MARSHALL, ALAN
I Can Jump Puddles
World Publ., Cleveland and New York, 1956
An Australian boy conquers polio.

MARUGG, JIM and ANNE WALTERS
Beyond Endurance
Hart-Davis, London, 1955
A man, for long in an iron lung with polio, eventually got back to his job on a newspaper.

OPIE, JUNE
Over My Dead Body
Dutton, New York, 1957
A woman who was completely paralyzed by polio.

PLAGEMANN, BENTZ
My Place To Stand
Gollancz, London, 1950
A man with severe polio won out and now can use crutches.

REVELL, NELLIE
Right off the Chest
Doran, New York, 1923
An able woman, suffering for four years with a broken back, wrote with the paper on her chest.

RUSSELL, HAROLD, with VICTOR ROSEN
Victory in My Hands

Creative Age Press, New York, 1949
A soldier who lost both hands and then succeeded marvelously.

THOMAS, GEORGE
My Mind a Kindom
Cape, London, 1938
The writer was one of four out of seven sibs who suffered from a great weakness of the muscles.

VISCARDI, HENRY, JR.
A Man's Stature
Day, New York, 1952
The thrilling story of a man, born with only stumps of legs, who became a great success in life. See his book, *Give Us the Tools.*

WALKER, TURNLEY
Rise Up and Walk
Dutton, New York, 1950
How a man fights polio.

WELLS, JUSTIN
Narrative and Reflections of Justin Wells Peirce
Boston, 1852
A man who one day suddenly found himself paralyzed all over. He remained that way.

CHRONIC INVALIDS

ACKISON, BELLE
The Sunny Side of a Shut-in's Life: A Book of Amusing, Interesting and Helpful Letters
Ogilvie Publ., New York, about 1902
Rather dull letters of a woman who spent several years as an invalid in bed.

CLEAVES, MARGARET A.
The Autobiography of a Neurasthene, as Told by One of Them and Recorded by M. A. Cleaves
Badger, Boston, 1910
A fine description of how it feels to be on the verge of a nervous breakdown.

LUCAS, MRS. RACHEL
Remarkable Account of Mrs. R. Lucas
W. & J. Gilman, Newburyport, 1809; paper
Gives list of her many illnesses.

MARRS, WILLIAM TAYLOR, M.D.
Confessions of a Neurasthenic
Davis, Philadelphia, 1908
A good description of a neurasthenic who travels about always hunting for a cure.

PASTORELLI, FRANCE
Strength out of Suffering (from the French, "Servitude et grandeur de la malade")
Houghton, Mifflin, Boston, 1936
The story of an able pianist, confined to bed by heart disease and fighting the temptation to enslave her daughter.

TRASK, LEONARD
The Wonderful Invalid
Printed by David Tucker, Portland, 1858; paper-bound
The story of a man whose upper spine caved in remarkably.

YOUNG, C. HOWARD
Sunny Life of an Invalid
Publ. by author, Hartford, Conn., 1897
An educated man was confined to his bed for fourteen years with many illnesses.

THE TUBERCULOUS

CHALMERS, STEPHEN
The Penny Piper of Saranac: An Episode in Stevenson's Life
Houghton, Mifflin, Boston, 1912
A delightful picture of Robert Louis Stevenson and Dr. Trudeau.

ELLIS, ANNE
Sunshine Preferred: The Philosophy of an Ordinary Woman
Houghton, Mifflin, Boston, 1934
A cheery book by a woman with tuberculosis.

HAYES, EDWARD W., M.D. (with chapters by Laurence de Rycke, Ph.D.)
Tuberculosis as It Comes and Goes
Thomas, Springfield, Ill., 1943 and 1947
A helpful book. Both Hayes and Rycke had the disease.

MACDONALD, BETTY
The Plague and I
Lippincott, Philadelphia, 1948
The story of her tuberculosis, by the author of *The Egg and I*.

MANSFIELD, KATHERINE
Journal of Katherine Mansfield (ed. by J. Middleton Murry)
Knopf, New York, 1927
A gifted writer writes while going down hill with tuberculosis.

McCLINTOCK, MARSHALL
We Take to Bed
Cape and Smith, New York, 1931
A husband and wife, both with tuberculosis.

PYLE, MARJORIE McDONALD, M.D.
Help Yourself Get Well: A Guide

for TB Patients and Their Families
Appleton-Century-Crofts, New York, 1951
A book to help the tuberculous, written by a woman who had the disease.

SMITH, ISABEL
Wish I Might
Harper, New York, 1955
The story of a long fight with tuberculosis.

SPITZER, MARIAN
I Took It Lying Down
Random House, New York, 1950, 1951
A helpful book on tuberculosis.

MISCELLANEOUS ILLNESSES AND OPERATIONS

ANONYMOUS
I Lost My Memory: The Case as the Patient Saw It
Faber and Faber, London, 1932
An interesting account of an amnesia.

ANONYMOUS
Words in Pain
Bishop, London, 1919
A woman of thirty-five, who felt she was dying, wrote letters worth reading.

BLOOM, URSULA
No Lady in Bed
Chapman and Hall, London, 1944
A story of severe migraine.

DAUDET, ALPHONSE
Suffering (transl. by Milton Garver)
Yale University Press, New Haven, 1934
Daudet's story of his great suffering with the "lightning pains" of locomotor ataxia.

EHRLICH, NICHOLAS
The Life of a Laryngectomee
Froben, New York, 1937
Information about what can be done for persons who have lost their voice box.

GILFOND, DUFF
I Go Horizontal
Vanguard, New York, 1940
A woman correspondent got a pain in her head that would go away only when she lay down. Later, she got a paralyzing abdominal pain.

HARPER, HENRY HOWARD
The Story of a Nephrectomy: A True History of a Semi-tragic Episode
Plimpton, Norwood, Mass., 1927
The man had a kidney removed at Mayo's.

KARINTHY, FRIGYES
A Journey round My Skull (transl. by V. D. Barker)
Harper, New York, 1939
The story of a man who had a tumor growing in his brain. Fortunately, it was removed.

LEWIS, ABIGAIL
An Interesting Condition: The Diary of a Pregnant Woman
Doubleday, Garden City, N.Y., 1950
A study of the emotions of pregnancy.

PAAR, JOHN
How I Cured My Duodenal Ulcer
Joseph, London, 1951
A man thinks he cured his ulcer.

PUDER, DR. SÁNDOR
Condition Satisfactory: A Physician's Report of His Own Illness
(transl. by Hildegard Nagel)
Knopf, New York, 1937
A physician's description of his three operations.

SCHREINER, OLIVE
The Letters of Olive Schreiner
(ed. by S. C. Cronwright-Schreiner)
Little, Brown, Boston, 1924
Letters of a somewhat eccentric writer who suffered much from an asthma which may well have been largely psychic in origin.

RANTOUL, ROBERT
Shoot That Needle Straight
Humphries, Boston, 1947
A playful book about diabetes and the doctors.

TALBERT, WILLIAM F., with JOHN SHARNIK
Playing for Life: Billy Talbert's Story
Little, Brown, Boston, 1958
A star tennis player tells of his diabetes.

WOODWARD, KATHLEEN
Jipping Street: Childhood in a London Slum
Harper, New York, 1928
The beautifully written autobiography of a poverty-stricken girl in a London slum.

BLINDNESS

BARNES, ERIC W. (with an introductory chapter by Anne Morrow Lindbergh)
The Man Who Lived Twice: The Biography of Edward Sheldon
Scribner, New York, 1956
The story of one of the world's rare characters, blinded and paralyzed and bedridden but still full of life and interest.

BARRY, HENRY M.
I'll Be Seeing You
Knopf, New York, 1952
A man, blinded in battle, went on to create a new life.

BROWN, ELEANOR G.
Milton's Blindness
Columbia University Press, New York, 1934
A learned discussion of Milton's blindness, with his references to his handicap.

CRIDDLE, RUSSELL
Love Is Not Blind
Norton, New York, 1953
A man who lost his sight in a childhood accident got it back with a corneal transplant years later.

DAHL, BORGHILD
I Wanted To See
Museum Press, London, 1947
An able woman went though college in spite of her difficulty in reading.

DAY, MARY L.
Incidents in the Life of a Blind Girl
J. Young, Baltimore, 1859
An interesting story of blindness a hundred years ago, written by a graduate of the Maryland Institute for Blind.

FOX, MONROE L.
Blind Adventure
Lippincott, Philadelphia, 1946
A man facing a sightless future.

FURNISS, HENRY SANDERSON (Lord Sanderson)
Memories of Sixty Years
Methuen, London, 1930
    A man with but little vision triumphed over his handicap.

HENDERSON, MRS. LOIS T.
The Opening Doors: My Child's First Eight Years without Sight
Day, New York, 1954
    A mother tells the story of the first eight years of her boy who was born blind.

HUSSEIN, TAHA
An Egyptian Child: The Autobiography of Taha Hussein
(transl. by E. D. Paxton)
Routledge, London, 1932
    An Egyptian boy, early blinded, quickly memorized the Koran, and eventually became one of Egypt's most learned men.

KEITLEN, TOMI (with Norman M. Lobsenz)
Farewell to Fear
Bernard Geis Associates (distributed by Random House, New York, 1960)
    A blind woman tells how she skis, plays golf, and climbs mountains.

KELLER, HELEN
Helen Keller's Journal
Joseph, London, 1938
    The story of one of the world's most remarkable women.

KELLER, HELEN
The Story of My Life (with her letters 1887–1901 and a supplementary account of her education, including passages from the reports and letters of her teacher, Anne Mansfield Sullivan, by John Albert Macy)
Doubleday, New York, 1947
    A remarkable story.

KUGELMASS, J. ALVIN
Louis Braille: Windows for the Blind
Messner, New York, 1951
    At the age of three, Braille was blinded. Later, he devised printing for the blind.

MEHTA, VED
Face to Face: An Autobiography
Little, Brown, Boston, 1957
    A brilliant, blind Hindu boy came to this country and graduated from college.

PUTNAM, PETER
Keep Your Head Up, Mr. Putnam
Harper, New York, 1952
    At twenty-one, a blind man tells of learning to go about with a Seeing Eye dog.

SCAPINI, J. GEORGES
A Challenge to Darkness: The Life Story of J. Georges Scapini
(transl. with an introduction by Helen Keller)
Doubleday, Doran, Garden City, N.Y., 1929
    A brilliant man lost his sight in battle, and then carried on.

SHEPPARD, WILLIAM, with FRITZ BLOCKI
Out of My Darkness
Fell, New York, 1956
    A boy of eight lost his sight, and many years later got it back with a corneal implant.

SMITHDAS, ROBERT J.
Life at My Fingertips
Doubleday, Garden City, N.Y., 1958
    A man who was blind and deaf went through college.

ZELAYETA, ELENA
"Elena"
Prentice-Hall, Englewood Cliffs, N.J., 1960

A blind woman tells how she teaches cooking and writes cookbooks.

DEAFNESS

FRANKEL, GEORGE W., M.D.
Let's Hear It: Confessions of a Hard-of-hearing Doctor
Stratford House, New York, 1952
The doctor advocates the use of a hearing aid.

HECKMAN, HELEN
My Life Transformed
Macmillan, New York, 1928
A deaf-mute who became a dancer.

HEINER, MRS. MARIE HAYS
Hearing Is Believing
World Publishing, Cleveland and New York, 1949
An able deaf woman wrote a helpful book.

LEADER, PAULINE
And No Birds Sing
Vanguard, New York, 1931
Story of a deaf girl.

MURPHY, GRACE E. BARSTOW
Your Deafness Is Not You: New Design for Deafness
Harper, New York, 1954
A well-written and helpful book.

WARFIELD, FRANCES
Keep Listening
Viking, New York, 1957
A helpful book by a deaf woman who later recovered with operations.

HEART DISEASE

HARRISON, CHARLES YALE
Thank God for My Heart Attack
Holt, New York, 1949

A man shows how, in a number of ways, his heart attack did him good.

LAWTON, GEORGE
Straight to the Heart: A Personal Account of Thoughts and Feelings while Undergoing Heart Surgery
International University Press, New York, 1956
A man faced death on the operating table and won out.

McELDOWNEY, DENNIS
The World Regained
Beacon Press, Boston, 1957
The story of a man born with a badly deformed heart. He was cured by an operation.

PERRY, HENRY
I Had Heart Disease
Pageant, New York, 1955
A man with heart disease who got well.

SNYDER, EUGENE F., M.D. (with foreword by Paul Dudley White)
From a Doctor's Heart
Philosophical, New York, 1951
The story of a doctor's recovery from a heart attack.

STUART, JESSE
The Year of My Rebirth
McGraw-Hill, New York, 1956
The story of a man's fight to survive a severe heart attack.

CANCER

GABRIELSON, CATHERINE
The Story of Gabrielle
World Publishing, Cleveland and New York, 1956
A mother's distress as she watched her child die with cancer.

KAEHELE, EDNA
Living with Cancer
Doubleday, Garden City, N. Y.,
1952
A woman with an arrested
cancer.

MACLEOD, LILY
Return to Life
Lippincott, Philadelphia, 1950
A woman's struggle with cancer.

SUSSMAN, BEN
My Fight against Cancer
Privately printed, New York,
1938
A diet enthusiast.

WERTENBAKER, LAEL TUCKER
Death of a Man
Random House, New York, 1957
A man who had cancer and in
the end took his own life—his
wife letting him—after much
thought and discussion.

ARTHRITIS

GOVAN, ADA CLAPHAM
Wings at My Window
Macmillan, New York, 1942
Crippled with arthritis and
racked with pain, she wrote a
best seller about the birds she attracted to her window.

LENT, EDWARD B.
*Being Done Good: An Amusing
Account of a Rheumatic's Expe-
rience with Doctors and Special-
ists Who Promised To Do Him
Good*
Brooklyn Eagle Press, Brooklyn,
N. Y., 1904
The story of a man who tried
every type of treatment.

SCOTT, ANN (pseudonym)
*Woman with Arthritis: The True
Story of a Recovery*
Abelard-Schuman, New York,
1957
A remarkable story of a
woman with deep sexual problems who got well during psychotherapy.

SOUTAR, WILLIAM
Diaries of a Dying Man (ed. by
Alexander Scott)
Chambers, London, 1954
A Scottish poet, dying with se-
vere arthritis of the spine.

STUART, MRS. GRACE
Private World of Pain
Allen and Unwin, London, 1953
A story of thirty years with
rheumatoid arthritis.

LEPROSY

BURGESS, PERRY
Who Walk Alone
Holt, New York, 1940
An American soldier in the
Philippines got leprosy.

BURGESS, PERRY
*Born of Those Years: An Auto-
biography*
Holt, New York, 1951
The man who wrote *Who
Walk Alone* became a physician
and dedicated his life to the
lepers.

GREAVE, PETER
The Second Miracle
Holt, New York, 1955
A leper is cured.

LAWSON, E. T.
No More Unclean!
Davies, London, 1957
A story of leprosy.

MARTIN, BETTY (pseudonym)
Miracle at Carville (ed. by Evelyn Wells)
Doubleday, Garden City, N. Y., 1950
A leper was cured.

MARTIN, BETTY (pseudonym)
No One Must Ever Know (ed. by Evelyn Wells)
Doubleday, Garden City, N. Y., 1959
Betty and Harry Martin, after twenty years in a leper colony, are cured.

COLLECTIONS OF STORIES

ASWELL, MRS. MARY LOUISE (ed.)
The World Within
McGraw-Hill, New York, 1947

A collection of stories about psychoses and neuroses. Some may be autobiographical.

KAVAN, ANNA (pseudonym)
Asylum Piece
Doubleday, Garden City, New York, 1940–1946
A series of stories said to be fictional, by a woman who had for long cared for insane people. The book is said to be a classic.

WINSLOW, DR. L. FORBES
Mad Humanity
Mansfield Publ., New York, 1898
An able psychiatrist got a number of his patients to write up their experiences with insanity or psychosis.

ALPHABETICAL LIST OF BOOK TITLES, WITH AUTHORS

John Clare: A Life
    J. W. and Anne Tibble
Journal of a Disappointed Man, The
    W. N. P. Barbellion
Journal of Katherine Mansfield
    Katherine Mansfield
Journal of a Young Artist, 1860–1884, The
    Marie Bashkirtseff
Journals of André Gide, The, vol. 2, 1914–1927
    André Gide
Journals and Letters of The Little Locksmith, The
    Katharine Butler Hathaway
Journey round My Skull, A (transl. by V. D. Barker)
    Frigyes Karinthy
Just One More: Concerning Problem Drinker
    James L. Free
Justice and the Justices
    Basil H. Pollitt
Keep Listening
    Frances Warfield
Keep Your Head Up, Mr. Putnam
    Peter Putnam
Kingdom of the Lost, The
    J. A. Howard Ogdon
Lady Sings the Blues
    Billie Holiday
Lambs, The
    Katherine Anthony
Last Confessions of Marie Bashkirtseff, The
    Marie Bashkirtseff
Last Diary, A
    W. N. P. Barbellion (Bruce Frederick Cummings)
Late Liz, The
    Elizabeth Burns
Laughing Torso
    Nina Hamnet (reminiscences of)
Lawyer's Story, The
    Basil Hubbard Pollitt

Layman Looks at Doctors, A
    S. W. and J. T. Pierce
Le Rêve et la vie
    Gérard de Nerval
Leaves from the Diary of an Old Lawyer
    A. B. Richmond, Esq.
Legends, Autobiographical Sketches
    August Strindberg
Letters of Charles Baudelaire, The
    Charles Baudelaire
Let's Hear It
    George W. Frankel, M.D.
Letters of a Lunatic
    G. F. Adler
Letters of Olive Schreiner, The
    Olive Schreiner
Letters to a Friend
    Marcel Proust
Liber Amoris, or the New Pygmalion
    William Hazlitt
Life of a Laryngectomee, The
    Nicholas Ehrlich
Life and Loves of a Prodigal Daughter, Being the Intimate Memoirs of Gervée Baronte
    Gervée Baronte
Life and Sufferings of Leonard Trask, The
    Leonard Trask
Life at My Finger-tips
    Robert J. Smithdas
Life of Mason Long, The (converted gambler)
    Mason Long
Life Story of Sarah M. Victor, The
    Sarah M. Victor
Life Struggle, Fall and Reformation of Thomas N. Doutney, The
    Thomas N. Doutney
Like a Lamb
    Ella Hales
Literary Sketches and Letters
    Charles Lamb

Movers and Shakers (vol. 3 of Intimate Memories)
Mabel Dodge Luhan
My Childhood
Maxim Gorki
My Father—My Son
Edward G. Robinson, Jr., *et al.*
My Fight against Cancer
Ben Sussman
My Fight for Sanity
Judith Kruger
My Fight To Conquer Multiple Sclerosis
Hinton D. Jonez, M.D.
My First Life, a Biography
Brenda Dean Paul
My Last Drink
Joseph H. Francis
My Left Foot
Christy Brown
My Life
Isadora Duncan
My Life as a Dissociated Personality
B. C. A.
My Life in Crime
John Bartlow Martin (reported by)
My Life Transformed
Helen Heckman
My Mind a Kingdom
George Thomas
My Place To Stand
Bentz Plagemann
My Sister and I (transl. by Dr. Oscar Levy)
Friedrich Nietzsche
My Story
Mary Astor
My Years of Indiscretion
Cyril Scott
Narrative and Reflections
Justin Wells
Needle in a Haystack: The Exciting Adventures of a Federal Narcotics Agent
William J. Spillard (as told to Pence Janos)

New Armor for Old
William O'Sullivan Molony
New Lands
Charles Fort
No Bed of Roses
O. W.
No Hiding Place (the story of Vincent Tracy)
Beth Day
No Hiding Place: An Autobiography
William Seabrook
No Lady in Bed
Ursula Bloom
No More Unclean
E. T. Lawson
No One Must Ever Know
Betty Martin
Odyssey of a Lonely Woman, The
Alma M. Karlin
Old Game, The
Samuel G. Blythe
One Man
Robert Steele
Opening Doors, The
Lois T. Henderson
Opium-eating, an Autobiographical Sketch
An Habituate
Opium, the Diary of a Cure
Jean Cocteau
Other Half, The
John Worby
Other Side of the Bottle, The
Dwight Anderson
Our Lady of the Flowers
Jean Genêt
Out of My Darkness
William Sheppard
Out of the Depths
Anton T. Boisen
Out of the Running
G. Gertrude Hoopes
Out of This Century
Peggy Guggenheim
Out on a Limb
Louise Baker

Shoot That Needle Straight
  Robert Rantoul
Sister of the Road
  Box-car Bertha
Sketches in the Life of John
Clare (written by himself)
  Edmund Blunden
Snake Pit, The
  Mary Jane Ward
Son of a Servant, The
  August Strindberg (transl. by
  Claud Field)
Spectacle of a Man, The
  John Coinard (written by
  Dr. Alvan Barach)
Sterile Sun
  Caroline Slade
Stone Wall, The
  Mary Casal
Story of Gabrielle, The
  Catharine Gabrielson
Story of a Lover, The
  Mabel Dodge Lunan
Story of Mary Maclane by Her-
self, The
  Mary Maclane
Story of My Life, The
  Helen Keller
Story of My Psychoanalysis, The
  John Knight (pseudonym)
Story of a Nephrectomy, The
  Henry Howard Harper
Story of a Terrible Life, The
  Basil Tozer
Straight to the Heart
  George Lawton
Strange Confession of Monsieur
Mountcairn, The
  Monsieur Mountcairn
Strength out of Suffering
  France Pastorelli
Stricken Deer, The: Or the Life
of Cowper
  Lord David Cecil
Stubborn Wood, The
  Emily Harvin
Suffering
  Alphonse Daudet

Sunny Life of an Invalid
  C. Howard Young
Sunny Side of a Shut-in's Life,
The
  Belle Ackison
Sunshine Preferred
  Anne Ellis
Taste of Ashes, The
  Bill Stern (with Oscar Fraley)
Testament of Caliban, The
  David Edstrom
Testament: The Confessions of a
Drug-taker
  G. P. Robinson
Thank God for My Heart Attack
  Charles Yale Harrison
These Are My Sisters
  Lara Jefferson
They Sell Sex
  Sara Harris
Third Strike, The
  Jerry Gray
Thirty-two Years of the Life of
an Adventurer
  John H. Drake
This Is My Life
  Agnes Hunt
This Is Norman Brokenshire
  Norman Brokenshire
Thousand Faces, A
  Florence S. Thompson and
  George W. Galvin
Three Faces of Eve, The
  Corbett Thigpen, M.D. and
  Hervey M. Cleckley, M.D.
Three Loves of Dostoevsky, The
  Marc Slonim
Three Steps Forward
  Vera Dean
To Beg I Am Ashamed
  Sheila Cousins
To Hell and Back
  James H. Ellis
Too Much, Too Soon
  Diana Barrymore
Torments of a Frigid Woman,
The
  J. Biezin, Jr., M.D.